The New Lean Toolbox
TOWARDS FAST, FLEXIBLE FLOW

By
John Bicheno

Lean Enterprise Research Centre, Cardiff Business School

and

University of Buckingham

Production and Inventory Control, Systems and Industrial Engineering Books

(PICSIE Books)

Buckingham, England
2004

To the Masters of Lean Operations who have helped make 'peeling the Lean onion' both fun and instructive.

Sam	Ainsworth	Ocular Sciences	Justin	Ovens	Visteon
John	Arnold	Multitone Electronics	Dave	Peacock	BNFL
Kate	Bailey	Toyota	Dave	Price	Rolls Royce
Steve	Baker	TPMI	Phil	Rees	Nordam Europe
Ole	Bang	Parker Hannifin	Clive	Rendle	
Tom	Banks	Polestar Petty	Keith	Riley	BNFL
Paul	Barson	BCL Technologies	Brett	Riley	MG Rover
Owen	Berkeley-Hill	Ford	Jacqueline	Royall	Perkin Elmer
Jeremy	Brown	VAW Motocast	Huw	Samuel	Corus
Joseph	Bujak	TMD Friction	Larry	Sheehan	Bausch & Lomb
Laurie	Cullen	Ford	Edward	Simkiss	Rolls Royce
Gareth	Duggan	Corus	Bob	Smith	Johnson Controls
Terry	Edwards	Ordnance Survey	Steve	South	Federal Mogul
Glyn	Finney	Celestica	Gary	Steele	SA Partners
Lee	Flinders	Linpac Plastics	Andy	Stepney	Ilmor Engineering
Adrian	Gordon	Benteler	Bo	Sundahl	Danfoss
Dan	Gurney	Grunwick Labs	Neil	Trivedi	Masterfoods
Dave	Hennessey	Rolls Royce	Sue	Turner	Avesta Polarit
Richard	Hill	Corus	Kevin	Wadge	SA Partners
Melvyn	Hooper	Ocular Sciences	Darren	Walsh	JPM International
Owen	James	Ford / LERC	Peter	Watkins	GKN
Brian	Johns	Cooper Standard	Fraser	Wilkinson	Ortho Clinical
Jeremy	Jones	Bombardier	Allyn	Williams	Excel Electronic
Tony	Kennedy	Bausch & Lomb	Dave	Williams	BNFL
Christian	Lees	Thermo King	Ian	Wilson	TPMI
Graham	McKendry	Westinghouse	Emma	Wilson	Ford
Wayne	Nicholls	Delphi	Julian	Winn	Celestica

FOREWORD

By
Peter Hines

I am frequently asked by firms on their lean conversion journey what should they read. Another question often asked involves finding out what tools should be used. A third involves how do apparently competing subjects such as lean, theory of constraints and six sigma fit together. My usual response refers people to this publication and its forerunners.

The New Lean Toolbox sets out in a clear and reader friendly way how lean fits together. It is an invaluable resource for staff right across an organisation. It provides a ready reckoner for directors wanting to know what is going on in their business, a guide to the improvement agent as well as an insight to those involved as part of a project team.

Whilst no organisation will ever use all of the tools illustrated here, understanding what is available and how these can be pulled to the needs of the organisation is an excellent starting point. Those who are likely to be most successful will integrate their approach into a systematic change programme taking into account the needs of the customer, business strategy as well as the needs of the people in the business. In order to start from the right place I would suggest reading this publication right through at an overview level before developing your own implementation plan. After that it will be a handy reference text towards your own desired future state.

Good luck on your lean journey.

Professor Peter Hines
Director
Lean Enterprise Research Centre

CONTENTS

Theory of Constraints and Factory Physics

Quality

Improvement

People and Sustainability

New Product Development and Introduction

Lean Supply

Accounting and Measurements

Index

A Lean Chronology

1797 Henry Maudslay builds the world's first metal precision screw cutting machine. This was the 'parent' machine of the machine tool industry.

1810 Maudslay and Marc Brunel (father of Isambard) set up the first mechanised production line that produced 160k pulleys per year with 10 men, for the Royal Navy.

1893 F.W. Taylor begins work as a "consulting engineer".

1896 Vilfredo Pareto publishes law of economic distribution.

1898 F.W. Taylor begins his time studies of shovelling of iron.

1904 Cadillac begins building cars using interchangeable parts.

1908 Ford Model T.

1909 Frank and Lillian Gilbreth study bricklaying. Beginnings of motion study.

1911 Wilson EOQ formula.

1913 Ford establishes Highland Park plant using the moving assembly line.

1922 Gantt "The Gantt Chart: A Working Tool for Management".

1925 "Mass Production" phrase coined by Encyclopaedia Britannica.

1926 Henry Ford "Today and Tomorrow".

1927 Establishment of Toyota Motor (Toyota Looms established in 1922).

1927-
1930 Mayo and Roethlisberger studies at Hawthorn Plant of Western Electric.

1931 Walter Shewhart. "Economic Control of Quality of Manufactured Product", Van Nostrand. First book on SPC and PDCA.

1934 H.B. Maynard coins the term "Method Study".

1936 An engineer at General Motors coins the term "automation".

1942 Juran: Reengineering procurement for Lend Lease (90 days to 53 hours).

1943-
1944 Flow production of bombers at Boeing Plant II and Ford Willow Run.

1945 Shigeo Shingo presents concept of production as a network to JMA.
Also identifies batch production as the main source of delays.

1948 Deming first sent to Japan.
Lectures on waste as being the prime source of quality problems.

1949 Juran first goes to Japan.

1950 Eiji Toyoda visits Ford's River Rouge plant. Ohno visits in 1956.

1950 Ohno begins work on the Toyota Production System following strikes.

1951 Deming Award established in Japan.

1951 Juran "Handbook of Quality Control" (first edition). Includes cost of quality, Pareto analysis, SPC. (Fifth edition published 1999.)

1961 Shigeo Shingo devises and defines "pokayoke", book published in 1985.

1961 Ishikawa devises Quality Circles, and first are set up in 1962. Juran introduces the concept in Europe in 1966.

1961 Feigenbaum, "Total Quality Control", McGraw Hill.

1969 First microchip designed at Intel by Ted Hoff.

1971 Mudge, "Value Engineering: A Systematic Approach", McGraw Hill.

1974 Wickham Skinner "The Focused Factory", HBR.

1975 Orlicky, "Material Requirements Planning", McGraw Hill.

1975 Burbidge, "The Introduction of Group Technology", Heinemann.

1978 APICS MRP Crusade.

1978 First articles on "Just in Time" appear in US magazines.

1980 NBC television screens "If Japan Can, Why can't We". Kawasaki opens factory in USA running 'Kawasaki Production System', based on TPS.

1981 Motorola begins a methodology called "Six Sigma".

1982 Deming "Quality, Productivity and Competitive Position", MIT Press and "Out of the Crisis", MIT Press - contains his 14 point plan.

1982 Schonberger "Japanese Manufacturing Techniques", Free Press.

1983 Hall, "Zero Inventories", Dow Jones Irwin APICS.

1983 Monden, "Toyota Production System", Ind Eng and Management Press.

1984 Eli Goldratt, "The Goal".

1984 Hayes and Wheelwright, "Restoring our Competitive Edge", Free Press.

1984 Kaplan "Yesterday's Accounting Undermines Production", HBR and 1987 Kaplan & Johnson "Relevance Lost: The Rise and Fall of Management Accounting".

1985 Shingo: "SMED", Productivity.

1985 Skinner, "Manufacturing: The Formidable Competitive Weapon", Wiley.

1986 Hill, "Manufacturing Strategy", Macmillan.

1986 Maasaki Imai, "Kaizen – The Key to Japan's Competitive Success".

1986 Goldratt and Fox, "The Race".

1987 Baldridge award established.

1987 Stan Davis in "Future Perfect" makes first mention of Mass Customisation.

1987 Boothroyd and Dewhurst, "Design for Assembly".

1988 Nakajima "Introduction to Total Productive Maintenance".

1988 Akao introduces QFD into manufacturing.

1988 Cooper and Kaplan, "Measure Costs Right: Make the Right Decision", HBR (First paper on ABC).

1989 Ohno and Japanese Management Association, "Kanban – Just in Time at Toyota", Productivity Press.

1989 Camp "Benchmarking: The Search for Industry Best Practices", ASQ Quality Press.

1990 Stalk and Hout: "Competing against Time", Free Press.

1990 Hammer "Reengineering Work: Don't Automate, Obliterate", HBR, and 1994 Hammer and Champy, "Reengineering the Corporation".

1990 Stuart Pugh "Total Design", and 1991 Concept Selection.

1990 Womack and Jones, "The Machine that Changed the World", Rawson.

1990   Schonberger, "Building a Chain of Customers", Free Press.

1990   Quick Response initiative initiated by WalMart.

1990   Osborn, Moran, Musselwhite, Zenger, "Self Directed Work Teams", Business One.

1992   Jack Stack, "The Great Game of Business", Currency Doubleday.

1992   EFQM award established.

1993   Hajime Ohba becomes general manager of Toyota Supplier Support Centre, and begins teaching TPS to US companies, many of them outside automotive.

1993   Pine, "Mass Customisation", Harvard.

1994   AME begins promotion of "Kaizen Blitz" (Book by Laraia, Moody and Hall published in 1999).

1994   Altshuller, First English translation of book about TRIZ.

1996   Womack and Jones, "Lean Thinking", Simon and Schuster.

1996   Hopp and Spearman, "Factory Physics", Irwin (Second edition, 2000).

1997   Clayton Christensen, "The Innovator's Dilemma", Harvard.

1998   Rajan Suri "Quick Response Manufacturing", Productivity Press.

1999   Rother and Shook, "Learning to See", Lean Enterprise Institute.

1999   Spear and Bowen, "Decoding the DNA of the Toyota Production System", HBR.

2000   Internet supply established by Big Three.

2000   Johnson and Bröms, "Profit Beyond Measure", Nicholas Brearley.

2001   C. Martin Hinckley, "Make No Mistake!", Productivity.

2001   Schonberger, "Let's Fix It!", Free Press.

2001   R.I. McIntosh et al, "Improving Changeover Performance", Butterworth-Heinemann.

2001   AME-UK established.

2002   Jones and Womack, "Seeing the Whole", Lean Enterprise Institute.

2003   Large scale trials of RFID (radio frequency inventory identification).

Note: HBR denotes Harvard Business Review.

Note and Thanks: This sequence builds on an original produced by Frank Sperotto of PICSIE Books, South Africa and the S.A. Institute of Industrial Engineers.

Philosophy

Lean

It is now 20 years since Richard Schonberger and Robert Hall wrote the two books that effectively launched (or some would say re-launched) Lean in the West. It is over 10 years since Womack, Jones and Roos wrote their seminal book naming the approach "Lean". Huge changes have taken place, yet it is also true that for the majority of operations organisations the Lean potential has hardly been tapped.

The New Lean Toolbox

You might respond to the title of this book, in three ways. First, it could be rejected out of hand. Lean is not an eclectic selection of tools, but a system. This is true. But hopefully it is useful to collect up the tools and concepts that Lean draws upon.

Second, as the *New* lean-toolbox. Lean, as an extension of Toyota Production System (TPS), continues to evolve. This book is a considerable update on the second edition of the Lean Toolbox. It is appropriate to think of this book as a supplement to Womack and Jones' classic *Lean Thinking*. We continue to learn more about Toyota and TPS. There remains huge potential in the vast majority of manufacturing organizations, and not just in repetitive manufacturing. Concepts of flow, 5S, standard work, kaizen, and the like, are surely universal in manufacturing (however 'agile') and in service, so this book attempts to consolidate and explore traditional Lean areas. However, thinking that TPS is the answer to all is also naïve – for example a value stream map is an excellent tool for value streams that do not share significant resources and for some clerical applications, but not for converging constraints or multi-contact customer service, and Toyota itself uses APS scheduling software. And, of course, Toyota would be the first to admit that they do not have all the answers – we do not all drive Toyota or Lexus – or even aspire to them. So there remain opportunities, for example, in creative design. The waste of not recognising and elevating a constraint will remain a huge challenge.

Third, as the *New-Lean* toolbox. Lean has now expanded out well beyond TPS. This is not to say that TPS has become passé – but building on TPS we have begun to realise how Lean can become an even more powerful concept as it integrates with 'fast flexible flow', with the theory of constraints, with 'factory physics', with service concepts, with much of six sigma, and with ERP. And Lean is expanding into new areas far removed from repetitive manufacturing – Lean construction, Lean project management, Lean health, Lean service, and even, wait for it, Lean defence and Lean public service. This surely constitutes *New Lean*. The New Lean Toolbox book attempts to address this growing target.

A central theme of the book is that the 'New Lean' comprises an amalgam of Traditional Lean, Theory of Constraints, Six Sigma, and a range of relatively new concepts for measurement, analysis, and transformation.

Bob Emiliani (from famous Lean company Wiremold) suggests that the focus for future Lean organizations needs to switch from around 75% on the manufacturing shop, 20% on product development, and the remainder on administration and behaviour to approximately 25% each on supply chain, product development, administration, and behaviour. This book does not achieve that, but lays a foundation to make it possible.

So, What is Lean?

In the *New Lean* context the word Lean is an unfortunate one. Unfortunate because it has connotations of both manufacturing (which it is by no means confined to), and mean-ness or cutting back (which may apply to waste, but Lean should mean fit for new activities not skinny or anorexic). This section explores the concept and the misconceptions.

George Davidson, retired manufacturing director of Toyota South Africa, says that the first principle of the

Toyota Production System (TPS) is "the customer first". And, George, how to you do that? "By creating thinking people', says he. And how do you do that, George? "By creating workplaces and organizations that are more human". Note what Davidson is NOT saying. It is not primarily about waste; waste is removed because you want to improve benefits to the customer. Hence Toyota is not averse to adding inventory where necessary – as indeed they have done recently. It is not about 5S – 5S is a just a tool for consistency and quality. It is not about SMED – SMED is just a tool for improving response time and service to the customer. TPS developed from first principles, with the customer in mind. In fact non-Lean systems do just the opposite. For instance, through "economic order quantities", "mass production", long lead times, reduced variety, "push" systems, and the location of plants in China purely for cost – all of which are designed with the producer in mind, not the customer!

One way of understanding Lean is to view it as a (proven) approach to dispense with increasingly inappropriate 'economies of scale' and to adopt 'economies of time'.

Lean is not Tools!

There is a danger that Lean is thought of as a box of tools to be cherry picked. No doubt some tools used individually give good results. The point is that it is an end-to-end value stream that delivers competitiveness. A great cell feeding into a morass of poorly controlled inventory is waste. A changeover reduction programme in a high capacity area is waste. A 5S programme without follow through into standard attainment is largely waste. Kanban working in a situation of unlevelled demand can be waste. And so on. Even if all these were sorted out through good value stream mapping and a well-directed kaizen programme, Lean may still fail to deliver its true potential.

Lean is Waste Prevention

One frequently hears that Lean is about waste or muda – it often is, but it should be more about waste prevention than waste elimination. Johnson and Bröms believe that the focus on elimination of waste is misleading, and argue that it is the subtle avoidance of waste whilst creating balanced flow that is the key. This is just like the total quality concept of trading the costs of prevention against the costs of inspection and internal and external failure. Spend more on prevention, but far less on failure and inspection. Russell Ackoff talks about resolving problems (by discussion), but better is solving problems (by fact-based scientific study), and best of all is dissolving problems (by tackling root causes). Non-Lean practitioners resolve "inefficiencies", beginning Lean practitioners solve problems to remove waste, but the experienced Lean practitioner dissolves waste.

Lean is Value

Lean practitioners do go after waste. This is appropriate given the high levels of waste in most value streams. Although there will always be another layer of waste to address, the more experienced need to return to Value – to the first and second Lean principles of customer and value stream. Like the Quality concept of quality of design and quality of conformance, waste elimination or prevention is but one half of the total picture. Rethinking the value side is at least as important. This leads to seeking out new opportunities…

Lean is System

Water is a liquid at normal temperatures. Its constituents, oxygen and hydrogen, are gases. You can never understand the properties of water by studying oxygen and hydrogen. Likewise Lean and Lean tools. Lean is a system – more than the sum of its components. Systems are in constant interplay with their environment – where the boundary is, is not obvious (what should be outsourced, the extent to which customers and suppliers are involved). Systems adapt continuously but at a faster rate when threatened, like ant colonies (true kaizen culture). Systems evolve – like bugs combating insecticides. So Lean must learn to recognise and kill off inappropriate tools whilst developing new and stronger ones.

Another analogy is the human body. Layout, supermarkets and buffers provide the skeleton, kanban and material are the circulation system. Eyes and brain give vision and strategy; control, deployment and measurement come from the nervous system, quality and improvement from the muscular system, energy and getting rid of waste come from the digestive system. The body needs them all for fast, flexible flowing human action.

Lean is Process

The Lean Thinker does not think in terms of 'optimising' functions or departments, but in terms of end-to-end value streams comprising the integration of marketing, sales, design, engineering, manufacture, distribution, and service. Note that the shop floor is only a small part. Note also that these are tied together by information. The closer to the customer, and the quicker the response, the better. This means a different type of organization- different structure, different measures, and different careers. Jim Womack identifies the 'perfect process' as one where every step is valuable, capable, available, and adequate, and where all steps are linked by flow, pull, and levelling.

"Mechanical", "Managerial" and "Innovative" Lean

Mechanical Lean is the implementation of Lean tools in a piecemeal fashion. Managerial Lean is the implementation of Lean tools in an integrated manner. Innovative Lean is takes Lean beyond the shop floor, beyond the organisation to create new opportunity, new value, and new customers. Lean often begins with the Mechanical or 'Demonstration'. Since piecemeal benefits are small, executives may then decide to abandon the Lean initiative. Unfortunately they will often have burned their fingers – in time, if not money – and are then discouraged taking further initiatives. Worse, they may even claim to have "done Lean – and it didn't do us much good". In the mid 1990's more powerful tools arrived (or more correctly were rediscovered) – value stream mapping, policy deployment, and the new type of improvement events – and there was increased recognition that Lean must be built on a sound foundation of 5S and standard operations. These enabled a more systematic, more balanced, and more efficient approach. (But note 5S for appearance sake is just decoration.)

Innovative Lean is altogether another matter. Here the question is what business and product opportunities

does Lean create? Like – Vision Express and the one-hour pair of spectacles; like – home bread makers; – like South West Airlines breaking the rules of established carriers. In these examples the customer is primary. Waste reduction and value enhancement are for the customer, not the producer. There may be no greater waste than cutting waste for the producer whilst increasing it for the customer. Stand back and look at the customer being the "object" of one-piece flow. Line up the stages in process order so that the customer can benefit – then use lean concepts of waste, cells, changeover, pull, small machines, OEE and so on to contribute to customer value.

Lean is Revolution and Evolution

The Toyota Production System (TPS) grew through revolution and evolution. Revolution rejected the concepts of mass production and economies of scale, and steered the organisation. Evolution developed the details and the tools. When TPS began there were few Lean tools - most developed from first principles over several decades, but fitting in with the top-level concept. Lean ideas developed from first principles; Taiichi Ohno believed in developing managers by the Socratic method – asking tough questions rather than providing answers. This is in line with the practice of Hoshin or Policy Deployment, whereby top management sets the strategic direction (the what and the why) but evolves the detail level by level by a process of consultation (the how). In the reverse direction decisions are taken locally, only migrating upwards in exceptional circumstances. This is much like the human body's management system. A top-level system that imposes the detailed (Lean) tools, but takes decisions that are in conflict with Lean, is precisely the wrong way around.

Lean is Distributed Decisions

Ohno saw the TPS ideal as minimising the amount of information and control, like the human body where much routine operation is decentralised and self-repair takes place locally. Excess information must be suppressed, said Ohno. Perhaps the greatest opportunity for Lean is not on the shop floor, but in simplification and decentralisation that enable whole swathes of overhead and administration to be eliminated.

Today large ERP systems, with data warehouses are "in". In Lean we have learned about the waste of centralised inventory warehouses as opposed to strategically located supermarkets. The world has learned about the failure of over-centralised economies. But during the late 1990's many manufacturers moved in the opposite direction by implementing large centralised systems – at great cost and often with mixed results. Today's need is for fast reacting distributed decision-making. There is a case for centralised strategic decisions, but for operational decisions, the Lean way is to deal at a localised level with schedules, maintenance, quality, cell design and even some aspects of design and supply at a localised level, but still keeping the end-to-end value stream in mind. This is not only more effective, but also more human. You may want MRP or APS for planning but definitely not for execution. Similarly you may use cost accounting for planning, but not for execution. Organisationally, the essence of the Hoshin process is nemawashi (consensus building) and ringi (shared decision making).

Lean is Service

Waste prevention and value adding are certainly applicable in service. But adaptation is necessary. A new service lean toolbox is emerging, with contributions from six sigma, business process reengineering, service quality, service operations and marketing. It contains adaptations on mapping, demand, service wastes, customer flows and "cells", TPM and OEE applied to the person not the machine. Some are described in this book.

Lean is Build to Order

Build to order was once the only way in which products were made but the then production methods confined benefits to the rich. Then came mass production that gave wide access to products but not to individual preferences. Mass customisation held out the promise of both. Lean concepts are at last making mass customisation a reality. Dell has been a pioneer, and the 3-day car study has worked through the barriers (mainly informational) that are in the way. No doubt Lean thinking and appropriate flow-based IT systems are about to make quick-response BTO a reality in whole

new industries – cars, white goods, furniture, clothing, education and music. For industrial customers, the BTO revolution is beginning in food and electronics.

Lean and Six Sigma

Lean and Six Sigma are no longer at odds, nor should they be. Lean is better at the big picture, at establishing the foundation through activities such as 5S and standard operations, whilst six sigma offers a powerful problem solving methodology through DMAIC. The Lean value stream mapping tools are generally superior but synergistic with those used in six sigma, and concepts such as cellular manufacturing, quality at source, pokayoke, and TPM are entirely synergistic. Six Sigma has shown a lead in the costing of projects, something that is under-developed in Lean. Through the green- and black-belt programs, Six Sigma is succeeding in bringing many improvement and analysis tools to people throughout organisations. To be sure, there are also doubtful practices in Six Sigma, as pointed out by one of the originators, Keki Bhote ex-Motorola quality guru.

However, much of six sigma itself is waste! What can be done to reduce or eliminate that variation before it even arises should be a prime question. Why is Toyota not falling over itself to get after six sigma or alternatively how has it been able to achieve six sigma levels of performance without legions of black belts and statistical software?

Lean is Green

Recently we have seen that not only is it possible to be Lean and 'Green', but in fact that by focusing on the wastes of materials and energy it is positively both profitable and attractive to customers. Pamela Gordon in *Lean and Green* has researched many examples of the successful adoption the three 'R's' (Reduce, Reuse, and Recycle). Hawken, Lovins and Lovins in *Natural Capitalism* go further, giving examples of a carpet made from recycled material that lasts four times longer, is stain proof and can be water cleaned, or windows that remain cool at high temperatures and warm at freezing temperatures thereby drastically reducing the need for air conditioning and central heating. Surely, this is ultimate Lean.

Lean is only beginning

Robert 'Doc' Hall has pointed out that even mighty Toyota regards itself as some way off the Lean ideal. According to Doc, Toyota regards many of its plants as being at stage B on a C to A+ scale. Few Toyota suppliers are at stage B, and most other manufacturers are at stage C. A mastery of tools and principles will only achieve stage B. To achieve stage A+ requires an organization-wide embedding of a questioning, ever-improving culture, innovation and flexibility. The ultimate stage of "Ba" is where there is complete integration of purpose with the customer.

Finally, Lean is Core

In developing the Five Lean Principles Womack and Jones were contributing to the emerging universal principles of operations – which is Lean. Hopefully the days of arguing between "Lean vs. Agile", "Lean vs. APS", "Lean and Six Sigma", "Lean and Theory of Constraints", "Lean and Manufacturing Strategy", and the practice of including a chapter on Lean (or JIT) in operations management textbooks, is passing. (Perhaps not – academics are often the last to change!). Lean is at the core. The principles, good sets of which are set out by Schonberger (see Audits) are universal. It is merely a question of the extent to which other concepts can add to the central developing core of Lean, and vice versa.

Further Reading

Richard Schonberger, *Japanese Manufacturing Techniques*, Free Press, 1982
Robert Hall, *Zero Inventories*, Dow Jones / Irwin/ APICS, 1982
Womack, Jones, and Roos, *The Machine that Changed the World*, Rawson, 1990
EEF, *Catching Up with Uncle Sam*, 2002
Bob Emiliani, 'Lean Behaviours', *Management Decision*, Vol36 No 9, MCB, 1998
Jinichiro Nakane and Robert Hall, 'Ohno's Method', *Target*, First Quarter, 2002
Richard Schonberger, *World Class Manufacturing: The Next Decade*, Free Press, 1996
H Thomas Johnson and Anders Bröms, *Profit Beyond Measure*, Nicholas Brealey, London, 2000
See series of articles by Robert Hall in *Target*, in 2001 and 2002.

Jim Womack, *The Perfect Process*, Presentation, AME Conference, Chicago, 2002

Fast, Flexible Flow

Fast, Flexible Flow is the basis for both 'old' and 'new' Lean in manufacturing and in service. These are a set – all three are necessary. Finding a way of combining them is the best way to achieve huge productivity and quality gains simultaneously. This is the exact opposite of 'batch and queue' operations.

In Lean, Vision is needed. Going for waste reduction, value stream analysis, and policy deployment will not suffice in transformation. Fast, flexible flow is the vision. It turns out to be universal in service and in manufacturing. Whilst fast, flexible flow is the vision or goal, waste and variation prevention and reduction are principle means.

Fast, because speed is at the heart of Lean. To quote Taiichi Ohno, *"All we are doing is looking at the time line…from the moment the customer gives us an order to the point when we collect the cash. And we are reducing that time line by removing the non-value added wastes"*. Think economies of time, not economies of scale. Stalk and Hout made the case eloquently in their seminal work on time-based competition (see separate section). Sufficient speed can be an order-qualifier. But speed is increasingly an order-winner. First to market used to be a risk but increasingly it is a risk not to be first. Customers are often prepared to pay a premium for fast delivery, particularly in service – where a customer's time, whether at work or leisure, is the most finite of commodities. More fundamentally, if 'fast' is the goal it leads automatically to waste reduction, to improved layout, to reduction of 'over-production', to closer working relationships, to better quality, to smaller batches, and to value stream thinking. 'Fast' cuts bureaucracy. Fast development cycles eventually means being a whole generation ahead of the competition.

Flexible, because being a fast flow operation like Henry Ford's Model T is no longer sufficient. Ohno in fact stated that the whole basis of TPS (Toyota Production System) was low cost flexibility. The ideal state of flexibility is a batch size of one and the ultimate market segment is one. A batch size of one offers huge productivity gains from the point of view of the customer but, counter-intuitively, will often be the best policy for the provider. Unfortunately the world has become conditioned to batches; in manufacturing with the so-called economic batch quantity; in public transport where passengers queue and compromise on destination; in education where batches of students of differing ability all follow the same schedule; even at the bakery.

Contrast this with built to order computers, the popularity of cars and road freight, internet education, and home bread making. Flexibility does not mean high variation, however (quite the opposite). Low variation standard work elements can be combined such as at any good restaurant or mixed model line, with suitable mass customisation concepts such as postponement and modularity being used, and with flexible yet standardised labour practices as at BMW. Standardised capacity is added in small increments, not 'monuments', and flexible right-sized technology (not necessarily flexible automation) made use of.

Holweg has usefully examined the types of flexibility and strategies available to a Lean organisation, as shown in the table.

Flow, because 'keep it moving' operations bring waste to the surface. Flow means working steadily at the customer rate, not hurry-up-and wait as in batch and queue, or concentrating on the value-adding seconds whilst ignoring the non-value adding hours. Flow means

Process Flexiblity	Product Flexiblity	Volume Flexiblity	Labour Flexiblity
• **Link customer requirements directly to production,** so that decisions are based on real customer demand, rather than on demand forecasting.	• **Bring customisation closer to the cusotmer** to avoid relying on stocks of finished products.	• **Reduce dependency on full capacity** by negotiating with workers and suppliers.	• Capacity / Time flexibility, in order to adjust labour to demand levels.
• **integrate suppliers** to make orders visible to all value chain partners.	• **Manage product variety** by understanding the cost and profit implications of choice.	• **Diversify production plants,** using dual-plant or multimodal plant strategies to cope with volume variability.	• Skill flexibility, whereby people can fulfil various tasks.
• **Perpetuate sales data through the supply chain** to avoid any time delays and enable a fast response to changes.	• **Make support structures more mutable** to support total responsiveness.	• **Use incentives to manage demand and profits,** rather than reactively discount excess stock.	• Geographical flexibility (ability to move workers between plants).

that value will be added steadily. Flow along a supply chain discourages amplification of demand. 'Going for flow' means not only competitiveness through more satisfied customers but also greater productivity through reducing waiting and inventory. But the focus must be on the customer or object that needs to keep moving, not the operator or service provider. Seek never to delay a value adding activity by a non-value adding activity. Once again, the conventional batch and queue mindset is that flow is non achievable or too costly. The opposite is almost invariably the case. Think takt time for products and customers, maintenance, hospitals, education, and general service. To allow for flow will frequently mean manipulating demand and managing capacity. Convert the job shop to the cell or line, get information to flow, convert static build or maintenance to flow line or 'pulse line', segment patient so they can be 'flowed' in a hospital. Think how customers can be flowed in service situations like quick check-in or checkout, like self-service, like single or fast track queues. Pull systems encourage flow to take place at the rate of demand.

Fast, flexible flow means breaking down barriers between traditional departments. Think value streams, takt time, concurrency, flexible labour, adaptive layouts, small machines, making maximum use of any repetitiveness, appropriate use of buffers, and demand and capacity management.

Roger Schmenner has recently argued that "Swift, Even Flow" is a concept that can be used to explain why some service companies have been more successful and productive than others. This is totally compatible, and evenness is a point worth emphasizing, like heijunka and demand smoothing. Schmenner argues that the trend in service companies is towards low throughput time, low variation operations.

Further reading:
Roger Schmenner, 'How Service Businesses have survived and prospered', *Proc. EurOMA – POMS Conference*, Como, Italy, 2003
Matthias Holweg, *The Three Day Car Challenge*, PhD Thesis, University of Wales, 2002

The Five Lean Principles

In *Lean Thinking*, Womack and Jones renewed the message as set out in *The Machine that Changed the World* (that Lean was, at least in automotive, literally Do or Die), but extended it out beyond automotive. These reflective authors have given manufacturing, but to an extent also service, a vision of a world transformed from mass production to lean enterprise. The five principles set forth are of fundamental importance. Reading the Introduction to *Lean Thinking* should be compulsory for every executive.

In this section, whilst using Womack and Jones' 5 principles, some liberties have been taken. Some managers are upset by the five principles, believing them not to be feasible within their industry. But this is to miss the point, which is vision: you may not get there within your lifetime, but try - others certainly will.

The starting point is to **specify value from the point of view of the customer**. This is an established marketing idea (that customers buy results, not products - a clean shirt, not a washing machine). Too often, however, manufacturers tend to give the customers what is convenient for the manufacturer, or deemed economic for the customer. Womack and Jones cite batch-and-queue airline travel, involving long trips to the airport to enable big batch flights that start where you aren't and take you where you don't want to go, via hubs, and numerous delays much like the aluminium cola can. How often are new product designs undertaken constrained by existing manufacturing facilities rather than by customer requirements? Of course we have to know who is the customer: the final customer, or the next process, or the next company along the chain, or the customer's customer. Start with need – 'holes not drills!'

Then identify the **Value Stream**. This is the sequence of processes all the way from raw material to final customer, or from product concept to market launch. If possible look at the whole supply chain (or probably more accurately the "demand network"). Again, an established idea from TQM / Juran / business processing. You are only as good as the weakest link; supply chains compete, not companies. Concentrate on the viewpoint of the object (or product or customer), not the viewpoint of the department or process step. Economies of time rather than economies of scale. The value stream should be mapped, and a whole section of this book is devoted to this topic. Focus horizontally, not vertically.

The third principle is **Flow**. Make value flow. If possible use one-piece flow. Keep it moving. Avoid batch and queue, or at least continuously reduce them and the obstacles in their way. Try to work according to Stalk and Hout's Golden Rule - never to delay a value adding step by a non value adding (although temporarily necessary) step - try to do such steps in parallel. Flow requires much preparation activity. (A whole chapter is devoted to this). But the important thing is vision: have in mind a guiding strategy that will move you inexorably towards flow.

Then comes **Pull**. Having set up the framework for flow, only make as needed. Pull means short-term response to the customer's rate of demand, and not over producing. Think about pull on two levels: on the macro level most organizations will have to push up to a certain point and respond to final customer pull signals thereafter. The idea is to push this point further and further upstream. On the micro level, there is responding to pull signals from an internal customer that may be the next process step in the case of kanban or an important stage in the case of Drum/Buffer/Rope or CONWIP (see Scheduling section). Attention to both levels is necessary. Of course, pull needs to take place along the whole demand flow network, not only within a company. So this ultimately implies sharing final customer demands right along the chain. Each extension of pull reduces forecast uncertainty.

Finally comes **Perfection**. Having worked through the previous principles, suddenly now "perfection" seems more possible. Perfection does not mean only quality - it means producing exactly what the customer wants, exactly when (with no delay), at a fair price and with minimum waste. Beware of benchmarking - the real benchmark is zero waste, not what the competitors are doing.

One quickly realises that these five principles are not a sequential, one off procedure, but rather a journey of continuous improvement. Start out today.

Further Reading:
James Womack and Daniel Jones, *Lean Thinking*, Simon and Schuster, New York, 1996

The 20 Characteristics of Lean

The literature on JIT and Lean contains several seminal books, amongst them by Womack and Jones, Schonberger, Hall, Goldratt, and Imai. These built on the "greats": Deming, Juran, and Ohno. To distil them is a daunting task, but certainly there are common themes. These 20 seem to be at the core:

- *Customer*. The external customer is the starting and ending point. Seek to maximise value to the customer. Optimise around the customer, not around internal operations. Understand the customer's true demand, in price, delivery and quality - not what can be supplied.

- *Simplicity*. Lean is not simple, but simplicity pervades. Simplicity in operation, in system, in technology, in control, is the goal. Simplicity is best achieved through avoidance of complexity, rather than by 'rationalisation' exercises. Think about ants that run complex adaptive systems without any management information system. Simplicity applies to product through part count reduction and commonality. Simplicity applies to suppliers through working closely with a few trusted partners. Simplicity applies in the plant, by creating focused factories-within-a -factory. Beware complex computer systems, complex and large automation, complex product lines, complex rewards. Select the smallest, most simple machine possible consistent with quality requirements.

- *Waste*. Waste is endemic. Learn to recognise it, and seek to reduce it, always. Everyone from chairman to cleaner should wear "muda spectacles" at all times. Seek to prevent waste by good design of products and processes.

- *Process*. Organise and think by the process view. Think horizontal, not vertical. Concentrate on the way the product moves, not on the way the machines or people or services move. Map to understand the process.

- *Visibility*. Seek to make all operations as visible and transparent as possible. Control by sight. Adopt the visual factory. Make it quick and easy to identify when operations or schedules are diverging.

- *Regularity*. Regularity makes for "no surprises" operations. We run our lives on regularity (sleep, breakfast, etc); we should run our plants on this basis too. Seek "repeater" products and run them in the same time slots - this cuts inventory, improves quality, and allows simplicity of control. "Time pacing" in new product introduction shortens the development cycle and makes innovation the norm.

- *Flow*. Seek "keep it moving at the customer rate", "one piece flow" manufacture. Synchronise operations so that the streams meet just in time. Flow should be the aim at cell level, in company and along supply chains. Synchronise information and physical flows. If you can't flow, at least pulse one at a time or in small batches.

- *Pull*. Seek for operations to work at the customer's rate of demand. Avoid overproduction. Have pull-based demand chains, not push-based supply chains. Pull should take place at the customer's rate of demand. In demand chains this should be the final customer, not distorted by intermediate "bullwhip" effect.

- *Postponement*. Delay activities and committing to product variety as late as possible so as to retain flexibility and to reduce waste and risk. This characteristic is closely associated with the concept of avoiding overproduction, but includes plant and equipment, information, and inventory. Note that this is not the same as simply starting work at the last possible moment, but is about retaining flexibility at the right levels.

- *Prevention*. Seek to prevent problems and waste, rather than to inspect and fix. Shift the emphasis from failure and appraisal to prevention. Inspecting the process, not the product, is prevention. Seek to prevent errors through pokayoke.

- *Time*. Seek to reduce overall time to make, to deliver, and to introduce new products. Use simultaneous, parallel, and overlapping operations in operations, design, and support services. Seek never to delay a value-adding step by a non value-adding step. Time is the best single overall measure. If time reduction is a priority you tend to do all the right things – waste, flow, pull, and perfection.

- *Improvement*. Improvement, and continuous improvement in particular, is everyone's concern. Make improvement both "enforced" and passive, both incremental and breakthrough. Improvement goes beyond waste reduction to include innovation.

- *Partnership*. Seek co-operative working both internally between functions, and externally with suppliers. Seek to use teams, not individuals, internally and externally. Employees are partners too. Seek to build trust. Another way of saying this is *Win-Win*, which is one of Stephen Covey's principles of highly effective people. You can find a win-win, never win-loose, or you should walk away.

- *Value Networks*. The greatest opportunities for cost, quality, delivery and flexibility lie with co-operating networks. Supply chains compete, not companies. But each member also needs to add value. Expand the concept of the one-dimensional supply chain to a two-dimensional value network.

- *Gemba*. Go to where the action is happening and seek the facts. Manage by walking around. Implementation takes place on the floor, not in the office. Encourage the spirit of Gemba throughout.

- *Variation reduction*. Variation in time and quantity is found in every process from supply chain demand amplification to dimensional variation. It is great enemy of Lean. Seek continually to reduce it. Measure it, know the limits, and learn to distinguish between natural variation and special events. Manage it. Build in appropriate flexibility. Shockproof the system.

- *Participation*. Give operators the first opportunity to solve problems. All employees should share responsibility for success and for failure. True participation implies full information sharing.

- *Thinking Small*. Specify the smallest capable machine, and then build capacity in increments. Get best value out of existing machine before acquiring a new one. Break the 'economy of scale' concept by flexible labour and machines. Specify a maximum size of plant to retain 'family focus' and to develop thinking people. Locate small plants near to customer sites, and synchronise with their lines. Internally and externally make many small deliveries rather than few big ones.

- *Trust*. If we truly believe in participation and cutting waste, we have to build trust. Trust allows great swathes of bureaucracy and time to be removed internally and externally. In supply chains, Dyer has shown how trust has enabled Toyota to slash transaction costs (that represent as much as 30% of costs in a company), and enable huge savings in time and people to be made. Building trust with suppliers gives them the confidence to make investments and share knowledge. Internally, trust allows a de-layered, streamlined, and more creative organisation.

- **Knowledge**. Since Peter Drucker's original work on knowledge workers being the engine of today's corporation, the importance of not only building knowledge but distributing it has become increasingly important. Spear and Bowen have shown how Toyota builds knowledge in a systemic, scientific way. Dyer has shown how Toyota cultivates both explicit knowledge (such as tools in this book), but also tacit knowledge, involving softer or stickier skills. It is tacit knowlege that is hard to copy and gives sustainable advantage.

Value

Womack and Jones' first Lean principle is about understanding value; the second is about removing waste. Activities that do not contribute value are waste – either total waste or temporarily necessary non value adding. So we need to understand these concepts a little more deeply. This section considers value, the next section considers waste.

Value enhancement is arguably more important than waste reduction, especially in service. Thus, for example in car servicing, it may prove highly effective to get the technician to 'waste his time' by talking to customers directly rather than through a service agent. And improve value by giving a discount to those owners who do not avail themselves of a courtesy car.

Porter says, "In competitive terms, value is the amount buyers are willing to pay for what a firm provides them. Value is measured by total revenue, a reflection of the price a firms' product commands and the units it can sell".

From a Lean perspective, this is a little too simple. First, there is present value – what present customers are willing to pay for. This is the usual way of identifying waste. Then there is future value – what tomorrow's customers are willing to pay for, but todays may not be. This is relevant in research and development and design. These represent different value streams – so you should not judge a current manufacturing stream in the same way as an R&D stream.

Similarly there are today's customers and tomorrow's customers. And today's customers come in different categories – those that are very valuable, an intermediate set, and a third set that are just not worth having. Possibly your products or services are inappropriately focused. So waste may be different depending on the customer group, for instance the pensioner chatting to a checkout attendant and a time-hassled businessman.

One straightforward interpretation of value is Perceived Benefit / Perceived Sacrifices. (Saliba and Fisher). Benefits may accrue before, during, or after the event. (Think of drink or sex!). Sacrifices may be in terms of cost, convenience, time, or exchange. There are probably upper bounds on sacrifices that a customer is willing to pay, and lower bounds on benefits – like Kano basics. Both are dynamic.

Zeithaml and Bitner talk about four meanings for value. First, 'value is low price'. For these customers, lowest price is best. This is the ultimate Lean – cut all activities that do not directly contribute to product or service value in the short term. No frills. Second, 'value is whatever I want in a product or service'. This focuses on benefits, not price. This is the classic marketing approach – selling the experience of owning a top-brand pair of trainers rather than the shoes themselves. Or of a drill company selling holes not drills. Here, the Lean company needs to understand their customer's requirements deeply – so 'wasted' market research or image creation may not in fact be waste. The classic marketing statement – 'we know half of our promotional activities are waste, but we don't know which half' comes to mind. Third, 'value is quality I get for what I pay' – here expectations are directly linked to price – pay more, expect more. Having standby services or extra inventory may be expected because the price is so high. Fourthly, 'value is what I get for what I give' - all benefits against all sacrifices, not just money. A luxury car may be worth the price and the wait but of course, customer satisfaction may increase if the wait decreases.

To borrow from service management, value is a "Moment of Truth" experience – the totality of all the experiences. So value is getting the exact product you require, in the right quantity, at the right time, with perfect quality of course, and at the right price. This is a multiplicative effect – a car on which you compromise for colour, delivered a week late, with minor faults, and including extras which you don't want but are asked to pay for.

Kano, speaking about quality, talks about "Basics", "Performance Factors", and "Delighters". (See separate section). Much the same can be said about value. There are some activities that are basic to value – defect free has become a basic in some industries. There is "performance" value – lead time for example in some businesses, and "delighter" value. Moreover, as in the Kano model, value is dynamic.

Reference:
Michael Saliba and Caroline Fisher, 'Managing Customer Value', *Quality Progress*, June 2000, pp63-69
Valerie Zeithaml and Mary Bitner, *Services Marketing*, second edition, McGrawHill, 2000

Waste (Muda)

Muda" is Japanese for waste. Waste is strongly linked to Lean. But
- Waste elimination is a means to achieving the Lean ideal – it is not an end in itself.
- Waste prevention is at least as important as waste elimination.
- Value is the converse of waste. Any organisation needs to continually improve the ratio of value adding to non-value adding activities. But there are two ways to do this – by preventing and reducing waste, but also by going after value enhancement specifically.

Taiichi Ohno, father of the Toyota Production System, and patriarch of Lean Operations, originally assembled the 7 wastes, but it was Deming who emphasised waste reduction in Japan in the 1950's. Today, however, it is appropriate to add to Ohno's famous list, presumptuous though that may be. The section after next begins with Ohno's original seven, then adds "new" wastes for manufacturing and service.

TPS refers to 'Muda, Mura and Muri'. Mura refers unevenness – one should be particularly concerned with self-induced unevenness, for example end-of-month sales targets which induce the end-of-month 'hockey stick' demand pattern. Muri refers to work that is hard to do – not the waste of motion to be discussed later, but difficult or awkward, such as a difficult adjustment or calculation that is required to be performed. Note that there are service parallels here. Mura – a bunching of customers at check-in. Muri – confusing data entry.

Type 1 and Type 2 Muda, Elimination and Prevention

Womack and Jones usefully talk about two types of waste. *Type 1 Muda* are activities that create no value but are currently necessary to maintain operations. These activities do not do anything for customers, but may well assist the managers or stakeholders other than customers or shareholders. Type 1 should be reduced through simplification. It may well prove to be greatest bottom-line benefit of Lean. Moreover, Type 1 muda is the easiest to add to but difficult to remove, so prevention of type 1 muda should be in the mind of every manager in every function. *Type 2 Muda* creates no value, in fact destroys value, for any stakeholder, including customers, shareholders, and employees. Elimination should be a priority. Type 2 tends to grow by 'stealth', or carelessness.

Waste Elimination is achieved, as Dan Jones would say, by 'wearing muda spectacles' (a skill that must be developed), and by kaizen (both 'point' and 'flow' varieties). Elimination is assisted by 5S activities, standard work, mapping, level scheduling and by amplification reduction. Ohno was said to require new managers to spend several hours in a chalk circle, standing in one place and observing waste. This should happen more frequently in offices, in warehouses, and in factories.

Waste Prevention is another matter. Womack and Jones talk about the eighth waste – making the wrong product perfectly – but it goes beyond that. Waste prevention cannot be done by wearing muda spectacles, but requires strong awareness in system, process, and product design. It is known that perhaps 80% of costs are fixed at the design stage. Of that 80%, a good proportion will be waste. System design waste prevention involves thinking through the movement of information, products and customers through the future system. (For instance, questioning the necessity for ERP and the selection of far-removed suppliers). Process design waste prevention involves the avoidance of 'monuments', the elimination of adjustments, and working with future customers and suppliers to ensure that future processes are as waste-free as possible. (For instance, selecting as much flexibility as possible in machines and plant layout). Product design waste prevention involves the rationalisation of parts – perhaps through Group Technology, of operations - perhaps through Design for Assembly; and of variability – perhaps through Design for Six Sigma. Prevention involves much more careful pre-design considerations. It also involves keeping options open via 'mass customisation' and recycling considerations. Of course, pokayoke is a prime technique for defect prevention in service and manufacturing.

In the opinion of the author, waste prevention is likely to assume a far greater role than waste elimination in the Lean organisation of the future – in the same way that prevention in quality is now widely regarded as more effective than inspection and fault elimination.

Ohno's 7 Wastes

You can remember the seven wastes by asking, "Who is TIM WOOD?" Answer: Transport, Inventory, Motion, Waiting, Overproduction, Over-processing, and Defects. (This idea came from the Lean Office at Cooper Standard, Plymouth, UK.)

In all these wastes, the priority is to avoid, only then to cut.

The Waste of Overproduction

Ohno believed that the waste of overproduction was the most serious of all the wastes because it was the root of so many problems and other wastes. Overproduction is making too much, too early or "just-in-case". Working a bottleneck resource with the wrong product or an inappropriate batch size. The aim should be to make exactly what is required, no more and no less, just in time and with perfect quality. Overproduction discourages a smooth flow of goods or services. "Lumpiness" (i.e. making products or working in erratic bursts) is a force against quality and productivity. By contrast, regularity encourages a "no surprises" atmosphere that may not be very exciting but is much better management.

Overproduction leads directly to excessive lead time and storage times. As a result defects may not be detected early, products may deteriorate, and artificial pressures on work rate may be generated. All these increase the chances of defects. Taking it further, overproduction leads to excessive work-in-process inventories that lead to the physical separation of operations and the discouragement of communication. Overproduction also impacts the waste of motion – making and moving things that are not immediately required.

Yet overproduction is often the natural state. People do not have to be encouraged to overproduce; they often do so "just to be safe". Often this is reinforced by a bonus system that encourages output that is not needed. By contrast, a pull system helps prevent unplanned overproduction by allowing work to move forwards only when the next work area is ready to receive it. It has application in service also. Hamburgers are only made at a rate in line with demand and clerical operations are most effective when there is a uniform flow of work. The motto "sell daily? make daily!" is as relevant in an office as it is in a factory.

Overproduction should be related to a particular timeframe – first reduce overproduction (or early delivery) in a week, then a day, then an hour.

Quality guru Joseph Juran noted that in Japan in the 1950s there were severe disruptions in power supplies, with production sometimes possible for only 3 hours per day. In such circumstances making the wrong product, or making it too early, or working on an already defective item was something to be strongly avoided. Likewise the transport infrastructure was awful. Transporting the wrong item, too early, or if defective was also a huge waste. It was in these circumstances

that Taiichi Ohno developed the JIT system, and led him to conclude that overproduction is the worst sin of all.

The Waste of Waiting

The waste of waiting is probably the second most important waste. It is directly relevant to FLOW. In Lean we are more concerned with flow of product than we are with keeping operators busy.

In a factory, any time that materials or components are seen to be not moving (or not having value added) is an indication of waste. Waiting is the enemy of smooth flow. Although it may be very difficult to reduce waiting to zero, the goal remains. Whether the waiting is for parts in a factory or of customers in a bank there should always be an awareness of a non-ideal situation and a questioning of how the situation can be improved. Waiting is directly relevant to lead time – an important source of competitiveness and customer satisfaction.

When operators and employees are waiting for work or simply waiting for something to do, it is waste. Can the time not be better spent on another operation or on training, cleaning, maintaining, checking, and practising changeovers or even deliberate relaxation? All of these are forces for improved quality and productivity. But they require management to have developed a contingency plan on the best use of time.

A bottleneck operation that is waiting for work is a waste. As Goldratt has pointed out in his book "The Goal", "an hour lost at a bottleneck is an hour lost for the whole plant". Effective use of bottleneck time is a key to regular production that in turn strongly influences productivity and quality. (See the section on Scheduling). By the way, a non-bottleneck waiting for work may also be a waste – of opportunity for improved flow through smaller batches.

Examples: materials waiting in queue, operators waiting, operators slower than line, operators watching machines, late delivery, queuing at a tool crib.

The Waste of Unnecessary Motions

Next in importance is probably the waste of motion.

Unnecessary motions refer to both human and machine. The human dimension relates to the importance of ergonomics for quality and productivity and the enormous proportion of time that is wasted at *every* workstation by non-optimal layout. (A QWERTY keyboard for example is non-optimal). If operators have to stretch, bend, pick-up, move in order to see better, or in any way unduly exert themselves, the victim is immediately the operator but ultimately quality and productivity.

An awareness of the ergonomics of the workplace is not only ethically desirable, but economically sound. Toyota, famous for its quality, is known to place a high importance on "quality of worklife". Toyota encourages all its employees to be aware of working conditions that contribute to this form of waste. Today, of course, motion waste is also a health and safety issue.

The machine dimension involves poor workplace layout, leading to micro wastes of movement. These wastes are often repeated many, many times per day – sometimes without anyone noticing. In this regard 5S (later section) can be seen as the way to attack motion waste.

Examples: bending, reaching, double handling at the workplace, more than one turn to loosen a nut, walking between widely spaced workcentres.

The Waste of Transporting (or Conveyance)

Customers do not pay to have goods moved around (unless they have hired a removal service!). So any movement of materials is waste. It is a waste that can never be fully eliminated but it is also a waste that over time should be continually reduced. The number of transport and material handling operations is directly proportional to the likelihood of damage and deterioration. Double handling is a waste that affects productivity and quality.

Transporting is closely linked to communication. Where distances are long, communication is discouraged and quality may be the victim. Feedback on poor quality is inversely related to transportation length, whether in manufacturing or in services. There is increasingly the awareness that for improved quality in manufacturing or services, people from interacting groups need to be located physically closer together. For instance, the design office may be placed deliberately near the production area.

As this waste gains recognition, steps can be taken to reduce it. Measures include monitoring the flow lengths of products through a factory or paper through an office. The number of steps, and in particular the number of non-value adding steps should be monitored. See the Section on Mapping.

Many conveyors represent poor practice because they "freeze in" the waste of transporting. A forklift truck is often a bad idea in several ways – too big, too inflexible, moving too large a batch, and having to wait for it to arrive.

The Waste of Overprocessing (or Inappropriate Processing)

Overprocessing refers to the waste of "using a hammer to crack a nut". Thinking in terms of one big machine instead of several smaller ones discourages operator "ownership", leads to pressure to run the machine as often as possible rather than only when needed, and encourages general purpose machines that may not be ideal for the need at hand. It also leads to poor layout, which as we have seen in the previous section, leads to extra transportation and poor communication. So the ideal is to use the smallest machine, capable of producing the required quality, distributed to the points of use.

How many have fallen into buying a machine centre, that accountants then demand to be kept busy, so routings are changed and batches encouraged, soon to be followed by complex routings and schedules, leading to demands for a finite scheduling system?

Inappropriate processing also refers to machines and processes that are not quality capable. In other words, a process that cannot help but make defects. In general, a capable process requires having the correct methods, training, and tools, as well as having the required standards, clearly known. The ideal is to have machines with available capacity exactly matched to demand.

Note that it is important to take the longer-term view. Buying that large machining centre may just jeopardise the possibility of cells for many years to come. Think "small is beautiful". Smaller machines avoid bottlenecks, improve flow lengths, perhaps are simpler, can be maintained at different times (instead of affecting the whole plant), and may improve cash flow and keep up with technology (buying one small machine per year, instead of one big machine every five years).

Examples: "monuments", variation between operators, variation from standard, having to use a "fast" machine shared between several lines.

The Waste of Unnecessary Inventory

Although having no inventory is a goal that can never be attained, inventory is the enemy of quality and productivity. This is so because inventory tends to increase leadtime, prevents rapid identification of problems, and increases space thereby discouraging communication. The true cost of extra inventory is very much in excess of the money tied up in it. "Push" systems almost invariably lead to this waste.

Note the three types of inventory: raw material, work in process, and finished goods. The existence of any of these is waste, but their root causes and priorities for reduction are different. FGI must sometimes be held to meet demand, but is best regarded as a 'wall of shame'. It also represents risk of obsolescence. Raw material may be temporarily necessary due to supplier constraints – quality and reliability. WIP is entirely under your own control.

Just-in-time (JIT) manufacturing has taught that inventory deliberately hides problems by covering them up. So, perhaps, a quality problem is not considered important because there are always extra parts available if one is defective. JIT encourages deliberate inventory reduction to uncover this sort of problem. Cut the safety inventory. If nothing happens - fine, you have learned to operate with a leaner system. If stoppage occurs - good, because the problem has been recognised and can now be attacked at its root cause.

Examples: inventory exceeding specified quantity limit, so much inventory at workplace that double handling is needed, and excessive safety stock.

The Waste of Defects

The last, but not least, of Ohno's wastes is the waste of defects. Defects cost money, both immediate and longer term. In Quality Costing the failure or defect categories are internal failure (scrap, rework, delay) and external failure (including warranty, repairs, field service, but also possibly lost custom). Bear in mind that defect costs tend to escalate the longer they remain undetected. Thus a faulty microchip discovered when made might cost just a few dollars to replace, but if it reaches the customer may cost hundreds, to say nothing of customer goodwill. So, central themes of total quality are "prevention not detection", "quality at source", and "the chain of quality" (meaning that parts per million levels of defect can only be approached by concerted action all along the chain from marketing, to design, to supply, to manufacture, to distribution, to delivery, to field service.) The Toyota philosophy is that a defect should be regarded as a challenge, as an opportunity to improve, rather than something to be traded off against what is ultimately poor management.

In service, "zero defections" has become a powerful theme, recognising that the value of a retained customer increases with time.

Examples: scrap, rework, less than perfect yield, complaints.

The New Wastes

These may be added to Ohno's original list, and are appropriate in service and manufacturing:

The Waste of Making the Wrong Product Efficiently.

This is Womack and Jones' eighth waste. It is really a restatement of the first Lean principle.

The Waste of Untapped Human Potential

Ohno was reported to have said that the real objective of the Toyota Production System was "to create thinking people". So this "new" waste is directly linked to Ohno. The 1980s were the decade of factory automation folly. GM and many others learnt the hard and expensive way that the automated factory and warehouse that does not benefit from continuous improvement and ongoing thought is doomed in the productivity race.

Today we have numerous examples, from total quality to self directed work teams, of the power of utilising the thoughts of all employees, not just managers. Of numerous examples, that of Proctor and Gamble that ran several similar factories differentiated only by worker empowerment is one of the most striking. The "empowered" plants were up to 50% more productive. Several sections of this book, on Hoshin, on People, on 5 S, on improvement, on TPM, have as their foundation the liberation of operator involvement and creativity.

Human potential does not just need to be set free. It requires clear communication as to what is needed (both from management and to management), it requires commitment and support (because uncapping human potential is sometimes seen as a real threat to first line and middle managers), it requires a culture of trust and mutual respect (which cannot be won by mere lofty words, but by example, interest and involvement at the workplace ("Gemba")). Basic education is also necessary. The retort to the question, "What happens if I train them and they go?" should be "What happens if you don't train them and they stay!"

Examples: Not using the creative brainpower of employees, not listening, thinking that only managers have ideas worth pursuing.

The Waste of Inappropriate Systems

How much software in your computer is never used (not the packages, but the actual code)? The same goes for MRPII, now repackaged as ERP.

The Lean way is to remove waste before automating, or as Michael Hammer would say "don't automate, obliterate!" The waste of inappropriate systems should not be confined to computers and automation. Indeed, how much record keeping, checking, reconciling, is pure waste? (Recall the categories of waste)

Recently, for example in the 3 Day Car project the waste of inappropriate systems has been highlighted. It is the order processing system, not the Shopfloor that is the greatest barrier. Often, it's not the operations that consume the time and the money; it's the paperwork or systems. And we now understand a little more of the dangers of demand amplification, of inappropriate forecasting, and of measurement systems that make people do what is best for them but not best for the company. All this is waste.

Wasted Energy and Water

Energy here refers to sources of power: electricity, gas, oil, coal, and so on. The world's finite resources of most energy sources (except sun and wind) were highlighted in a famous report "The Limits to Growth" written by the Club of Rome in 1970. Their dire predictions have not come to pass but the true impact of unwise energy use on the world's environments is growing. Wasting these resources is not only a significant source of cost for many companies, but there is also the moral obligation of using such resources wisely.

Although energy management systems in factory, office and home have grown in sophistication there still remains the human, common sense element: shutting down the machine, switching off the light, fixing the drip, insulating the roof, taking a full load, efficient routing, and the like. (By the way, the JIT system of delivery does not waste energy when done correctly: use "milkrounds", picking up small quantities from several suppliers in the same area, or rationalise suppliers so as to enable mixed loads daily rather than single products weekly.)

Several companies that have "institutionalised" waste reduction, Toyota included, believe that a good foundation for waste awareness begins with everyday wastes such as switching off lights and printers. You get into the habit.

Wasted Materials

Today conservation of materials is not only environmentally responsible, but is beginning to be profitable. To reduce the waste of materials a life cycle approach is needed, to conserve materials during design, during manufacture, during customer usage, and beyond customer use in recovery and remanufacturing.

Seven Service Wastes

Most of the above wastes are seen from the organisations perspective. What about the customer's perspective? Perhaps an improvement programme should begin with the service wastes:

- *Delay* on the part of customers waiting for service, for delivery, in queues, for response, not arriving as promised. The customer's time may seem free to the provider, but when she takes custom elsewhere the pain begins.

- *Duplication.* Having to re-enter data, repeat details on forms, copy information across, answer queries from several sources within the same organisation.

- *Unnecessary Movement.* Queuing several times, lack of one-stop, poor ergonomics in the service encounter.

- *Unclear Communication*, and the wastes of seeking clarification, confusion over product or service use, wasting time finding a location that may result in misuse or duplication.

- *Incorrect Inventory.* Out-of-stock, unable to get exactly what was required, substitute products or services.

- *Opportunity Lost* to retain or win customers, failure to establish rapport, ignoring customers, unfriendliness, and rudeness.

- *Errors* in the service transaction, product defects in the product-service bundle, lost or damaged goods.

Further reading:
Taiichi Ohno / Japan Management Association, *Kanban: Just-in-Time at Toyota*, Productivity Press, 1985
James Womack and Daniel Jones, *Lean Thinking*,

Simon and Schuster, New York, 1996
John Bicheno, *The Quality 75*, PICSIE Books, Buckingham, 2001

Agile Operations

The term 'Agile' is sometimes touted as an 'alternative' to Lean. There are two issues:
- What is meant by Agile?
- Where and how can it be used?

What is Agile?

'Agile', as of now, seems to be a vague concept – meaning flexible automation to some, or excess capacity, or rapid response, or virtual networks of cooperating companies, or even 'being like a gazelle' (to quote one proponent). Nevertheless, being agile is a useful if not essential goal for *all* operations.

In the opinion of the writer, there has been a large amount of frankly incorrect, misleading waste written attempting to compare lean with agile and to identify market segments for each, or claiming 'distinct differences' by using selective quotations. For instance, one comparison shows product variety as low for lean supply and high for agile supply, and customer drivers being cost for lean and availability for agile.

Harrison and van Hoek have made a serious attempt to identify the characteristics of Agile but equate Lean with waste reduction, saying "where demand is volatile, and customer requirement for variety is high, the elimination of waste becomes a lower priority than responding rapidly to the turbulent marketplace". Five points: (1) In Lean waste is the *means*, not an end in itself. (2) The first Lean (and TPS principle) is to begin with the customer; it is not primarily about waste, it is about the customer's value which implies reducing waste as something that does not contribute to the customer (3) *appropriate* inventory, people, and machines is not waste – especially when combined with TOC where the deliberate location of inventory is a requirement; and (4) reduction in lead time is a central

Lean objective and the best route to rapid response is by the adoption of Lean concepts. If you do not use Lean concepts, how do you respond rapidly? Excess capacity? (5) Is fast, flexible flow Lean or agile – it doesn't matter.

Take Dell. Computers are assembled in small cells grouped into lines for desktops, laptops, and servers. Cells are opened and closed at short notice. Operators are often moved to busier lines. Inventory is minimised and flow is maximised. Design for assembly is used extensively. It is also a 100% customer pull system. Waste reduction – in reducing inventory, packing boxes, components, space, and most of all time – is extensive. Dell also manages orders by giving customers 'special offers' and free upgrades that help with inventory turns and reduce risk of obsolescence. Is this Agile or is this Lean? At Dell, it seems, all 5 Lean principles are in place.

Kidd makes the useful statement that Lean Operations are necessary but not sufficient for Agile Manufacturing. Ansari however says, "Lean Production is a broad concept and encompasses terms such as flexible manufacturing, mass customisation, and even agile manufacturing". A supreme example of Agility built on Lean was shown in the case of the Aisin fire. This single-source Toyota supplier of P-valves suffered a catastrophic fire in February 1997. Within days, the network of Toyota suppliers, many of which had no experience in manufacturing these products, were sending them to Aisin for inspection prior to shipment to Toyota. The problem-solving mentality and spirit of partnership fostered by Toyota were probably the main reasons why only a few days assembly line production was lost. Other reasons were the breadth and depth of engineering skills, the willingness to solve the problem first and sort out compensation later and the existence of a supplier association. If anything, the experience reinforced the commitment to JIT and Lean.

What about Flexibility and Agile? A quick view is that Flexibility has been added to the Cost, Quality and Delivery (time and reliability) objectives of Lean. Holweg and Pils say that 'the best way to reduce waste in the overall system is to build to order (BTO). This requires flexibility across the entire value chain –

material, information, and design. They suggest that in a BTO strategy, the first question to ask is the impact on customer value (How much is the customer willing to pay for reduced leadtime, more variety, etc), and then to address the questions in terms of three flexibility dimensions: Process flexibility (linking production more closely to actual demand, small machines, supply chain cooperation), Product flexibility (bringing customisation and variety closer to customers), and Volume flexibility (via working arrangements such as annualised hours, or plant diversification, and managing demand). This is useful, and worthy of consideration by any manufacturer. (See page 9).

Perhaps it is useful to distinguish between 'tight' Lean and 'loose' Lean – in much the same way as tight and loose kanban. Loose Lean would place more emphasis on flexibility.

Agile Networks

From a wider perspective, "Agility" may involve bringing together core skills and competencies from several organisations in order to achieve convenience, flexibility, cost and service. An agile partnership may be for a short or longer period, and will involve partners who often regard each other as equals irrespective of differences in size. The important thing is that each partner brings certain unique core skills to the party.

An Agile manufacturer may be a "virtual" organisation (like virtual computer memory) that may not exist physically as one unit, but appears to customers as a single unit. An agile manufacturer may be dominated by a single organisation (referred to as a "prime web") or not (referred to as a "democratic web"). In a prime web, the largest company may not be the prime site - what counts is the core product.

Benetton is an agile manufacturer of the prime web type, which co-operates with many designers and manufacturers in Italy, and with many shops throughout the world, most of which use the name but are privately owned. Benetton itself also contributes design and manufacturing competence but leverages itself with computer technology. In another case, Ross Operating Valves of Georgia USA uses its own CAD software capability to design valves on a customer's site, and then download to its own manufacturing facilities or those of a third party which may be better placed geographically. Mass customisation principles are applicable in both these cases. See the separate section on the topic.

With the extension of Internet use, the possibilities for establishing and running agile manufacturing improves every day but is generally yet to emerge. Small companies and even individuals are apparently moving towards becoming members of agile or virtual manufacturing companies. Thus an agile or virtual manufacturer may be able, simultaneously, to achieve fast time to market, at low cost, whilst minimising risk, and gaining access to markets beyond the scope of most of the partners taken individually. But is that just theory?

Conclusion: Of course it would be dangerous and dogmatic to say that there is no alternative to Lean and to dismiss Agile. At this stage, "Agile" remains a vague concept but a worthy goal. Do challenge any Agile advocate to say *exactly* what they would do in a *specific* situation. How would they decide on capacity and inventory and how would they layout, schedule, design and purchase? Compare their answers with Lean concepts.

It seems that to be Agile is indeed an objective of many manufacturing operations. The term is entering into common usage. But at the same time, there is no distinct body of knowledge relating to agile – at least not yet. To be agile you have to be Lean. They are inextricably linked. To quote Anand Sharma, "A lean operation that matches production to current orders maintains agility".

Where and how can Agile be used?

Harrison and van Hoek give three ways in which Lean and Agile can combine. The first is via the Pareto curve – with Lean adopted for the 20% A class, high volume products having 80% of demand, and Agile used for the 80% products accounting for 20% of demand. Two points: (a) Even in high variety manufacturers there is frequently commonality in subassemblies, and (b) one should always strive to convert 'strangers' into 'repeaters' and 'repeaters' into runners'. Nevertheless,

thinking in terms of Pareto analysis for priority areas for Lean implementation is useful. See the section on The Essential Paretos.

The second way is by use of the Decoupling Point or postponement principle. Generic product is made up to the decoupling point, and customer variety added beyond it. They suggest using Lean up to the decoupling point and Agile after the decoupling point. Three points: (a) Postponement is a long-established concept in Lean. In fact, Ohno spoke about winning the bet on every horse race by placing the bet just before the horse crosses the line. (b) As waste is removed and lead time shortened, so the decoupling point can be moved upstream. The ultimate is complete Lean Build to Order where customer-expected lead time is longer than the build time. (c) There is no reason not to use the full suite of Lean concepts on both sides of the decoupling point – as Mercedes Benz does in building the 3 billion variants of the E class, downstream, but also building buffers of sufficient variety upstream. In a Lean system we often locate the single 'pacemaker' at the decoupling point – see the section on Future State (2). But, thinking strategically about decoupling is useful in Lean design.

Harrison and van Hoek's third method is to differentiate between 'Surge' demand and 'Base' demand. Use Lean for base and Agile for surge. From a Lean perspective, the first questions must be 'why is there surge demand?' and can it be reduced? (See the sections on demand amplification and demand management.) Then the next questions relate to how best to manage the fluctuations – via supermarket inventories ("wall of shame") and if so, *where* in the company and the supply chain, or via excess capacity – machine, labour, both, flexitime, annualised hours, subcontracting, and so on. For example, you may be able to run a very Lean but responsive system using annualised hours. Under TPS there is a hierarchy for managing fluctuating demand: first, finished goods; second, limited overtime; third, adjust takt time and vary the number of operators. Nevertheless the long established idea of base and surge demand is useful to Lean.

Conclusion? These three methods of 'combining Lean and Agile' are three useful considerations, but they are not about the integration of two systems.

Further Reading:
Steven Goldman, Roger Nagel, Kenneth Preiss, *Agile Competitors and Virtual Organisations*, van Nostrand Rienhold, New York, 1995
Michael Cusumano and Kentaro Nobeoka, *Thinking Beyond Lean*, The Free Press, New York, 1998
Toshihiro Nishiguchi and Alexandre Beaudet, The Toyota Group and the Aisin Fire, *Sloan Management Review*, Fall 1998, pp 49-59
Alan Harrison and Remko van Hoek, *Logistics Management and Strategy*, FT Prentice Hall, London, 2002
Matthias Holweg and Frits Pil, "Successful Build to Order Strategies start with the Customer", *MIT Sloan Management Review*, Fall 2001, pp 74-83

Time Based Competition

The reduction of lead time – in manufacturing, in supply chains (including information flows), and in design is central in Lean. Stalk and Hout's classic work, *Competing Against Time*, was one of the first to identify the importance of time to the competitive edge. In the book, Stalk and Hout set out four "rules of response" which are provocative rules of thumb, but apparently based on research by the Boston Consulting Group.

- *The 0.05 to 5 rule*, states that, across many industries, value is actually being added for between 0.05% and 5% of total time. (This is no longer a surprise; see for instance the earlier section on Lean Thinking).

- *The 3/3 rule*, states that the wait time, during which no value is added, is split 3 ways, each accounting for approximately one third of time. The three ways are waiting for completion of batches, waiting for "physical and intellectual rework", and waiting for management decisions to send the batch forward.

- *The 1/4-2-20 rule*, which states that for every quartering of total completion time, there will be a doubling of productivity and a 20% cost reduction.

- *The 3 x 2 rule*, states that time based competitors enjoy growth rates of three times the average, and twice the profit margin, for their industry.

Note that there may be good reasons for emphasising speed or reduction in lead-time even though customers may not be interested in reduced lead times. This was revealed in the 3 Day Car project where it was found that some customers were not interested in having a car in three days, but this fact could allow those that require short lead times to be catered for.

Becoming a time-based competitor is really what this book is all about. Like Womack and Jones, Stalk and Hout recommend process mapping. They talk about the "Golden Rule of Time Based Competitiveness" which is never to delay a customer value adding step by a non-value adding step. Instead, seek to do such steps in parallel.

Further reading:
George Stalk and Thomas Hout, **Competing Against Time**, The Free Press, New York, 1990

Gemba

"Gemba" is the place of action – often but not necessarily the workplace. But this Japanese word has taken on significance far beyond its literal translation. Taiichi Ohno, legendary Toyota engineer and father of TPS, said, "Management begins at the workplace". This whole philosophy can best be captured by the single word: Gemba. Of course, Gemba is by no means confined to the factory.

Contrast the Gemba way with the traditional (Western?) way. The Gemba way is to go to the place of action and collect the FACTS. The traditional way is to remain in the office and to discuss OPINIONS. Gemba can be thought of in terms of the "four actuals": Go to the actual workplace, look at the actual process, observe what is actually happening, and collect the actual data.

Under Gemba, if your organisation has a problem or a decision, go to Gemba first. Do not attempt to resolve problems away from the place of action. Do not let operators come to the manager, let the manager go to the workplace. Spend time on the factory floor or at the service counter. This is the basis of so much Japanese management practice: that new Honda management recruits should spend time working in assembly and in stores, that marketers from Nikon should spend time working in camera shops, that Toyota sends its Lexus design team to live in California for three months, and so on. Ohno was famous for his "chalk circle" approach - drawing a circle in chalk on the factory floor and requiring a manager to spend several hours inside it whilst observing operations and taking note of wastes. The West too has its devotees. John Sainsbury who ran the supermarket chain in its heyday could pass a shelf and see at a glance if prices were wrong. His retirement may account for the decline of a once-great chain. An open plan office, with senior management sitting right there with "the troops" is Gemba.

Gemba is, or should be, part of implementation. How often is the Western way based on "change agents", on simulation, on computers or information systems, on classroom-based education? These have a place, of course, but Gemba emphasises implementation by everyone, at the workplace, face-to-face, based on in-depth knowledge. And low cost.

Gemba is often combined with other elements. The 5 Whys, Muda (or waste), Hoshin, Kaizen, 5 S, 7 tools, and as a central part of Total Quality. Gemba is the glue for all of these. So today one hears of "Gemba Kanri", "Gemba Kaizen", and "Gemba TPM". The word has already appeared in the English and American dictionary.

Further reading:
Masaaki Imai, *Gemba Kaizen*, McGraw-Hill, New York, 1997

Lean Frameworks

In this section the map of the book is developed, which is intended to help with the grouping of the tools that follow. The sections are presented as steps a hierarchical fashion, from top level to detailed level.

This book is really about Lean Transformation. It may describe tools, but unless the tools are organized in an appropriate sequence they will be futile. So this section sets out the steps to Lean Transformation beginning at the general level in the first box and then in greater detail in the boxes that follow. Each of the 12 main steps to Lean Transformation contains steps within itself. Each of these sub-steps is cross referenced to a section in the book.

Although presented in a uni-directional hierarchical manner, in fact there will be numerous feedback loops. It is as well to have in mind that transformation will involve moving around Plan Do Check Act cycles, and cycles within a cycle.

Lean Transformation

Graham McKendry of Wesinghouse believes there are five stages for Lean Transformation. These are (1) Building the business case, (2) Establishing 'Gemba' leadership - where leaders have bought into a hands-on, participaticve style, (3) Developing key people and the culture - including freeing up key people (a transformation cannot be done part-time), (4) Mapping and analysis, (5) Focused improvement and systematic improvement - both are necessary. Graham talks about 'right to left' transformation - beginning with the vision and working back to what is needed, rather than left to right, moving slowly and incrementally ahead from the current state. Certainly, direction is needed at an early stage. Full-blown Policy Deployment comes later. Some strategies will only emerge after Lean capability is established. The framework below is therefore iterative.

Step	Activity
1	Understanding the principles
2	Understanding Customers
3	Strategy, Planning and Communication
4	Understanding the System and Mapping
5	Product Rationalization and Lean Design
6	Implementing the Foundation Stones
7	The Value Stream Implementation Cycle
8	Building a Lean Culture
9	Working Lean Supply
10	Working Lean Distribution
11	Costing and Measuring
12	Improving and Sustaining

1. Understanding the Principles

No	Description and Book Section
1	Lean Thinking
2	Fast, Flexible Flow
3	Five Lean Principles
4	Value and Waste
5	20 Characteristics of Lean
6	Time Based Competition
7	Gemba

2. Understanding Customers

Step	Activity	Book sections
1	Understanding customers	Lean Principles, Value, Kano
2	Segmenting customers	Supply chains
3	Understand demand	Demand management
4	Understand product characteristics	Manuf Strategy (order winners), Quality Function Deployment

3. Strategy, Planning, and Communication

Step	Activity	Book sections
1	Establishing the Strategy and Vision	Manufacturing Strategy, Value stream economics, Disruptive Technology, Value and Waste
2	Clarify tradeoffs	Time, Cost, Performance, Resources, Design (4 objectives)
3	Form focus factories	Product Family Analysis
4	Planning	Scenarios, Target Costing
5	Deployment	Hoshin / Policy Deployment,

4. Understanding the System and Mapping

Step	Activity	Book sections
1	Audit	Lean Audits
2	Pareto Analysis	The essential Paretos; Part, material and tool simplification
3	Product Family Analysis	Product Family Analysis
4	Basic Mapping	Basic Mapping Tools
5	Activity Sampling	Activity Sampling
6	Secondary Mapping	Detailed mapping tools
7	Supply Chain Mapping	Seeing the Whole
8	Shop floor Mapping	Work combination, Cell layout

5. Product Rationalization and Design

Step	Activity	Book Sections
1	Simplify parts	The essential Paretos; Part, Material and tool simplification
2	Organize for Lean design	Set Based Design
3	Link products to Customers	Quality Function Deployment Target costing
4	Consider design objectives and tradeoffs	Four objectives and six tradeoffs. Concept screening, Value engineering
5	Design the product	TRIZ, Design for manufacture, Modularity and Platforms

6. Implementing the Lean Foundation Stones

The Lean foundation stones are applicable in all situations. Whilst they do not have to be fully implemented for further implementation, a weak foundation leads to a weak and non-sustaining general implementation.

Stone	Description	Relevant Sections in the book
1	5S Housekeeping	5S
2	Standard work	Standard work
3	Improvement cycles	PDCA, DMAIC, Kaizen
4	7 Tools of Quality	(In *The Quality 75*)

7. The Value Stream Implementation Cycle

Value Stream Implementation is a central, ongoing cycle within wider Lean transformation. The table below lists the main steps and relevant tools. Each step is briefly explained below. More detailed explanation of the tools is given in relevant sections.

Step	Description	Relevant Tools
1	Organizing	The Implementation Team Lean Promotion Office, Value Stream Implementation Cycle
2	Pre-mapping workshop	Pre-mapping workshop
3	Basic Mapping	Value Stream mapping. Spaghetti diagrams, Demand amplification, Quality Filter maps
4	Current state data collection	Lean assessment, Activity sampling, OEE, Basic data collection
5	Current state workshop	Current state workshop
6	Short Term Actions	Kaizen 'blitz', 5S
7	Detailed Mapping	Detailed mapping tools
8	Future state workshop	Future state workshop, Constraints, Creating Flow, Cell and Line Design, Creating the Future State (2). See below (7.8)
9	Simulation, Measures, Costing	Costing and Performance measurement, Implementation cycle.
10	Internal implementation plan	Internal implementation, Hoshin, People
11	External implementation plan	Lean Supply
15	After Action Review	After action reviews, PDCA

8. Building a Lean Culture

Step	Activity	Book sections
1	Lay the foundation	People basics
2	Understand the pitfalls	People pitfalls
3	Build team spirit	What is Lean?, Gemba, Vision
4	Skill up	Team Skills, Problem solving skills; 5S, Standard work, Kaizen Flag
5	Take positive actions	Gemba, Communication, Waste walks, Audits, Hoshin
5	Tackle anchor draggers	Adoption Curve
6	Change behavior	Culture
7	Build and sustain	Sustainability

9. Working Lean Supply

Step	Activity	Book sections
1	Define the supply chain	Supply Chain Thinking, S-C Basics
2	Understand demand	Demand management, Runners Repeaters and Strangers
3	Rationalizing parts and materials	Essential Paretos: Part rationalization
4	Select channels	S-C Channels, S-Chain mapping
5	Rationalize the supply base	Supplier Strategy and rationalization
6	Consolidate, Simplify and Schedule Supply	The Building Blocks, Ten Scheduling Tools, Milkrounds
7	Manage amplification	S-C Amplification
8	Develop suppliers	S-C Basics, Supplier partnerships, Supplier associations

10. Working Lean Distribution

Step	Activity	Book sections
1	Defining distribution channels	The Right Supply Chain Partnership, Trust
2	Establish build to order principles	Creating the Future State (1 and 2)

11. Costing and Performance Measurement

Step	Activity	Book sections
1	Understanding the basics	Throughput, Inventory, Operating expense; Constraints, Pareto analysis
2	Measuring the right things	Balanced scorecard. Performance Prism
3	Measuring things right	Performance measurement
4	Costing it out	Lean accounting

7.8.1 Designing a Pull System with Heijunka

Pull system design is a late step in Lean implementation – recall, 'pull' is Womack and Jones' fourth principle. The main steps are given below, based partly on Rother and Shook's 8 steps to create a Future State from Learning to See. Each step is briefly explained below. More detailed explanation of the tools is given in relevant sections.

These sub-sections detail the necessary steps within section 7.8 above – the Future State Workshop. These are the detailed steps for Pull System design (this section), and Cell design (next section).

Step	Description	Relevant Tools
1	Ensure demand is smoothed as far as possible	Demand Smoothing
2	Product family identification	Product Family Analysis
3	Value Stream Mapping	Value Stream Mapping Identification of constraints
4	Strategy and subcontract issues	Value stream economics, Manufacturing strategy
5	Segment the map into Value Stream loops	Value Stream Loops
6	Calculate takt time	Takt time
7	Identify constraints convergences and variation	Theory of Constraints, Factory Physics, Six Sigma.
8	Decide container size or move quantity	Move quantity, Kanban
9	Decide pitch increment	Takt and Pitch time
10	Build to finished goods or directly	10 Scheduling Concepts, Supermarkets
11	Investigate continuous flow possibilities	10 Scheduling Concepts
12	Locate supermarkets	Supermarkets
13	Decide on the pacemaker	Pacemaker, Material Handler
14	Level production at the pacemaker	Heijunka, Mixed Model production, Material handler
15	Calculate batch sizes at changeover stages	Batch sizing, Priority kanbans, EPE (every product every)
16	Design kanban loops	Kanban, CONWIP, DBR
17	Design material handling routes	Material handling route
18	Form cells	Cell and Line Design
19	Improve	Kaizen

7.8.2 Cell and Line Design

Cell and line design is a hierarchical process, from factory layout to detailed workstation ergonomics. The table below lists the main steps and relevant tools. More detailed explanation of the tools is given in relevant sections. Note that these steps are done at the 'focus factory' level.

Step	Description	Relevant Tools
1	Product family or value stream identification	Product Family Analysis P-Q analysis Group Technology
2	Value Stream Mapping, and shared resource analysis	Value Stream Mapping Spaghetti diagram Constraint analysis
3	Strategy and subcontract issues	Value stream economics Manufacturing strategy
4	Plant layout and location of supermarkets	Lean plant layout, Supermarkets, Building Blocks
5	Activity timings and sampling	Activity timing Determine VA, NVA, NVAU Activity sampling
6	Calculate takt and cell cycle time	Takt time Cell cycle time
7	Identify any constraints	Theory of Constraints, Drum Buffer Rope, CONWIP
8	Paper kaizen	Paper kaizen and waste analysis.
9	Theoretical minimum activity times	Minimum activity times calculation
10	Theoretical minimum operators	Minimum operator calculation
11	Cell reference cost and Savings calculation	Cell costing Lean accounting
12	Cardboard simulation	Cardboard simulation
13	Cell layout design	Cell layout, 5S Pokayoke Material handling / Runner
14	Operator balancing (and plus one and minus one analysis).	Cell Balancing Yamazumi board Work Combination chart Cell layout chart Standard work
15	Workstation ergonomics and workstation design	Ergonomics Cell workstations
16	Pull system design	Kanban and Pull, Heijunka

Value, Strategy, Planning, Deployment

Manufacturing Strategy

Unlike many topics in this book, Manufacturing Strategy is concerned with the longer term. It is concerned with developing policies with regard to location, capacity, technology, suppliers and the supply chain, and people and organizational aspects. These must be made compatible with the future requirements of customers and markets. The manufacturing strategy process involves translating the future needs of customers into cost, quality, delivery (lead time and reliability), flexibility and service support. These policies are moving targets in as far as customers, the economic environment, suppliers, production volumes, and competition is all evolving.

A later section discusses the Policy Deployment or the Hoshin process. Policy Deployment should be seen as a stage after the formulation of manufacturing strategy. However, this should not be seen as a one-way process. Manufacturing strategy is 'emergent' with strengths in Lean enabling a manufacturer to adopt strategies that are simply not open to the non-Lean. No manufacturing strategy can compensate for an incompetent operation.

There are a number of classic approaches to manufacturing strategy.

An early but still useful view is the Product Process Matrix. See the Figure. The feasible region implies that the process or layout must evolve as the volume increases. Failure to adjust leads to a system that is out of alignment. Moreover there are appropriate, but overlapping, scheduling systems for each region. In the one-off project management area (e.g. new product introductions, large constructions) critical path analysis

The Product Process Matrix

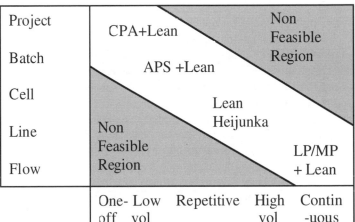

is an appropriate tool. For job shops with shifting bottlenecks an APS (Advanced Production Scheduling) is appropriate. MRPII is appropriate in batch production. Lean scheduling in the repetitive area, and Linear and mathematical programming in process plants such as oil refineries. Note that Lean techniques overlay all these areas to a lesser or greater extent.

Terry Hill's approach begins with corporate objectives – manufacturing strategy is seen as contributing towards these objectives. Corporate objectives lead to marketing strategy. In fact, the development of links between the marketing and the manufacturing strategy is central to the Hill approach. Marketing identifies appropriate markets, product mix, services, and the degree to which the company needs to customize and innovate. Marketing strategy leads into the identification of required 'order winners' and 'order qualifiers'. This is more or less similar to the Kano model dimensions. (One problem that several users have found is that it is difficult to identify clearly the 'order winners' amongst different customers.) They in turn lead to articulation of the manufacturing strategy, including the detail of 'process choice' (inventory, processes, capacity, location, etc.) and 'infrastructure' (planning and control systems, organization, reward systems, etc.). The whole strategy formulation process is iterative, learning as it goes. Gaps are identified between the requirements and the actual situation.

The Platts and Gregory procedure begins with a SWOT analysis, a market evaluation, and a manufacturing audit. From this a profile is developed for the critical dimensions – typically cost, lead-time, quality, reliability, capacity, production control, product features, design capability, human resources, suppliers, and distribution. For each dimension the strategic (market) requirements are plotted, and the current performance. The profile reveals gaps that must be closed. This is a variation on the spider diagram often used in Lean audits, but focuses on strategic rather than operational dimensions. A Spider version is shown below.

The procedure is often carried out in a series of workshops. Ian Sadler, of Victoria University, uses 7 workshops of two hours each over two months, with cross-functional attendance. Sadler's workshops are market requirements and competitive criteria, basic data on product groups, order winning criteria, currents ops performance, assessing current strategy, strategy derivation, and action plan. Once again, iteration is the norm – Sadler believes that results are often poor first time around but improve significantly.

The Slack and Lewis' approach is probably the most comprehensive available. They say there are three levels to the operations strategy process. "Fit" involves concepts like the three approaches discussed above, but is seen more generally as an alignment between market requirements and resource capability. "Sustainability" is the next level. Sustainability is about keeping up with change – running just in order to stand still. It is about developing the capabilities that will allow it to adapt to new markets, or developing itself to be a better player in existing markets, or both. There will be changes in markets and in capabilities. Strengths may turn out to be a hindrance – like a Disruptive Technology (See separate section) This aspect deals with the necessary flexibility. Finally "Risk" is the deliberate consideration of unexpected factors and assumptions. A 'what if' or scenario analysis.

Slack and Lewis use a matrix of five performance objectives (quality, speed, dependability, flexibility, cost) that lead to market competitiveness, against four decision areas (capacity, supply network, process technology, and development and organization) that are

Strategy and Audit

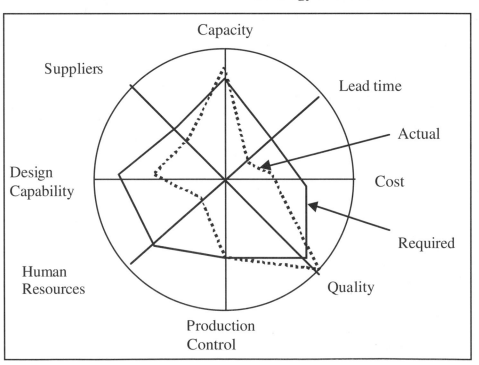

the resource usage issues. This gives a matrix of 20 blocks, just a few a few of which will be critical to success. These need to be developed and thought through on each of the three levels above.

David Walters uses a "value chain approach". A value chain starts and ends with customers, and involves a series of parallel, overlapping processes comprising customer expectations, design and development, production, procurement, marketing, logistics, service, and value delivery. Developing a strategy involves considering how these value chains can be developed and integrated. This seems to be an extension of value streams discussed in this book. A customer value model (what customers value) leads to a value proposition (key operations factors and partnership issues). This leads into a value positioning and competitive advantage strategy (a mix of factors of technology management, relationship management, and knowledge management) leading to the design of the organization and operational processes of production, logistics, and service. All a bit theoretical, although Walters claims wide applicability.

Note:
A framework for strategic decision making is given in the Scenario section on page 37.

Further Reading:
Terry Hill, *Manufacturing Strategy: Text and Cases*, Macmillan, 2000
DTI, *Competitive Manufacturing*, 1990, (for Platts-Gregory procedure)
Nigel Slack and Michael Lewis, *Operations Strategy*, FT Prentice Hall, 2002
David Walters, *Operations Strategy*, Palgrave, 2002

The Kano Model

Dr. Noriaki Kano is a Japanese academic who is best known for his excellent "Kano model". The Kano Model has emerged as one the most useful and powerful aids to product and service design and improvement available.

The Kano model relates three factors (which Kano argues are present in every product or service) to their degree of implementation or level of implementation, as shown in the diagram. Kano's three factors are Basic (or "must be") factors, Performance (or "more is better") factors, and Delighter (or "excitement") factors. The degree of customer satisfaction ranges from "disgust", through neutrality, to "delight".

A Basic factor is something that a customer simply expects to be there. If it is not present the customer will be dissatisfied or disgusted, but if it is fully implemented or present it will merely result in a feeling of neutrality. Examples are clean sheets in a hotel, a station tuner on a radio, or windscreen washers on a car. Notice that there may be degrees of implementation: sheets may be clean but blemished. Basic factors should not be taken for

THE KANO MODEL

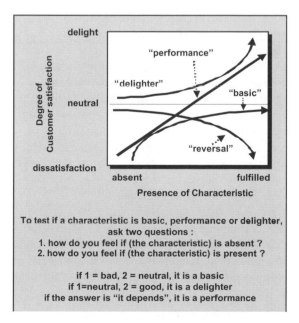

To test if a characteristic is basic, performance or delighter, ask two questions :
1. how do you feel if (the characteristic) is absent ?
2. how do you feel if (the characteristic) is present ?

if 1 = bad, 2 = neutral, it is a basic
if 1=neutral, 2 = good, it is a delighter
if the answer is "it depends", it is a performance

granted, or regarded as easy to satisfy; some may even be exceptionally difficult to identify. One example is course handouts that a lecturer may regard as trivial but the audience may regard as a basic necessity. If you don't get the basics right, all else may fail - in this respect it is like Maslow's Hierarchy of Needs: it is no good thinking about self esteem needs unless survival needs are catered for. (In fact, the Kano model is based partly on the Herzberg Motivator-Hygiene theory of motivation.) Market surveys are of limited value for basics (because they are simply expected). Therefore a designer needs to build up a list by experience, observation and organized feedback.

Notice the non linear shape of the curve. This is in line with economic theory that suggests that most people have such non-linear responses. If you had a 50/50 chance of winning or losing $1 million would you do it? Most people would not even accept a bet with a 90% chance of winning $1 million if they had a 10% chance of losing $1 million.

A Performance factor can cause disgust at one extreme, but if fully implemented can result in delight. This factor is also termed "more is better" but could also be "faster is better" or "easier is better". Performance factors are usually in existence already, but are neutral, causing neither disgust nor delight. It is not so much the fact that the feature exists; it is how it can be improved. The challenge is to identify them, and to change their performance. Examples are speed of check in at a hotel, ease of tuning on a radio, or fuel consumption. Performance factors represent real opportunity to designers and to R&D staff. They may be identified through market surveys, but observation is also important, especially in identifying performance features that are causing dissatisfaction. Creativity or process redesign is often required to deliver the factor faster or more easily, and information support may play a role as in the "one minute" check-in at some top hotels.

Finally, a Delighter or Excitement factor is something that customers do not expect, but if present may cause increasing delight. Examples are flowers and wine awaiting guest arrivals in some hotel rooms, or a radio tuner that retunes itself when moving out of range of a transmitter. By definition, market surveys are of little

use here. Once again, it is creativity, based on an appreciation of (latent) customer needs that can provide the breakthrough. But we need to be careful about Delighters also: a true Delighter is provided at minimal extra cost - it would certainly cause customer delight to give them all a complimentary car, but would be disastrous for company finances. Therefore, perhaps a more appropriate hotel Delighter would be to give guests a choice of sheet colour, pillow type (English or German), and sheet type (linen, satin, or cotton). There are risks with providing Delighters – customers may come to expect them – as may have happened with Ford and GM car discounts.

Kano factors are not static. What may be a Delighter this year may migrate towards being a Basic in a few years time. Also, what may be a Delighter in one part of the world may be a Basic in another. Thus it is crucial to keep up to date with changing customer expectations. Benchmarking may be a way to go. From Kano we also learn that a reactive quality policy, reacting to complaints, or dissatisfiers, will at best lead to neutrality but proactive action is required to create delight.

The Kano Model works well with Quality Function Deployment and is increasingly being used with TRIZ. Basics should be satisfied, and delighters can be explicitly traded off in the "roof" of the QFD matrix (for example fuel consumption may suggest a lighter car, but safety suggests a stronger one - so the quest is to find material that is light, strong, and inexpensive.)

Further reading:
Special Issue on Kano's Methods: *Center for Quality of Management Journal*, Vol 2, No 4, Fall 1993 (Several articles, including administering Kano questionnaires).
Joiner, B.L., *Fourth Generation Management*, McGraw Hill, New York, 1994
Lou Cohen, *Quality Function Deployment*, Addison Wesley, Reading MA, 1995

Scenarios

Why be concerned about Scenarios in a book on Lean? Because conventional forecasting using extrapolation is more likely to lead to mass manufacture. Scenarios are better at picking up possible discontinuities, thereby encouraging a more flexible, lean approach.

When making longer term plans or decisions, a forecast can be notoriously unreliable (consider the effects and difficulty of predicting the outcome of the Iraq War, the Euro, the pensions crisis, or a new and outstandingly successful car from a competitor). So instead use a few scenarios. For instance, most medium and larger companies in the UK should be considering the implications of the matrix of four scenarios, one of which will certainly come to pass: In or out of the Euro, and will the Euro succeed or fail. At Shell, all major projects are judged against two or three scenarios. All projects are expected to demonstrate robustness against all the scenarios. This is a powerful supplement to traditional financial evaluation such as payback or ROI / IRR, where figures are sometimes (always?) massaged. The use of scenarios instead of forecasts is also consistent with "pull" decision-making (starting in the future and working back) rather than "push" (starting from the present and selecting from apparent alternatives).

Ilbury and Sunter have developed a most useful matrix, referred to as the 'foxy' matrix – since foxes are supreme adapters. It has two axes, certainty – uncertainty, and absence of control – full control. This gives four cells that turn out to be a useful way of developing and using scenarios but also for general strategic thinking. We will use an example of a food-packaging manufacturer considering Lean and Six Sigma. The first cell and starting point is certainty and absence of control. Here the 'rules of the game' are established. These are the facts of the situation. (Note an interesting slant on facts from Walter Shewart discussed in the Measures section of this book.) This includes the developing business environment and demographics. The first cell may include benchmarking on cost, quality, lead-time, delivery, and inventory turns. The second cell is uncertainty and absence of control. Here

there are two activities – identifying the key uncertainties and developing the scenarios. In manufacturing key uncertainties may be alternative products and strength of the Euro. Scenarios may include a narrative on growing public reaction against non-degradable packaging, growing supermarket insistence on involvement in the supply chain and integration with non-food manufacturers, and the shift in demand for food as populations age and decline. Developing the scenarios involves lateral thinking. The third cell is uncertainty-control where options are identified. Options may include Leaning the plant and supply chain, implementing Six Sigma but not Lean, relocation of some lines to China, and developing a complete new product line. The fourth cell, control – certainty is where Decisions are made. The food packager decides the appropriate response, weighing up the work in cells two and three.

Ilbury and Sunter claim this matrix switches emphasis from SWOT analysis (strengths, weaknesses, opportunities, threats) to OTSW – thinking about opportunities and threats first because they are outside our control, and then matching them with strengths and weaknesses. In the third cell, options are expanded from TINA (there is only one alternative) to TEMBA (there exist many better alternatives).

Peter Schwartz in *Inevitable Surprises* says that the future is not as unknown as we think. He lists some 'future shocks' that should not surprise including where age 60 becomes the equivalent of 40, American economic might but the simultaneous existence of a disorderly set of nations with the ability to create disruption, and patterns of human migration.

The concept of the "Business Idea" is important in building scenarios. Any company should have a "distinctive competence" which is the basis of competitive advantage, survival and profit. But distinctive competencies degrade over time. So it is important to understand the business idea as a feedback loop that allows the business to survive and prosper. Then, scenarios can be developed relating to external events that impact the business idea. For instance, a company may have a competence in the fabrication of steel frames used to support the suspension and engine in cars. This allows the company, with the aid of lean manufacturing techniques and a growing car market, to prosper. So instead of basing plans purely on sales projections, look at some scenarios: the car market declines due to saturation, the particular makes of car which they supply become uncompetitive relative to others, or car makers demand that such suppliers take over responsibility for actual assembly at the car plant itself. According to Davis good scenarios are built from the present, are not easily dismissed, should be internally consistent, and genuinely challenge the user's mental map.

According to van der Heijden there are three ways to build scenarios: Inductive, Deductive and Incremental. The inductive method builds stepwise from existing data, stringing known and chance events together. For instance, in the car example new models may be scheduled at particular points in the future. But perhaps the levels of demand are unknown. A framework of coloured cards (one for each level of demand) that maps new model introduction is assembled. Then an external trend or event (such as given in the previous paragraph) is introduced, and the scenario team talks through the consequences. Tight questioning is desirable ("why does that happen?), but destructive criticism ("that's stupid") is not allowed. Also, scenarios must be equally plausible. The test of this is whether the events are worth planning for; an earthquake that destroys the plant is not, unless you live in California or Kobe.

The Deductive method begins by identifying a series of events about which there is uncertainty, and then uses a "decision tree" as a framework. For instance in the car example: Do we win the Ford business? If yes, does the market grow? And if yes again, will car manufacturers require first-tier suppliers to assemble on site? The "no" branches are also explored. Probabilities can also be attached to each branch, thereby preventing the exploration of very unlikely scenarios.

The Incremental method simply uses conventional forecasts and projections. This is the "official" view into which, often, considerable time and effort has been sunk. The scenario team then examines this as the baseline, and may question various assumptions and

trends. For instance, is a straight-line projection of car sales sustainable? For how long? In this way, "break points" may be established. From these points, alternative stories are developed. Needless to say, this can involve treading on the toes and vested interests of some managers, so the scenario team would be well advised to have top-level protection! Like so much planning, it is the process that is at least as important as the actual results. Good scenario planning needs to be redone and updated, examining how to do it better next time.

Further reading:
Kees van der Heijden, *The Art of Strategic Conversation*, John Wiley, Chichester, 1997
Pierre Wack, "Scenarios: Uncharted waters ahead", Harvard *Business Review*, Sept/Oct 1985, pp73-90
Pierre Wack, "Scenarios: Shooting the Rapids", Harvard *Business Review*, Nov/Dec 1985, pp131-142 (these are two classic articles)
Ged Davis, "Foreseeing a refracted future", *Scenario Strategy and Planning*, April-May 1999, pp13-15
Chantell Ilbury and Clem Sunter, *The Mind of a Fox*, Human and Rousseau, Cape Town, 2001
Gill Ringland, *Scenarios in Business*, Wiley, Chichester, 2002

The Right Supply Chain

Marshall Fisher's Harvard Business Review article is already a classic with great relevance to Lean strategy. Fisher claims that the reason why so many supply chain (and Lean?) implementations fail is that that they are wrongly configured according to demand. He claims that there are two categories of demand – Functional (typically predictable, low margin, low variety, with longer life cycles and lead times, and no need to mark down at end of season), and Innovative (typically less predictable, high margin, high variety, shorter life cycles and lead times, with end of season discounting common). Functional demand requires an efficient process or supply chain, innovative requires a responsive process. Mismatches between demand and process give problems, as do transferring successful managers from one type of supply chain to the other.

Fisher says that the loss of contribution as a result of stockout is markedly different between functional and innovative products. In the former, a typical contribution margin of 10% and stockout of 1% translate to 0.1% of sales (negligible) but in the latter, rates of 40% and 25% respectively translate to 10% of sales (very significant).

For Lean strategy the implications are that a product requiring a responsive supply chain would be inappropriate in a low cost distant location, but that may be just the right thing for functional demand. (Refer also to the next section.) This may well mean having more than one type of facility and demand chain to cope with different demand segments. Can one equate efficient with Lean and responsive with 'agile'? Certainly not! Both need many Lean principles in place. But responsive requires, in addition to fast, flexible flow strategic inventory buffers, or better still reducing order lead times and uncertainty by faster information flows (EDI, EPOS, ECR) including process re-engineering. Fisher gives three alternatives – reduce uncertainty (faster information or mass customization), avoid uncertainty (reduce leadtime) or hedge against uncertainty (buffer inventory).

Fisher says that many companies find themselves in the mismatch quadrant of 'innovative demand' and efficient supply chain. If located in this mismatch segment there are two possibilities – either by making products and demand more functional (product line rationalization, or design) or by making the supply chain more responsive by the three approaches mentioned. An organization would need to balance the options.

SAB Miller is a case in point. They have massively efficient, low flexibility, high volume 'base' breweries and more flexible but less efficient flex breweries. An individual brewery therefore cannot be judged on its own. The Systems Approach.

Further reading:
Marshall Fisher, 'What is the Right Supply Chain for Your Product?', *Harvard Business Review*, March/April 1997

Value Stream Economics: What to Make Where

Questions of what to make, where to make, and what to outsource have become increasingly pressing questions with the rise of low cost, high capability manufacturing countries such as China, India or Eastern Europe. The last section is particularly relevant, but here we consider internationalization and the issue of what to make where.

The Outsourcing and International Location Question.

The first principle of value stream economics is to seek to adopt a Systems Approach. In other words try to include all the variables for both now and the future. Consider their interactions. A system is like a child's mobile – touch one part and everything moves, some in unexpected directions. (Build a scenario? – see earlier section). Also, take a longer-term view. The following is a tentative checklist of factors that need to be added to the ex-works direct cost of the product made abroad. (Note: direct costs means that all overhead must be excluded).

1. No doubt, the biggest factors are often lead-time and flexibility. How much does the business compete on lead-time and responsiveness? What opportunities are to be gained, and what lost by a change in lead-time. (See the section on time-based competitiveness.) Consider, at least, the counter argument to outsourcing – what opportunities will be created by insourcing? (See part rationalization).
2. Outsourcing and overseas relocation were tremendously fashionable in the late 1990s and early 2000s. Beware of fashion – think of the stockmarket.
3. Loss of core competence.
4. Normal transport costs from the supplier's site to home markets – less any costs saved where the new location serves an overseas market.

5. Extra transport costs (e.g. airfreight) and an estimate of the frequency with which this will occur as a result of quality problems or imperfect forecasts (Seldom zero). Note this may include shipping back of defective items for rework.

6. Staff redundancy costs – possibly amortized.

7. Overhead costs – will the overhead be saved, or will it have to be allocated to another product? What overheads will be incurred at the new location, and how will they be allocated?

8. Will any space savings actually result in a saving – can the space saved be used for another purpose.

9. Currency fluctuation insurance costs.

10. International taxes and duties. Note that these may vary in relation to international agreements, but also in accordance with 'tariff wars' that may be imposed at short notice.

11. Customs clearance time and resources need for extra paperwork.

12. The extra inventory held in the pipeline and the one-off cost of that inventory – possibly amortized over the life of the product.

13. The extra inventory held as a result of demand uncertainties over the longer lead-time horizon.

14. The extra inventory held initially whilst ramp-up takes place. (Is it reasonable to assume that there will be no hiccups in early days)? Will utilization be as good?

15. The extra inventory held as a result of quality problems or damage. (Remember the vessel containing a full cargo of new 7 series BMWs that sunk in the English Channel in 2003.) Hence insurance costs.

16. Increased obsolescence risks – e.g. computers with chips in transit

17. General costs of quality: internal failure costs (scrap, rework) and external failure costs, including increased warranty costs

18. Ramp-up costs in general – including training, sorting out problems, visits by home engineers.

19. Loss of customer goodwill, or loss of customers – period – as a result of quality, service, support, customization opportunity, etc.

20. Marketing costs – can you sell a longer lead-time?

21. Costs of loss of design expertise for future products. Difficult to assess.

22. Costs of loss of manufacturing expertise. Difficult to assess, but real – think about the next product that has to be developed from afar.

23. Political risk costs (Naïve to assume zero?). And bribes?

24. Finally, allow a percentage for data inaccuracy – several of the above will be guesstimates.

25. Against this list, you can subtract any incentives gained and opportunities in the new market. A 'benefit' may be transfer pricing – (cooking the books?) – so that the profit is made in low tax locations. Lean accounting?

Note: Jim Womack wrote another checklist in a LEI newsletter of 10 January 2003. It overlaps.

The Location Issue – Vertical Splits

Think about products and channels. Consider relocating that part of the plant that deals with stable, runner products whilst retaining locally products requiring a more flexible shorter lead-time. Or a mixed approach that involves retaining products locally during ramp-up or de-bugging (to sort out quality, standard work, kaizen, cell design), and only then relocating the stable or mature line.

The Location Issue – Horizontal Splits

Locating subassemblies away from base involves adding to scheduling and coordination complexity whilst possibly reducing engineering and accounting complexity. But at what level in the bill of material is a split appropriate? An interesting case is Dell, which chooses to insource assembly, as opposed to several less successful computer manufactures that choose to outsource.

Disruptive Technologies

Two of the primary rules in Lean are listening to your customers, and continuously improving. Also, benchmark! Are there situations in which this is not only misguided but also deadly? Perhaps so – where there are so called Disruptive Technologies at work.

Clayton Christensen of Harvard has produced an inspiring analysis. Christensen distinguishes "sustaining technologies" from "disruptive technologies". A disruptive technology is one that classically starts small, is simpler than the existing technology, and is ignored or even scorned at early stages by customers and managers alike. But the technology develops until suddenly it becomes a serious proposition. Customers "don't know that they want it until they want it". Meanwhile the sustaining or established technology continues to improve, often outstripping the needs of many customers. There is the danger that companies compete by continuous improvement, often putting their best people on this, but ignoring the challenge of the new approach. Witness vacuum cleaners and Dyson.

Improvement can create a void that the typically low cost disruptive technology fills. Customers think they want it, but don't know about the alternatives. By then it is often too late for companies with the sustaining technology to catch up. Witness Amazon.com as against established booksellers who offered sofas and coffee. Other examples are mini computers displacing mainframes, and eventually being displaced themselves by networked PCs. Or department stores being displaced by discounters. Or Visa and MasterCard displacing Sears' dominant store card. Note here that "technology" refers to a concept rather than a physical technology.

Christensen states that with a disruptive technology many of the normal rules of business don't apply. Thus market research, allocating resources, killing off low return business, investment hurdles, and continuous improvement are all good policy for sustaining technologies, but may be the very policies that prove deadly in the presence of a disruptive technology.

"Markets that don't exist can't be analyzed". This is not a failure of poor management; it is the very fact that they have done everything right that causes them to fail. The "innovator's dilemma" is that continuing innovation, listening to customers and going after more lucrative developments is precisely wrong.

Precisely because a disruptive technology displays minimal initial impact on corporate growth or existing markets it fails to attract the interest of executives who must look for far bigger gains. Christensen suggests that the way to deal with disruptive technologies is to establish a completely separate division, perhaps geographically separated but certainly organizationally separated from the parent, where small innovations are still viewed with excitement. This happened in the successful start-up of IBM's PC division or HP's inkjet printer division. Christensen suggests that the management of disruptive technologies requires different resources, different processes, and different values to those required for sustaining technologies. Strong visionary leadership is required, but also a different sort of leader to those skilled at managing sustaining business. Reading Christensen's brilliant analysis leaves the open question, "Is that why so many kaizen or lean initiatives fail to deliver?" (Because the mindset is about sustainability, not radical change.)

Christensen points out that imitation is sometimes precisely the wrong thing to do. It may build only yesterday's competitive advantage. Successful strategies need to have a deep understanding of the processes of developing competition, not the transient 'solutions'.

(Refer also to the Supply Chain section of the book.)

Further reading:
Clayton Christensen, *The Innovator's Dilemma: When New Technologies Cause Great Firms to Fail*, Harvard Business School Press, 1997
Clayton Christensen, "The Past and Future of Competitive Advantage", *MIT Sloan Management Review*, Winter 2001, pp 105-109
Clayton Christensen et al, "Skate to Where the Money Will Be", *Harvard Business Review*, November 2002, pp 72-83

Time Pacing

"Time pacing" is the undertaking of events such as new product introduction, factory relayout, or staff training at regular intervals. This is distinct from traditional "event pacing" which waits until action is needed before initiating such change events. Intel for example, introduces new microprocessors at regular intervals rather than waiting for design breakthroughs or market pressures.

Time pacing is absolutely in line with Lean Operations. It follows the Lean principle of regularity, whereby products are manufactured at regular intervals attempting to make this week's schedule as much like last week's schedule as possible. (See the section on Runners, Repeaters, and Strangers.) The advantages are huge; everyone from supplier to operator to marketing knows when a product is due for manufacture. As pointed out, we run our lives on this basis - we don't need a finite scheduler to decide when the family should have breakfast every day. Time pacing is like inventory cycle counting; counting a few parts every day with clear accountability, rather than when the auditors require it and resulting in a panic set of arrangements.

In new product introduction, time pacing cuts development time because each new product is not a complete new adventure, but resources are geared to a momentum to achieve immovable deadlines. Regularity breeds "choreography". It creates a relentless sense of urgency. So new chocolates are introduced in time for Easter, new model cars in time for the Motor Show. Moreover, with time pacing planning for the product after next, the factory after next has already begun.

Eisenhardt and Brown make the point that there are two related disciplines for Time Pacing. These are Managing Transitions and Managing Rhythm. Both are absolutely in line with good Lean Thinking. Managing Transitions is the process of change management in moving from one product to another. Eisenhardt and Brown say that although new product development is carefully managed, the transition from old to new often is not. Toyota has a whole team that focuses minimising the waste of materials in moving from one model to

another. It introduces new models on the line in a mixed model fashion - first one, then a small batch with space before and after, then a day's run and finally the transition is complete without any stoppage. As this transition process becomes regularised it becomes more routine, better choreographed, and less traumatic. The best transition management style sets out to learn from each transition - what went wrong and what can be done better next time.

Managing Rhythms is the process of setting the drumbeat, the frequency with which transitions take place. "Without rhythm, managers tend to be reactive and to see change as an unwelcome surprise" say Eisenhardt and Brown. So this is the task of establishing how frequently batches are run, re-layouts are done, new products introduced, shelf stocking policies reviewed, re-training or job rotation is required, university courses are revisited, or performance is reviewed. The idea is not to be too fast or too slow. Regularity is the key. Capacity must be provided and set aside for this purpose. A programme should be developed which is within the capabilities of the organization - much like cycle counting again, with A, B, C category frequencies. Eisenhardt and Brown point out that it can be as harmful to increase the frequency of the rhythm, as it is to have no rhythm.

Time pacing should become a central strategy for new products, for improvement, for performance review, for personnel development, and the extension of lean. Begin by making a list of activities that can benefit from regularity. Decide the feasible frequency. Then do it, and expect it.

Further reading:
Kathleen Eisenhardt and Shona Brown, "Time Pacing: Competing in Markets that Won't Stand Still", *Harvard Business Review*, March-April 1998, pp 59-69
Kathleen Eisenhardt and Shona Brown, *Competing on the Edge*, Harvard Business School Press, 1998

The Essential Paretos

Pareto Analysis (or the 80/20 rule) has been called the single most important management concept of all time. Quite a claim! Certainly, there are four essential Pareto analyses that every operations manager, and especially every aspiring Lean manager, should be aware of in relation to their own plant.

Inventory ABC Analysis

Inventory ABC analysis is a long established procedure, but important for the Lean manager as an aid to inventory control and a guide to selection of pull (and push?) system, when combined with Runners, Repeaters and Strangers. (See Scheduling section). At the part or component level, A parts are a small percentage by number but a large percentage by value. B is intermediate. C parts are low cost, but there are typically many of them. Of course you need all types of part to complete a product, but you can afford to be less tight (more safety stock) with C items.

To construct, simply rank the parts from highest to lowest unit value in a long list. The top perhaps 15% of parts by value warrant special attention (tight kanban, low safety stock, careful monitoring and demand forecasts) – the middle 50% less so, and the remainder even less (2 bin system, more safety stock, automated monitoring). This ranking should also be the basis for cycle counting – count a few parts every day, such that A's are counted monthly, B's quarterly, C's once or twice per year. Ignore this at your peril – whilst not as glamorous as a six sigma project it is at least as important.

P-Q (or Product Quantity) Analysis.

P-Q analysis is a Pareto procedure that simply ranks parts or products by volume. It is also linked with the Runners, Repeaters and Strangers concept. (See

Scheduling section.) Top end items (Runners) can justify dedicated equipment. Mid range parts (Repeaters) may have to share cell facilities with other parts. Often some routing changes will be required. Parts in the tail of the Pareto (Strangers) are problematical for cells. The best case is that by clustering routings they can be brought into a cell. The worst case is that these parts will have to go into a

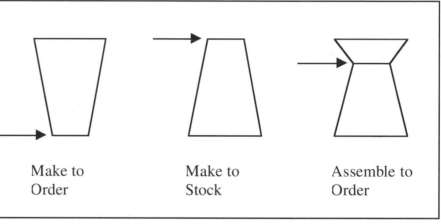

| Make to Order | Make to Stock | Assemble to Order |

residual cell or job shop – or they are candidates for outsourcing.

An important issue is at what level should you do a P-Q Analysis. A general answer is – the same level at which the Master Schedule is developed. See the figure above, showing bill of material structures, and the usual master scheduling level.

Note that you need two types of Pareto for P-Q analysis. See the figure on the next page. The value based analysis at the top may identify a small number of products where dedicated lines may be worthwhile irrespective of volume – for example a cosmetics line that is run on average one day per week, but thereby allows low inventories and extreme flexibility. The volume based analysis shown in the lower half may justify dedicated lines on volume.

But not so fast! By rationalization methods (design, modularity, etc.) stranger parts can be made into repeaters. Recall also that whilst end items or products may be unique, their subassemblies or components may not be. Therefore an upstream cell may be justified, even though a downstream cell may not be. Or, upstream you may have part family cells, but downstream the cells may be customer specific. The parts Pareto section below is of relevance.

Not so fast, part 2 – the direction of movement should also be noted. In other words a low volume product that is growing is more important than a slightly higher volume product that is declining.

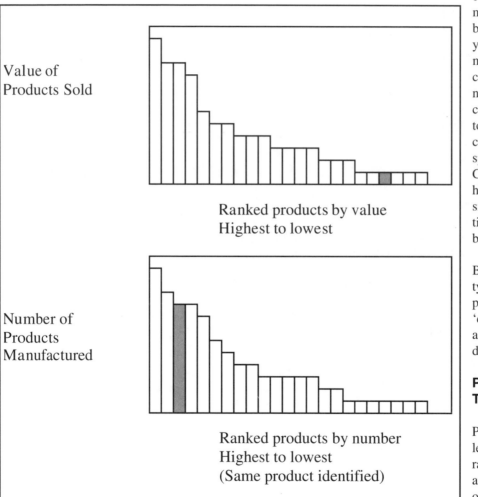

Value of Products Sold

Ranked products by value
Highest to lowest

Number of Products Manufactured

Ranked products by number
Highest to lowest
(Same product identified)

for the future state. Again, there are two sub-categories. The first is total contribution. Which products are making the greatest contribution, and which if any are making a loss? There may be strategic issues here – some products may have to be retained as loss leaders.

The second, and possibly more important, is contribution per bottleneck minute. If you have a clear bottleneck process (where you could make more money if you had more capacity) or a stage that is a near bottleneck (or constraint), then you need to divide the unit contribution by the time spent on the bottleneck. Clearly, you don't want to have products that make small contribution *and* that tie up your precious bottleneck capacity.

But do take care with this type of analysis – if you cut products, be sure that all the 'direct' costs you have assumed will actually come down.

Parts, Materials, and Tools Paretos

Parts, materials and to a lesser extent tool rationalization is a huge, and often untapped, field of opportunity in many companies. In fact, the potential often far exceeds taking out inventory as part of a scheduling, kanban, or value stream implementation. A series of Paretos is the way in. Where rationalization has not been done or specifically controlled for several years, part proliferation may be rampant. Getting after proliferation is big task, usually

Contribution Analysis

Refer to the figures opposite. Contribution is selling price minus direct costs (i.e. contribution to overheads). It is essential to know which products are making your money. This needs to be done for the current state and requiring a specific team, but with big payoff in inventory savings. But, more importantly, this activity allows the business to become much more flexible and in some instances literally to change the business model from long leadtime, high inventory build to stock to short leadtime, build to order.

The conversion of 'strangers' into 'repeaters' and 'repeaters' into runners' should a fundamental part of every lean transformation. For example, in one organization that the author was involved with, over 50

4 material types) enabled a short-leadtime pull system to be introduced with one pacemaker, replacing vast quantities of different material inventories (well over 100 part numbers), forecasting, purchasing, MRP transactions, long lead-times, and part shortages - (as Zorba would have said,' the full catastrophe!').

Rationalization may involve upgrading existing specifications, and so appear 'uneconomic' but the payoff is in simplicity of control, in flexibility, in inventory – but more importantly, in business opportunity.

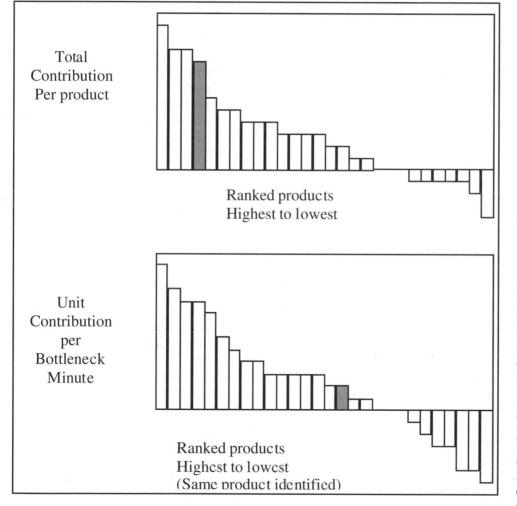

Rationalization requires high-level support – and will typically meet resistance from both accountants concerned with unit costs (but not system costs), and from designers concerned with optimal product design and 'waste' (but not with system design and even wider wastes).

The first step is to list the categories of major parts, components, materials, and tools. For example part categories may include fasteners, bushes, housings, and gears. Components may be motors, pc boards, transformers, and containers. Materials may include coil steel, bar stock, plastic for injection molding, fabrics, gloves, and packaging material. Tool categories may include hand drills, torque wrenches, welders.

types of bar stock were reduced to just 5; in another 28 types of fastener were reduced to just 6. In a third case, implementation of NC laser fabric cutting in-house (on

The second step is to decide which categories to tackle first. Set up a multi-function group from the lean promotion office, manufacturing, design, purchasing, accounting, and possibly marketing. Anticipate a stormy session, and get it chaired by a sympathetic system-thinking, top manager.

The third step is to draw up usage Paretos for the chosen categories. Rank by annual usage and rank by current inventory holding divided by annual usage last year. This second ranking will sometimes result in a few 'infinite' categories where usage has ceased. Examine the tail of the Pareto in the former case, and the head in the latter case.

Get the team to examine systematically each item from these two ends, always looking at the possibility of eliminating or combining items.

This standardization and rationalization activity must be ongoing. Part proliferation slowly creeps in, in the Design office and via Marketing. These functions do need to appreciate wider system economics.

Policy Deployment

In essence Policy Deployment (or Hoshin) is about 'nemawashi' (consensus building) and 'ringi' (shared decision making). There is the belief that "80% is greater than 100%" meaning that a set of decisions 80% correct but bought into by all will be better than an optimal 100% correct solution imposed by the 'experts'.

Policy Deployment has become a well-accepted way of planning and communicating quality and productivity goals throughout a Lean organization. In a Lean context it is more about Deployment than strategic choice, so this section should be seen as following the Manufacturing Strategy section. Here we will use Hoshin and Policy Deployment interchangeably, although strict Japanese style Hoshin is hugely bureaucratic and form-intensive so Policy Deployment is a preferable phrase to distinguish it from the rather non-Lean Hoshin.

Policy Deployment (PD) is used by leading Japanese companies (Toyota, Sony) and by leading Western companies (Hewlett Packard, Intel, Ford, Proctor and Gamble). It is, in essence, very simple but requires high levels of commitment and time. The objective is to communicate common objectives and gain commitment throughout the organization.

Policy Deployment is in fact the PDCA cycle applied on an organizational level. Witcher and Butterworth talk about the FAIR model beginning with the Act stage. Focus (act), Alignment (plan), Integration (do), and Responsiveness (check).

Cowley and Domb use a useful metaphor. This shows a road leading from the present position (the current state) to the destination (the vision or future state. The road is the plan or action plan. Along the road are scattered small rocks and large boulders – which are obstacles or problems. PD is used to remove the boulders one at a time. Kaizen is used to remove the smaller rocks, and importantly this is not what we are concerned with here. Also, there are boulders that are off the road. These should not be tackled – PD is about focusing on the 'vital few'. The vision must be shared, level by level. What not to do must be agreed. And alternatives must be developed. The road metaphor is even more useful when used with Route Learning Maps – increasingly used for lean transformation. See the discussion in the mapping section.

A "Hoshin" is a word that is increasingly being heard in Western companies, to mean those few breakthroughs or goals that are required to be achieved to meet the overall plan. At the top level there may be only 3 to 5 Hoshins. But at lower levels, the Hoshins form a network or hierarchy of activities that lead to the top level Hoshins. They are developed by consultation. Hoshin objectives are customer focused, based on company wide information, and measurable.

A good concept, with applications far beyond PD, is to use the Toyota concept of requiring all plans to be confined to a single side of one A3 size sheet.

PD starts with the concept of homing in on the "vital few". Where there is little change in operating conditions, a company still needs to rely upon departmental management, and top management planning is not required. However, where there is significant change, top management must step in and steer the organization. This requires strategic planning (for future alignment to identify the vital few strategic gaps), strategy management (for change), and cross functional management (to manage horizontal business processes). PD is, however, not a planning tool but an execution tool. It deploys the "voice of the customer", not just the profit goals.

An important aspect is Learning. The future is uncertain, although the destination is clear, Treat every unexpected event is an opportunity to learn and to adapt.

Departmental management should be relied upon for "kaizen" (i.e. incremental) improvements, but breakthrough improvements that often involve cross functional activities and top level support, should be the focus for PD planning.

Once the vital few strategic gaps have been identified by top management (see the Manufacturing Strategy section), employees and teams at each level are required to develop plans as to how to close the gaps. The premise is that insights and ideas are not the preserve of management. Moreover, commitment will be built by participation. This requires that employees have access to adequate up-to-date information - breaking down "confidentiality" barriers found in many Western organizations. There must be a clear link, or cause and effect relationship, between the organizational goals, key objectives, and activities. The employees themselves develop measures, including checkpoints. At each level, Deming's Plan, Do, Check, Act cycle operates. And, there is strong use of both the "7 tools" to analyze, quantify, and control. Further, root cause analysis, using the 5 Whys method (see separate section), is used at each level.

The main stages, explained by Cowley and Domb, are "What do we need to do?" "How should we do it?", and "How are we doing?" The first stage is strongly linked with the strategy process, but benefits from feedback from later stages ("What did we learn from the last time?") This stage also involves the identification of

Hoshins and other actions that are delegated to 'Daily Management'. In the second stage the nemawashi and catchball process then deploys the Hoshins. The third stage is about implementation, review, and corrective action.

PD uses the "outcome, what, how, how much, and who" framework. A Policy Matrix is useful here. At Board level, a visioning process covers the key questions of what is to be the required outcome for the company (e.g. 10% growth), what is to be achieved (e.g. reductions in lead time), how is it to be done (e.g. extend lean manufacturing principles), and how much (all shops to be on JIT by year end). Specific quality and productivity goals are established. Then, the "who" are discussed. Normally there will be several managers responsible for achieving these objectives. Appropriate measures are also developed.

The PD plans are cascaded in a Tree Diagram form. This cascading process is also different to most traditional models. In traditional models, cascading plans come down from the top without consultation, and there is little vertical and especially horizontal alignment. In PD, people who must implement the plan design the plan. The means, not just the outcomes, must be specified. And there are specific and ongoing checks to see that local plans add up to overall plans. The matrix is used to assure horizontal alignment.

The 'nemawahsi' process is the step during which consensus is built amongst all affected stakeholders. It involves consultation with all those affected. Hutchins (in discussing constraint Management but equally applicable here – see the Goldratt section) makes the useful point that there are five stages. They are (1) gain consensus on the issue (2) gain consensus on the direction of the solution (3) gain consensus on the benefits of the solution (3) overcome reservations, and (5) make it happen.

As deployment proceeds a group meeting takes place at each level. This is referred to as "Catch Ball" (ideas are tossed around like a ball) or "Huddles". Ideas flow from all directions, and agreement is arrived at by consensus and negotiation, not authority. If a goal is really infeasible the upper tier is informed. A Japanese word for this is the "Ringi" system. Much use is made of affinity diagrams and post-it notes. The process can and should be tied in with the Future State and Action Plans developed under Value Stream Mapping. A Master Schedule is the outcome. This Master Schedule shows the time-phased activities, usually in Gantt chart form. A progress line is shown on the Master Schedule

Master Schedules

Master Schedules are Gantt charts showing progress against all key objectives. They are on display in the Lean War Room or the Lean Promotion Office. Normally master schedules will cover Safety, Cost, Quality, Delivery, Morale, and Environment. Each of these areas is further broken down into detailed sub categories.

because progress is reviewed team by team, then group by group, and finally across the organisation. At each stage any lack of progress is questioned. The plan thus moves up and the plan moves down.

A final stage in the cycle is the Hoshin Review where achievements against plan are formally rolled up the organization. This uses visual results where possible. Exceptions are noted and carried forward. Hewlett Packard does this very formally once per quarter, "flagging up" (by yellow or red "flag") problem areas. Intel uses, against each Hoshin, a classification showing highlights, lowlights, issues, and plans. Again, root causes are identified.

The tools of PD are similar to QFD and Matrix Analysis. When the objectives have been discussed and clarified they are set down in a matrix against the

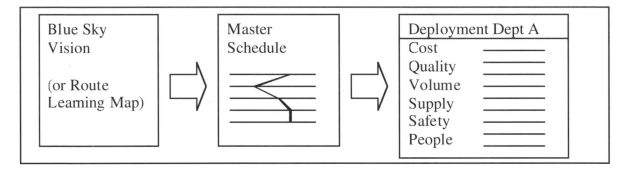

The Master Schedules are reviewed regularly in groups. A senior group discusses the top-level objectives say fortnightly. Middle level groups, one per key area and including a member from the senior group, will discuss weekly progress with relevant managers down to operators and consolidated into an Overall Master Schedule ("Nerve Centre'). A slippage procedure should be developed. Difficulties and constraints are identified and fed back to the level above who are required to act accordingly. Also, measures are taken and gaps identified. If a problem is identified, corrective action is taken in relation to the process, not the person. This "blame free" culture is critical.

A Master Schedule is a powerful deployment and learning mechanism. First because the whole plan is displayed activity by activity, level by level. Second

existing measures. An example, similar to those found in several Lean companies, is shown on the next page. Deployment then takes place using a series of matrices. First, objectives against processes. This identifies the most important processes. Second, processes against measures. This enables a review of measures identifying measurement gaps, redundant measures, and excessive measures.

So PD is in essence an expanded form of "team briefing" but requires written commitment, identification of goals, the setting of measures, and discussion at each level. In Western companies, top management sometimes spends much time on corporate vision but then fails to put in place a mechanism to translate the vision into deliverables and measures, at each level in the organization. Hoshin may go some way to explaining why in better Japanese companies the decision making process is slower, but implementation is much faster and smoother.

Hoshin Process

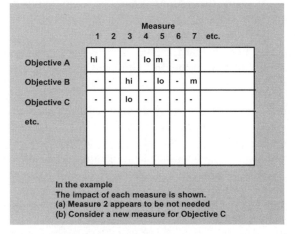

Adapted from Unipart and Oakland *TQM*

	Measure							
	1	2	3	4	5	6	7	etc.
Objective A	hi	-	-	lo	m	-	-	
Objective B	-	-	hi	-	lo	-	m	
Objective C	-	-	lo	-	-	-	-	
etc.								

In the example
The impact of each measure is shown.
(a) Measure 2 appears to be not needed
(b) Consider a new measure for Objective C

Further reading:

Y. Akao, *Hoshin Kanri : Policy Deployment for Successful TQM*, Productivity Press, Portland, 1991
Michael Cowley and Ellen Domb, *Beyond Strategic Vision: Effective Corporate Action with Hoshin Planning*, Butterworth Heinemann, 1997
Michele L Bechtell, *The Management Compass : Steering the Corporation Using Hoshin Planning*, AMA Management Briefing, New York, 1995

Preparing for Flow

The topics in this section are an integrated set. Takt time and activity times are basic building blocks for Lean flow. 5S provides the housekeeping basis. One of the 5S- perhaps the most important - is Standards. The 5Ss and particularly standards are closely related to the TPM methodology. Visual management is enabled by 5S, and makes TPM and standard work more effective. 5S, standard work, and TPM are also the basis for fast, consistent changeover operations. Finally, demand smoothing and small machines allow all the others to be more effective. Together, the topics are the foundations for fast, flexible flow. In combination these topics are an effective attack on Muda (waste), Muri (difficult work), and Mura (unevenness).

But beware. Making 5s or TPM an end in itself is huge waste. Convert to flow as soon as possible. Then come back and do more preparation.

Takt Time and Pitch Time

Takt time is the fundamental concept to do with the regular, uniform rate of progression of products through all stages from raw material to customer. Takt time is the drumbeat cycle of the rate of flow of products. It is the "metronome" (from the German origins of the word). Understanding takt time is fundamental to flow and mapping of Lean Operations.

Takt time is the available work time (say per day) divided by the average demand per day. Note that there are two variables – one to do with the customer, the other to do with the plant manager. Therefore, if demand changes a manager could maintain the same takt time by adjusting the available work time. The available time is the actual time after allowances for planned stoppages (for planned maintenance, team briefings, breaks).

Demand is the average sales rate (including spare parts) plus any extras such as test parts and (we hope not) anticipated scrap. It is expressed in time units: e.g. 30 seconds (or 30 seconds between completions).

Where there are multiple parts going down a line, the overall takt time is calculated by dividing the available time by the total number of parts. Say you have A: B: C parts in the ratio 3: 2: 1 with daily demand 120A, 80B, 40C. Available time is 200 minutes per day. Takt time is 200 / 240 = 0.83 min. = 50 secs. There would be a repeating sequence ABABAC every 6x50 = 300 seconds. In this regard, the ski chairlift analogy is useful – a constant flow of moving chairs but containing a mixed set of people.

Some companies allow for changeover times in càlculating the available weekly work time. This is not really good practice because the takt drumbeat must be maintained throughout the plant, including changeovers. Nor is it good practice to allow for an overall equipment effectives (OEE) percentage. Building in these wastes leads to a lower takt time that translates to more people.

Where demand is seasonal or variable, selection of the period over which demand is estimated is important. Selecting a longer period will stabilize build rate but at the expense of more supermarket inventory to smooth out the bumps. Moving towards build to order means reducing the time horizon and having more frequent takt time. This means that lines may have to be rebalanced, which in turn means that operators should be involved in the task of rebalancing and know the concept of takt time. As you become more Lean and flexible you can reduce the period over which takt is calculated.

Note that takt time is not cycle time, which is the time required to complete an operation or a machine cycle. Where such cycle times exceed takt, you have a constraint – requiring parallel processes or an additional shift. Also note that there may be several takt times within the same plant – for example one takt for cars, but one quarter of the time for the wheels. In some environments, such as chemicals made in tanks, takt may not be an immediately useful concept, but may still be useful for planning and control.

For machines and processes, working at the takt time may mean <u>slowing down</u>. Strangely and counter-intuitively, slowing down to achieve synchronization may lead to a reduction in lead-time. This is because queues do not build up after machines that run faster than the takt time. This simple realization, to try to get all machines in a plant running at the constant takt time, can have dramatic results. It changes the job shop into a pseudo assembly line.

Takt time should drive the whole thinking of the plant and the supply chain. In a plant it is the drumbeat. Consideration needs to be given to the number of parts per product sold. Thus if there are four wheels per trolley sold, and wheels are all made on the same machine, the wheel machine needs to have a takt time of approximately one quarter that of the main assembly line. (Approximately because there may be special demands for additional spare wheels). So takt times in a plant leads to overall synchronization.

Pitch Time

Pitch is the takt time multiplied by the container quantity or a convenient multiple of parts, typically 15 to 30 minutes. Instead of thinking the time to make one part, think of the time required to fill the standard container. The analogy of the ski lift is particularly appropriate – a constant rate of movement delivering 4 people at a regular spacing.

The pitch increment is the basic time slot used in Heijunka. The material handler in a Heijunka system should fit in with the pitch time. In that sense, pitch time is the vital drumbeat of the whole system, forcing regularity, visibility and flow.

Activity Timing and Work Elements

Activity timing is the long-established industrial engineering (or time and motion study) task of determining the duration of work elements. This is an essential input into cell balance (Yamazumi) boards, value stream maps, scheduling, and costing. In Lean, timing is best done by operators rather than by I.E.s – thereby encouraging ownership and avoiding the pitfalls of suspicion and 'slow-motion' work. In time and motion studies, the rule is to sort out and standardize the motions before timing them.

Preferably, make a video of the tasks. (This is better than live recording, because it allows backtracking, and slow motion. It also avoids the stress of several people with stopwatches standing over an operator.) Be sure to video at least 10 cycles on each shift. If several operators are used, film each of them. A very useful learning experience is to get operators from different shifts together to see if there is variation between operators, and to agree on the best method. This should be an essential step in determining standard work. If you are an outside observer, it will take time to familiarize yourself with the exact tasks – best of all is if you can do the work yourself. This is another good reason for using operators themselves to do the timing.

With the correct methods established, begin the timing. If necessary re-video. It is good to video several operators, from different shifts. First, break down the work sequence into work elements each with a clear start and end point. Agree on these points. Keep manual (work) times, walk times, and wait times separate and record each of these under separate columns. Machine cycles should be separately recorded. Make a list of the sequence of activities that an operator goes through in a complete sequence. Some of the manual times will turn out to be non-value adding, or non-value adding unavoidable. At this stage, just record each separately. When balancing the cell, try to reduce or eliminate wait and walk times. Critically examine the possibility of reducing NVA or NVAU steps.

Time at least 10 good cycles of each – by a 'good' cycle is meant a cycle where nothing goes wrong. Discard 'outliers'. Time to the nearest whole second. For each work element time, take the lowest more frequently occurring time. In other words, in 10 observed cycles of 4, 5, 6, 6, 7, 7,8, 8, 8, 8 take 6.

Note: In traditional time study, the time used is the observed time plus an allowance for 'PR&D' – personal, rest and delay. Do not add this allowance. Rather, give operators more frequent breaks.

5S

5S is the basic housekeeping discipline for lean, quality and safety. It applies in office and on shop floor equally. Everyone has the experience of working better and feeling better in a tidy room. But it's also a mindset thing – changing attitudes from "I work in a dirty factory" to "I work in a manufacturing laboratory". The team should carry out the following steps with their supervisor. They should not be done by an outsider.

SORT
Throw out what is not used. The first step is to CLASSIFY literally everything by frequency. A good idea is to do this with the team and to touch every item systematically. If used every day, is the quantity correct? If used weekly can it be brought out weekly? If used monthly should it rather be located in the store? If never, or in doubt, then red tag or throw out. A Red Tag is a label with the date; if no one accesses it within a specified period it should be thrown out, recycled or auctioned. The sort stage should be done regularly – say once every six months, but as a regular activity not a re-launch of 5S.

SIMPLIFY (or Set in Order or Straighten)
Locate what is used in the best place. A place for everything (using shadow boards, inventory footprints, tools and dies on trolleys or at the right height, and colour matching to link associated tools). And everything in its place (if not in place and not in use, a problem is indicated). Personal toolboxes are discouraged because the tools for the job should be located at

standardised locations. The standard is The "Dental Surgery". Why? Because all can relate to that standard of excellence, and know the consequences of failure. Try for 'One level' which means keeping dies, tools and parts at the same level as the workplace to minimise bending. Repeat this stage whenever products or parts change. Use a spaghetti diagram for analysis. Ergonomic principles should play a role here, and an ergonomic audit may help.

SWEEP (or Shine or Scrub)
Keep up the good work. This includes physical tidy up, on an ongoing basis, and "visual sweeping" whereby operators are always on the lookout for anything out of place, and try to correct it immediately. Some companies adopt a 5 minute routine whereby operators work out a 5 minute cleanup routine for each day of the week such that by week end everything has been covered the required number of times. Designate exactly who is responsible for what and what the standard is. The stage will require suitable cleaning equipment to be suitably located and renewed. There may be a sign-off chart for routine cleaning.

"Cleaning is Checking," means that these are integrated. You don't just clean up, you check for any abnormality and its root causes. The garage analogy is first clean up – this enables oil leakage to be identified. Continue to clean up any leakage that occurs. But then ask 'why is leakage occurring' and decide what should be done for prevention.

STANDARDISE (or Stabilize)
Only now is it possible to adopt standard work. This is the real bottom line for 5S. See the section on Standard Work. But 5S standards also need to be maintained. So develop standards for the first 3 S's.

SUSTAIN (or Self Discipline)
Everyone participates in 5S on an ongoing basis. Self-discipline is about participation and improvement. Carry out audits on housekeeping regularly. Some award a floating trophy for achievement.

Some companies add a sixth S – **SAFETY**. Although good to emphasize, a good 5S program should stress safety as an aspect of each of the five stages. It may confuse to list safety separately. Safety procedures and standards should also be developed, maintained and audited as part of the programme. Unsafe conditions should certainly be integral to 5S. Toyota and Ford, amongst others, do an ergonomic risk assessment exercise.

An alternative for 5S is CANDO – Cleanup, Arrange, Neatness, Discipline, and Ongoing improvement.

Some companies adopt regular walk about audits and competitions. (See below). The shift supervisor audits daily, the area manager weekly at random times, the production manager monthly – perhaps on the basis of

5S audit and scoring systems are becoming more common. The best do this regularly and display the result for all areas on a board showing comparisons with the last period.

The physical areas of responsibility must be clear. Display a layout diagram of the plant showing 5S boundaries.

Hirano suggests a host of activities including 5S days, 5S visits to outside companies. 5S model workplaces, 5S patrols, and a 5S month. Excessive?

	Inventory	Suppliers	Computer Systems	Costing Systems
Sort	Throw out all dead and excessive stock	Select the best two suppliers in each category. Scrap the rest.	Delete all dead files and applications	Do you need all those costs and variances? Prune them!
Simplify	Arrange in the best positions	Cut all wasteful, duplicate transactions	Arrange files in logical folders, hierarchies	Cut transactions. Review report frequency. Incorporate o/head directly
Sweep	Regularly review dated stock and ABC category changes	Improve supplier performance by supplier assoc & kaizen	Clear out inactive files regularly	Audit the use made of costing reports and transaction size & frequency
Standardise	Footprint	Milkrounds, payments	Systems, formats	Adopt reporting standards
Sustain	Audit ABC, RRS	Audit performance	Audit perform & response	Review and reduce.

drawing a number out of a hat in the presence of all cell leaders, whereupon all cell leaders and managers descend on the chosen area (office or factory) and give it a thorough evaluation. At weekly audit level, a floating trophy and wooden spoon are awarded.

Many companies now claim that they are doing 5S but are in fact doing 2S sporadically. Not completing all 5 means that sustainability will be low. This is waste. 5S will then require increasing effort to re-energise. The real productivity and quality benefits of 5S are in the later S's, particularly standardisation, not the relatively easy-to-do first two.

Extending the 5S Concept.
5S can be applied more widely. Four areas are given in the table. There are probably many more applications.

REMEMBER THE PRIME REASON FOR 5S IS STANDARD WORK.

Further reading:
Productivity Press Development Team, *5S for Operators*, Productivity, 2002
Hiroyuki Hirano, *5 Pillars of the Visual Workplace*, Productivity, 1995

Standard Work and Standard Operating Procedures

Standard work is a pillar of the Toyota Production System (TPS). Two useful quotations introduce this vital topic.

"To standardise a method is to choose out of many methods the best one, and use it. What is the best way to do a thing? It is the sum of all the good ways we have discovered up to the present. It therefore becomes the standard. Today's standardisation is the necessary foundation on which tomorrow's improvement will be based. If you think of 'standardisation as the best we know today, but which is to be improved tomorrow' - you get somewhere. But if you think of standards as confining, then progress stops."
(Henry Ford, *Today and Tomorrow*, 1926)

"In a Western company the standard operation is the property of management or the engineering department. In a Japanese company it is the property of the people doing the job. They prepare it, work to it, and are responsible for improving it. Contrary to Taylor's teaching, the Japanese combine thinking and doing, and thus achieve a high level of involvement and commitment."
(Peter Wickens, Former HR Director, Nissan UK)

Standard and Davies explain that there are 3 key aspects of standard work which need to be understood
1. Standard work is not static, and when a better way is found the procedure is updated
2. Standard work supports stability and reduces variation because the work is performed the same way each time. Moreover variations (defects, deviations, discrepancies) are easily recognised.
3. Standard work is essential for continuous improvement – moving from one standard to a better standard without slipping back.

Standards should cover three aspects: work time, work sequence, and standard work-in-process. All are necessary. On work time, both takt time and current cycle time (i.e. the time taken for one cycle of the process) should be recorded.

At the outset it should be said that Lean standards are not the rigid, work-study imposed, job specifications associated with classic mass production. Such standards have no place in the world of Lean. They lead to industrial sabotage and absenteeism. Beware of the human-relations based reaction against 'work standards' that is often confused with work-study. Allowing loose standards may lead to no standards, which in turn lead to decreased safety and productivity.

Also, beware of thinking that standards have no place in non-repetitive work such as maintenance, service, design, or senior management. Good, flexible maintenance and service work is built by combining various small standard work elements. Good design comes out of creativity combined with standard methods and materials, adhering to standard procedures and gateways. Management standards should exist for meetings, communications, budgets, and many other activities.

Spear and Bowen in a classic article discuss the apparent paradox of TPS that activities, communications and flows at Toyota are at once rigidly scripted yet enormously flexible and adaptable. They conclude that that it is the rigid specification of standards and communications that gives the system the ability to make huge numbers of controlled changes. Without standards and the scientific method, change would amount to little more than trial and error.

Despite what some people think about Frederick Taylor, there remains "one best way" to do any task that will minimise effort and maximise safety, quality and productivity, with available technology. To some this may sound like boring repetition, but the "new" standards are about participation in developing the best and safest way, mastery of several jobs, and the ability to adapt to changes in rate and mix in the short term.

Ohno realised that the achievement of standardised work, with minimum variance, was the essential ingredient to allow one-piece flow and JIT production. Deming, in proposing the PDCA cycle, saw improvement moving from standard to standard.

Juran emphasised the importance of "holding the gains" by establishing standards following a process improvement, rather than allowing them to drift back to the old ways. Recently the "Learning Organisation" has become fashionable, including "knowledge harvesting" from everyone in the organisation. How is this to be achieved? By documenting experience; in other words by establishing standards from which others may learn. Supervisors should have prime responsibility for maintaining and improving standard work.

At Toyota, emphasis is placed on workers documenting their own standards, and in mastering both a wider range of work tasks and greater responsibility for supporting tasks. Operators themselves establish work cycles within the specified takt time. It may be that they are assisted in this task by industrial engineers and supervisors, but the operators must write up the final documentation of work standards themselves. This achieves four goals. First, there can be no question that work standards are not understood. Second, the operator is forced to think about the best way in which he or she should do the work within the takt time. A trained operator will frequently do a better job than an uninvolved work-study officer. Third, the responsibility for setting the standard and then maintaining it is clearly up to the operator. There is motivation to update the standard when improved ways are found. And, fourth, because the standards reflect what actually happens rather than what might happen, learning can take place particularly when operators change jobs. In other words this is job enrichment and job mastery. The Toyota way takes time to train operators to do the analysis and standardisation themselves - they need to not only learn basic work-study principles but also to appreciate the reasons why they should do it. Toyota regards work standardisation as one of its most challenging management tasks. Robert Hall believes that this worker-oriented standardisation, requiring high levels of operator skill and motivation, takes much time but pays huge dividends.

Too many operations-based organisations delude themselves on standards. It is tempting to simply impose work standards by getting industrial engineers or work-study people to do the work and to post stand-

ards at workstations, or worse to keep them in a file. Then of course, there is no buy-in, no foundation for continuous improvement, and worst of all a great likelihood of large process variance. So the quick way turns out to be the least effective way and often a total waste. Traditional "Taylorism", is suitable only the sweat shop.

Monden gives the five steps of developing standard operating procedures as: (1) Determine the takt time (2) Determine the production capacity (net work time divided by process time plus changeover time). (3) Determine number of operators (sum of work elements divided by takt time). (4) Define the standard procedures – but first remove waste, develop the layout, standard locations. (5) Write the standard operating procedure chart. The last steps are iterative. (See the section on Cell Design for more detail.)

Standard operating procedures (SOPS) should contain the takt time, the detailed work sequence steps that are involved together with the time taken for each step (these should be written in the operators own words), and the standard inventory quantity or kanban quantity involved during the takt time cycle. Today good standards make extensive use of digital photos, with close-ups of any operation requiring clarification, and specifying tools, quality checks, and a note on any special operation that is required to be carried out periodically. A standard operating procedure can be colour coded to match the product that carries a label of matching colour. When an engineering change occurs, a number on the product should match the number on the standard procedure. Often, a standard should cover not only what to do when things are normal, but also what to do if things go wrong. Consider health and safety. There must be own responsibility for the standard, for publishing it, for keeping it at the workplace, and for keeping it up to date. At Intel where consistency is an absolute requirement, operators audit one another using the standard instructions. Jaguar makes videos of the same operation on different shifts, and then gets operators to critique one another.

Three forms are common. The Standard Work Combination Chart is a Gantt-type chart detailing the sequence of steps against time bars joined by 'squiggles' to indicate walk times. The takt time is shown as a vertical bar, and the longest accumulation of job element times should be within this takt time. The Standard Work Analysis Chart gives a birds-eye view (plan view) of the cell showing the standard route that operators follow when carrying out a standard cycle, and the standard locations and quantities of inventory. The Standard Work Element Sheet contains the steps, times and photographs. All three should exist in a cell. (See page 96).

When cellular manufacturing is established or when takt times change, operators in the cell are encouraged to rebalance the line themselves or to change their own work standards to the new takt time. This is referred to as the 'Yamazumi' board.

Robert Hall has pointed out that there are three stages of standardisation. The first is "outcome only" where the standard is established in a plan or drawing but how to get there is not specified. This generally leads to a high level of variation, and the need for inspectors. The second stage is "standardised processes" where variance is reduced by following standardised methods to achieve the outcome, supported by for instance SPC and pokayoke. The third stage is "standardised predictive methods" whereby a high level of consistency is achieved directly from the design by using standardised processes that work first time "without the need to prototype, test, or make special tools". Very few companies or processes are at this stage.

Further reading:
Robert W Hall, "Standard Work: Holding the Gains", *Target*, Fourth Quarter, 1998, pp 13- 19
Taiichi Ohno, *Toyota Production System*, Productivity Press, Portland, OR, 1988
Charles Standard and Dale Davis, *Running Today's Factory*, Hanser Gardner, 1999
Spear and Bowen, 'Decoding the DNA of the Toyota Production System', *Harvard Business Review*, Sept/Oct 1999
Fred Owen James, *How can standard operations be sustained on a short cycle manual assembly line?* MSc Dissertation, Cardiff Business School, 2001

Total Productive Maintenance (TPM)

TPM can be regarded as integral to Lean. Certainly no Lean implementation can be a success with a high level of breakdowns. TPM goes well beyond breakdown issues to cover availability, performance, quality, as well as safety and capital investment through making best use of, and extending the life of, equipment.

TPM has much in common with Total Quality. Everyone has a role to play, not just experts. In total quality there is the concept of 'the chain of quality'; the TPM equivalent is the equipment life cycle. Both aim at prevention. Both widen the scope to include the operator, the product, the process, and the environment. Both aim to 'spread the load' by getting front line staff to take over as much responsibility as possible thereby directing authority to where it is most effective and freeing up specialists to do more complex tasks (thereby creating a positive feedback loop). Both use 'management by fact'.

TPM can be viewed in relation to the 'Bathtub Curve', below.

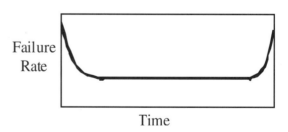

Time

TPM addresses all parts of the curve. It reduces breakdowns in the burn-in period by early equipment maintenance and by improved understanding of equipment usage. It reduces breakdowns during the plateau period by autonomous maintenance and the 9 step programme. The 9 step programme also extends the life of equipment. The upturn point is addressed through predictive and planned maintenance. Failures during the wear-out period are also reduced.

(Note: The author would like to thank Tony Purcell of BNFL Westinghouse for his inspiration leading to the sections that follow.)

The Six Big Losses and OEE

The six big losses and OEE concept is widely used in TPM. The six are divided into three categories (availability, performance, and quality), which are the basis for OEE. They are

Availability

Breakdown losses are unplanned stoppages requiring repair. Any unplanned stoppage greater than 10 minutes is usually considered breakdown. These may be electrical, mechanical, hydraulic, or pneumatic.

Changeover and adjustment losses occur when changing over between products. Often changeover is defined as the time from the last piece of the first batch to the first good piece of the next batch. But note that getting up to full production rate may take much longer, during which time adjustments may be required. The time lost is recorded.

Performance

Minor stops and Idling are often defined as stops taking less than 10 minutes. They result from a host of causes such as tip breakage, coolant top-up, jams, swarf removal, and small adjustments. When data is collected, minor stoppages are often revealed as (by far) the most significant loss. Since minor stops are so frequent and last such a short time they are often ignored because they are difficult to measure. Activity sampling may be an answer. Alternatively get the operator to just mark off each stoppage on a fence and gate ⊬ℸ chart, and sample the time taken for 20 actual minor stoppages to give an average.

Reduced Speed losses result from the machine running at less than the design speed. Typical causes are flow restriction, program errors on a CNC machine, and worn tools, feeds or belts.

Quality

Defects result in scrap or rework and are the result of any problem that causes the machine to work outside of the specification limits.

Start up losses result in scrap or rework during changeover. It is measured in pieces. (Note that in some systems the time lost in attaining full speed is recorded here rather than as part of changeover losses.)

OEE

OEE is Availability x Performance x Quality, expressed in percentage terms

An example: A shift takes 9 hours. Working time is 8 hours – planned maintenance and meeting time is one hour. Breakdowns take 20 minutes. Changeovers take 40 minutes. The standard machine cycle time is 1 minute. At the end of the day 350 parts have been produced of which 50 are scrapped, 30 of them during adjustment.

Availability: (8 x 60 – 20 – 40)/480 = 420/480 = 88%
Performance: actual working for 420 minutes, so 350/420 = 83%
Quality: 300/350 = 86%
OEE = 88% x 83% x 86% = 63%

For non-process industry world class OEE is in the range 85% to 92%. Note that figures in the 90's may indicate that insufficient time is being given to changeover, so batches may be too large.

Each of the elements of OEE should be graphed as well as the overall figure. Keep these at Gemba. Also, below each chart, it is good to have a fishbone diagram showing possible causes. Even better, keep a CEDAC (cause and effect with addition of cards) where progress is recorded on coloured cards (red still to do, yellow done, notes on the back).

Cautions on using OEE

* OEE say nothing about schedule attainment. It is useless having a high OEE if you are making the wrong products!

- You can improve OEE in good and bad ways. Good ways are to reduce minor stoppages and decrease the length of a changeover. A bad way is simply to do fewer changeovers. OEE should not be used alone, but alongside schedule attainment which tracks how many batches were supposed to be made. So do not make OEE an end in itself.
- There is a cost factor – reducing changeover at great cost may be counterproductive.
- Do not measure OEE plant-wide. Combining machine performance is meaningless. Target only critical machines. Pareto!
- There are other ways to cook the books – simply don't make products with higher defect rates or more difficult adjustments.

Focusing TPM Activities

An excellent way to focus TPM activities is to graph performance as follows:

To construct: Start with the working day. Determine planned maintenance, break time, and planned idle time. Split the remaining time into the six big losses and actual effective working time. Divide by typical planned production in units. The result is a stacked bar chart as shown.

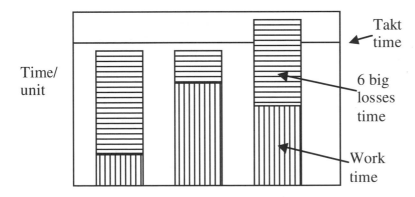

Consider the three machines. Machine 1 has the worst OEE. Machine 2 is closest to takt time. Machine 3 has a comfortable machine cycle but losses mean that total work cycle exceeds takt. Which to target? To target by worst OEE may be to miss the point. The question is, is this serious? To focus on machine cycle (as has been

suggested in various value stream mapping publications) is not relevant as long as total time is below takt time. Machine 3 is the machine to focus on, even though it has moderate OEE and comfortable machine cycle time.

And what to focus on, on Machine 3? Look at the 6 big losses. To take this analysis further, it would be good to repeat the analysis by days of the week, like a run diagram. And control using SPC principles.

The JIPM Model

The Japan Institute of Plant Maintenance has put forward probably the widely adopted framework comprising 9 steps, divided into three cycles. The 9 step process is a long and thorough one. Absolutely not a quick fix. Short cuts generally don't pay!

Measurement Cycle

1. <u>Collect Equipment History and Performance Analysis.</u> This step focuses the project (as above) and sets measurement objectives (e.g. cost, OEE, manning, material savings). Often this is for a machine or a cell, never for a plant – it would simply be too big a project. A small team is assembled. A TPM display board is set up at Gemba to show progress along the 9 steps. Collect manuals and drawings covering mechanical, hydraulic, electrical, and pneumatic. Assemble any available data on history – installation, working patterns, performance rates, replacements, and planned maintenance records. Also identify any accident black or brown spots.
2. <u>Define and Calculate OEE.</u> Clarify the meaning and interpretation amongst team members. Set up an OEE display board at Gemba. Brainstorm out possible causes and display on a chart. This step may involve several days, even weeks of data collection, to clearly identify the six big losses for different situations. Agree progress, methods and figures with plant management.

3. <u>Assess Six Big Losses and Set Priorities.</u> This will involve an analysis such as shown in the last section. Agree and sign off the priorities with management.

Condition Cycle

4. <u>Critical Assessment.</u> (This may be overlapped with step 3.) Produce a list of all components of the relevant machines. Discuss and understand the role of each component and their interdependencies – not superficially, but in detail. Why exactly was it designed that way? Identify the critical components – and why they are critical. Discuss the optimal conditions for the operation of each critical component (e.g. temperature, lubrication, cleanliness, sharpness). Publish the optimal conditions on a drawing of each component. Then define the normal operating conditions. Finally discuss the sources of accelerated deterioration for each component – equipment based, operator based, environment based. (This is a long stage of no immediate impact – but huge long term potential. Hang in there.) (Note: Only now, after several weeks, is the team ready to undertake specific improvement actions.)

5. <u>Initial Cleanup and Condition Appraisal.</u> Agree the cleaning areas. Source all necessary and specified cleaning equipment. Photograph the current state. Systematically inspect every part of the machine in detail. Clean and inspect, capturing all problems found. At the end of cleaning, fill in an appraisal form for each component (1 to 4) covering mechanical, hydraulic, electrical, and pneumatic. Develop a cleaning and inspection programme ("Cleaning is inspection"). Identify sources of contamination (internal and external) and develop a plan to eliminate, isolate, prevent, or if necessary clean. Discuss with plant management.

6. <u>Plan Refurbishment.</u> Develop a phased refurbishment schedule – covering item, labour hours, planned completion, and PDCA cycle stage. Discuss with plant management. Schedule the release of equipment. Implement elimination of contamination. Look into pokayoke and implement as far as possible. Examine the need for quick changeover and undertake this where necessary.

7. <u>Develop Asset Care.</u> Clearly define the role and the tasks of the operator. Produce a clean and check list, with appropriate frequencies. Develop a Kamishabi Board (see separate section), covering the phased and daily activities of maintenance, safety, quality, and operator checks. Identify, mark and colour code, all gauges, pipework, lubrication points, levels and sight glasses, nut positions. Etc. Label all components and tools – with cross references to manuals. Indicate flow directions and motor rotations. Install inspection windows.

Problem Prevention Cycle

8. <u>Develop Best Practice Routines and Standards.</u> Taking all that has been learned in previous steps, assemble a best practice manual. Develop Single Point Lessons (see separate section) where necessary. Review Standard Operating Procedures – amend where necessary, including pictures, in consultation with operators, and place at Gemba. Review the maintenance instructions. Review equipment spares – what needs to be kept, where, how much. Index the spares and cross reference with manuals and SOPS. Develop a spares catalogue associated with each machine. Locate the manuals appropriately – not in the office!

9. <u>Problem Prevention.</u> This is an improvement cycle. OEE leads to the particular loss leading to the problems that are tackled by the 5 whys leading to solutions. A method is P-M analysis - similar to the quality matrix of variation, mistakes and complexity vs. the 6 M's (see Quality section). The preference is for low cost / no cost solutions, but also takes in technical solutions, and support service solutions. All of this feeds back to earlier stages to complete the cycle.

Some Special Features of TPM

"At its worst when new". This provocative statement goes to the heart of TPM. Why should an item of equipment be at its worst when new? Because, it may not yet be quality capable, standard procedures not yet worked out, mistake proofing (pokayoke) devices not yet added, operating and failure modes not yet known, 6 big losses not yet measured or understood, and vital internal elements not yet made visible (through transparent covers) or monitored by condition monitoring.

Visibility. Like JIT, TPM aims to make what is happening clear for all to see. This means maintenance records need to be kept next to the machine, problems noted on charts kept next to the machine, and following a 5 S exercise, vital components made visible by replacing (where possible) steel covers with transparent plastic or glass. Also, following 5 S, any leaks or drips are more easily seen.

Red Tags. Red tags are a common form of visible TPM. Maintenance "concerns" are written on red tags and hung on a prominent board on the shop floor. They remain there until action is taken. Red tags usually cover concerns that cannot be dealt with by operators.

Failure Modes and Scheduled Maintenance. In classic Preventive Maintenance, a "bathtub" curve was often assumed (i.e. high failure rate early on, dropping to a low and continuing failure rate, then increasing at wear out). Routine maintenance is then scheduled just before the risk rate starts to increase. Today, we know that not all equipment has this pattern. Some may not have early high failure, some may not have sudden wear out, some may exhibit a continuous incline, etc. The point is you need to know the failure mode in order to undertake good scheduled maintenance practice. So, data needs to be recorded, the best way being automatically, for instance the number of strokes on a press for each die. And operators (who often have an inherent knowledge of failure modes) should be consulted. A maintenance cycle should be developed much like the cycle-counting concept, which visits important machines more frequently, allocates responsibility, and aims to improve not just maintain.

Condition Monitoring. Condition monitoring is a specialist function in TPM, but in some environments (for example heavy and rotating machinery) an important means to reduce cost. Methods include vibration detection, temperature monitoring, bearing monitoring, emission monitoring, and oil analysis. Today, there are hand-held, and computer linked, devices to assist.

Information Systems. Information systems were always an important part of PM, and remain so with TPM. However, their scope is extended from machines to include operator, safety and energy issues but also to allow for workplace data recording.

Design and Administration, and Benchmarking. Today, TPM is beginning to be seen in administrative and white-collar areas. Of course, there are computers, photocopiers, and fax machines but there are also tidy (?) desks, filing cabinets, and refreshment rooms. Progressive companies are beginning to cater for TPM in product design. And, benchmarking, as usual, is useful.

Further Reading:
Nick Rich, *Total Productive Maintenance*, Liverpool Academic, 1999
Seiichi Nakajima (Ed), *TPM Development Program*, Productivity Press, Cambridge MA, 1989
Seiichi Nakajima, *Introduction to TPM*, Productivity Press, Cambridge MA, 1988
Masaji Tajiri and Fumio Gotoh, *Autonomous Maintenance in Seven Steps*, Productivity, 1999
Peter Willmott, *Total Productive Maintenance: The Western Way*, Butterworth Heinemann, Oxford, 1994
John Moubray, *Reliability Centred Maintenance,* (Second edition), Butterworth Heinemann, Oxford, 2001

Visual Management

Visibility, visual management, or 'control by sight', is a key theme in Lean operations. Visual management should be integrated into 5S and standard work. In fact, visual management is the 'litmus test' for Lean – if you go into any operation and find that schedules, standard work, the problem solving process, quality and maintenance are not immediately apparent, and up to date, there is an excellent chance that the operation is far off Lean. Visibility has been joined by audio.

Visibility fits in well with several other Lean themes:
- Speed (no waste of time having to look for information), Improvement (progress should be for all to see, and celebrated).
- Up to date and clear schedules (via kanban, progress boards, automatic recording).
- Making problems apparent (via overhead Andon boards or lights).
- Involvement (clarity on who is doing what and who can do what).
- Teamworking (making visible the good work of teams, and skill matrix)
- Standardisation (keeping standards up to date by locating them at the workplace).
- Responsiveness (requiring quick response to maintenance and quality problems via for example a line stop chord or a red tag maintenance board).

Ford Motor Company makes a distinction between visual display, concerned with provision of information, and visual control, concerned with action.

The idea is to be able to gain the maximum amount of operating information and control without having to go off the shop floor, or go into a computer system - a variation of Gemba management. This applies to operators, supervisors, and managers. A few examples of visual management follow:

- Machines: Transparent plastic guards and covers used wherever practical to enable operators and maintenance people to see the innards of machines.
- OEE charts placed next to machines or at team meeting areas; there should be four graphs - one for overall OEE and one each for the three elements of OEE. Below each graph should be kept a fishbone diagram with the contributing factors.
- Changeover times should be graphed routinely, to prevent slippage.
- The Heijunka box is a visual display of the status of the day's schedule.
- Kanban priority boards used where there is changeover (triangle kanban) give a continually updated display of the urgency of the next products to be made.
- Lights to indicate status, with the overhead Andon Board linked to computer to record stoppages for later analysis (not blame!)
- Management: Is it possible to have the production control and scheduling office on the shop floor?
- Cost, Quality, Delivery performance should be a central trio on display, possibly joined by Safety, Leadtime, and Days of Inventory.
- Line rebalancing charts showing takt time, and with magnetic strips for each work element, kept in the team area.
- Keep teams informed of new products and developments by progress boards, including Gantt charts.
- People: A skills matrix (or I L U O chart) indicates achievement from beginner to instructor. Operators on one vertical axis, tasks on the horizontal axis.
- Employee suggestions and employee of the month are more common in service than manufacturing - why?
- Have a mirror with a slogan such as "You are looking at our most important source of ideas"
- Methods: Keep those standards and methods at the workplace!
- Materials: Don't forget to keep footprinting up to date. Kanban remains the most visible effective means for production control.
- Maintenance: A maintenance "red tag" board, showing all outstanding concerns.
- Money: There is a welcome tendency towards displaying company financial and sales data on the shop floor.

- Improvement: Keep a flipchart handy to note problems (which accumulate Pareto style) and suggestions with stage reached shown by filled in quadrant (suggested, investigated, being implemented, solved).
- Storyboards, showing the standard stages in kaizen events, recent successes and current progress.
- 5S: Display area responsibilities and 5-minute cleanup plans. Use shadow boards. Label and organise. Use kitchen organisation, not 'garage' organisation. Display audit results and winners.

Audio is also useful. At Toyota each robot cell has its own unique tune, which gets played over loudspeaker when there is a stoppage or problem. Maintenance engineers learn to listen out for the tunes they are responsible for. Tunes change with urgency.

Galsworth suggests appointing a "visual co-ordinator", and a management champion, who encourages and monitors the status of visual management in a plant. She makes the important point that visual management extends beyond the shop floor to the design of forms, to the presentation of information, to office layout, and to the home, together saving countless hours of waste spent searching and clarifying.

Further Reading:
Michel Grief, *The Visual Factory*, Productivity, Portland, OR, 1991

Gwendolyn Galsworth, *Visual Systems: Harnessing the Power of a Visual Workplace*, AmaCom, New York, 1997

Changeover Reduction

Changeover reduction is a pillar of lean manufacturing. The late Shigeo Shingo produced the classic work on "SMED", and until recently very little has been added to what he said. However, a significant advance has now been made by a group at the University of Bath (McIntosh et al, 2001). Also Six Sigma methods have added useful dimensions on variation.

Generally, for Lean, the reason to do changeover reduction is to allow for small batch flow and improved EPE performance.

What is Changeover?
There are three views. The first, narrow, view is the time that a machine is idle between batches (the 'internal' time). The second, and widely held, view is that it is the time from the last piece of the first batch to the first good piece of the second. A third view, supported by the Bath group, is that it is the time from the standard rate of running of the first batch to the standard rate of running the second. This view therefore includes rundown and ramp-up times.

The classic Shingo methodology is
- Identify and classify internal and external activities. Make a video?
- Separate "internal" activities from "external" activities. External or preparation activities should be maximized. Cut or reduce waste activities such as movement, fetching tools, filling in forms.
- Try to convert internal activities to external (for example by pre-heating a die).
- Use engineering on the remaining internal activities. There are many tricks, from quick release nuts, to constant platform shims, to multiple hole connections all in one. Both Shingo and McIntosh are an excellent source of ideas.
- Finally, minimize external activity time. (Why? Because in small batch production there may be insufficient time to prepare for the changeover during a batch run.)

To analyse, the process flow chart and spaghetti diagram are useful. To standardize, the work combination chart and standard operating procedures are useful. See separate sections on these standard Lean tools.

The Formula1 pit-stop analogy is useful. But note this is a high cost changeover with minimum time virtually the only goal. It also involves slowing down and speeding up. Safety is important but again costs big money. The wheel is held in place by only one screw. Is this acceptable? Another analogy is the standard seat belt, which has been safe, quick, reliable, adjustable and easy for all to use and widely acceptable. This is a design-led innovation – see below.

Changeover is part of OEE, so changeover reduction may be done under the auspices of TPM. The very thorough 9 step TPM approach will always be effective, but the effort to go through this level of detail is significant. TPM will also help highlight the importance of the changeover in relation to other losses, particularly when changeover is being done for capacity reasons.

To derive the target changeover time for mixed model flow, please refer to the Batch sizing section.

It is useful to think strategy: Is the changeover to reduce

McIntosh usefully divides changeover reduction into three phases. The table below has been developed from their work.

McIntosh et al make a strong case that there are two general approaches, organization-led (i.e. SMED) and design-led. For each, there are four areas to address: (1) 'On line activities' (by internal and external task reallocation, or by designs that allow the sequence to be altered – for example simultaneous rather than sequential steps); (2) Adjustment (by reducing trial and error by for example indicators and shims, or by design which allows 'snap-on' adjustment): (3) Variety (by standardization and standard operations or by design which reduces the possibilities of variation – pokayokes); and

Phases of Changeover (Adapted from McIntosh et al.)

Phase	Tasks	Issues
Strategic	Identify opportunities Focus priorities Identify the approach to use (Organization led or design led)	Internal team? Consultants? New equipment? Dedicated equipment? TPM / OEE approach?
Preparatory	Existing performance records. Variation in times? Postponement? Fix targets (e.g. via VSM)	5S of tools and dies Sequence dependencies? Use blitz? Involve different shifts?
Implementation	Video SMED methodology Engineering changes Pokayoke? Regularity and sequencing	Records Incentives? SOPS Sustainability

time, to reduce cost, to improve quality, to reduce manpower, to limit maintenance, or a combination. Is the aim to increase capacity or to improve flow? Generally you can't have them all.

McIntosh et al say there are four elements to successful changeover: Attitude, including workplace culture and receptiveness to change; Resources including time, money, personnel, training, tools; Awareness, including the contribution of changeover to (flow), flexibility, inventory, capacity and awareness of different possibilities of achieving quick changeover; Direction, including leadership and vision, priority and ranking, (and presumably impact on the value stream).

(4) Effort (by work simplification and preparation or by design which incorporates simplification – for example fixing multiple hoses by one fixture).

The choice between organisation-led and design-led, depends on objectives, on how much is willing to be spent, and on sustainability – design-led locks in improvements much more than organization-led.

McIntosh at al suggest that a 'Reference Changeover' be developed. This is what Lean practitioners would call a 'paper kaizen' activity. It involves collecting data (e.g. by video), identifying and cutting all waste, rearranging activities, and doing the changeover as efficiently as possible. This establishes the theoretical benchmark.

Six Sigma methodology has also been attempted on changeover. It is now clear that the SMED methodology is much more effective at reducing time, and should always be done first. But then Six Sigma analysis can be useful to examine the causes of time variation. If the changeover is important enough, building the distribution of changeover times and examining for normality of distribution and then seeking root causes of, for example, bi-modal time distributions can be worthwhile.

Design-led changeover involves a whole tranche of possibilities some of which are: First breaking task interdependencies and automating adjustments (for example incorporating a measuring scale); Making parts more robust or lighter; Second Pokayoke, incorporating built-in tools (e.g. welded spanner), improving access, and mechanization and robotics. Clearly there is overlap with TPM.

Finally a few tips

- Measure and record changeover times. Many changeover times have fallen by doing this alone.
- Put the pressure on reducing and keeping to setup times. See the comments on the 90/10 policy in the Batch Sizing section.
- Involve the team in analysis. Do not rely only on Industrial Engineers.
- Make a video, and get operators to record and critique. The video must remain their property. Put their ideas up on a board at the workplace.
- Consider a financial incentive for quick setup, whilst discouraging incentives for more production.
- Remember the equation: Changeover time x no of batches = constant. In other words as changeover time comes down, this must be converted into smaller batches. Resist the temptation just to gain extra capacity.
- Q:How do you get to Carnegie Hall? A:"Practice, man, practice". It's what grand prix teams do.
- Use trolleys onto which all tools and equipment are placed, and which can be wheeled to the changeover machine
- Regularity in the schedule helps. If everyone knows that Machine A is changed over every day at 9 a.m., then everyone from forklift driver to setter will be on hand.

- Tool and die maintenance is a vital, but sometimes overlooked, part of setup reduction. Don't compromise.
- At bottlenecks, use a team for the changeover, bringing in operators from non-bottleneck machines.
- Use appropriate quality control (such as SPC and Precontrol) procedures to verify good production.
- Be aware of the optimal sequence of changeover times.

Further reading:
Shigeo Shingo, *SMED*, Productivity Press, Portland, OR, 1985
R I McIntosh, S J Culley, A R Mileham, G W Owen, *Improving Changeover Performance*, Butterworth Heinemann, London, 2001

Small Machines, Avoiding Monuments and Thinking Small

The small machine concept is one of the least recognised lean facilitators. The general principle is to use the smallest machine possible consistent with quality requirements. Several smaller machines instead of one bigger, faster 'monument' allows flexibility in layouts, easier scheduling, reduction in material handling, less vulnerability to breakdown, less vulnerability to bottleneck problems, possibly reduced cost (through a mix of capability), and through phasing of machine acquisition, improved cash flow and more frequent technology updates. Do work improvement first, and only then do equipment improvement.

The related sunk cost principle means that the priority should be with minimising present and future costs, not with keeping machines working to "pay off" a cost that has already been incurred. Therefore utilisation is less relevant unless it is a capacity constrained machine. (Beware, however, a poorly utilised machine can become an effective constraint.)

Old Machines. The small machine concept can be extended to older machines. The best machine may well be an old machine that is quality capable, that is permanently set up, located just where needed, and that is written off in the books so that no-one cares about utilisation. It is throughput and lead-time that count. Beware of scrapping old machines that are still quality capable for machines that are faster.

Self Developed Machines. Why should a machine be "at its worst when new"? Because it may not yet have had pokayoke devices fitted, may not yet be quality capable, may not yet have had low cost automation devices integrated with it, and may not yet have been developed for multiple operations, and especially if variation has not been tackled.

Automation. The prime reason for automation in lean is for quality. The principle is not to automate waste. So simplify first. Ask whether a low cost solution is possible – a gravity feed rather than a robot. Good reasons for automation are dull, dirty, dangerous and hot, heavy, hazardous. Another good reason is reduction in variation. A bad reason is to reduce people. Beware, machines don't make improvement suggestions.

Schonberger offers excellent advice in what he terms 'Frugal Manufacturing'. In essence:
- Get the most out of conventional equipment and present facilities before implementing large-scale automation projects.
- Keep control over manufacturing strategy rather than turn it over to newly hired engineers and computer technicians or to a turnkey automation company.
- Build up your capability to modify, customise and simplify your machines. Do not expect commercially available general-purpose equipment to be right for your products. The ability to modify continually is becoming increasingly important as materials, technologies, quality standards and products change and improve.
- Approach bigger, faster machines and production lines with caution. High capacity and cost tend to dictate production policies, and immobility and inflexibility do not accommodate shortening product life cycles.

- Understand that big machines, separated equipment, and long conveyor systems disconnect people, obscure opportunities for merging processes, and result in divided accountability: automation has the potential to lower costs and minimise variations in quality, but it makes sense only when it solves clear-cut problems and when it costs less than simpler solutions introduced incrementally.

Small Machines are a part of a wider Lean issue – the advantages of thinking small. This goes back to Schumacher's classic work *Small is Beautiful*. Pil and Holweg discuss four advantages of small-scale operations. (1) Tapping into local networks, as decentralised R&D labs as opposed to large centralised facilities, are able to do in Cambridge (US and UK) (2) Responding to customers, as several manufacturers such as Nypro and Johnson Controls find when they set up facilities near customer sites. (3) Rethinking human resources – developing people more quickly by giving them greater responsibility in small operations. (South Africa has been a hotbed for the development of automotive CEO's, or training airline pilots in smaller airlines.)(4) Driving Innovation as per steel mini mills and discount airlines.

Further reading:
John Bicheno, *Cause and Effect Lean*, PICSIE Books, Buckingham, 2001
Richard Schonberger, 'Frugal Manufacturing', *Harvard Business Review*, 1987
Frits Pil and Matthias Holweg, 'Exploring Scale: the Advantages of Thinking Small', *MIT Sloan Management Review*, Winter 2003, pp33-39

Demand Management

Generally, the smoother the demand, the better the flow. Demand can never be entirely smooth – but at least do not make instability worse by your own actions. What is attempted here are a few pointers, for internal demand and external (supply chain) demand. (External demand can be converted to internal demand if what you regard as your supply chain changes.)

External Demand

- Try to avoid policies such as quantity discounts (rather give discounts for regular orders), or monthly sales incentives (rather give incentives for obtaining regular orders).
- Use the "variety as late as possible" concept. Do not add variety until the last possible moment. Design has an important role.
- Develop a build to order (BTO) policy with appropriate trigger points, where push meets pull. In cars this is body in white – at this stage actual orders are firmed.
- Use 'Yield Management' concepts – like hotels and airlines. Book ahead and get a discount; book late and pay more.
- Related to yield, segment demand into bands – fill in the troughs with longer lead time items
- Offer customers upgrades. For instance Dell offers customers free or bargain upgrades thereby helping to smooth variety and to shift inventory. Both customer and manufacturer benefit.
- Manage demand variation, report it, discuss it, and make people responsible for it - especially Sales and Marketing. Know the tradeoffs between promotions and "everyday low prices" (as Proctor and Gamble were surprised to discover).
- Avoid supply chain 'gaming' – for example running up inventories to appear more favourable at the next end of quarter statement. Have measures that work against such behaviour.
- Communicate along the supply chain. Try to make at the ultimate customer's rate of demand. Try to persuade supply chain partners to share information, and be willing to share it yourself.

Internal Demand Management

- Work further down the bill of materials. Perhaps the demands for various end items are erratic, but do these products share subassemblies, the demand for which may be much more regular? A related point is to aggregate demand. Demand for 1.6 litre, green, leather trim, sunroof Ford Focus may be erratic, but demand for Focus is much more stable.
- Have a policy to convert 'strangers' into 'repeaters' and 'repeaters' into 'runners'. See Design and Essential Paretos.
- Stabilize manufacturing operations by appropriate supermarkets.
- Use a single pacemaker, preferably for a whole supply chain.
- Reduce changeover times to make customer pull more possible. Much underlying demand is fairly stable, but becomes unstable when supply chain members distrust response times and available inventory.
- Use control limits, much like an SPC chart. As long as demand stays within these limits, don't change the plan. Or, use a CUSUM chart to detect changes to underlying demand. A CUSUM is one of the most effective ways of detecting shifts in demand patterns. (See *The Quality 75* for a section on CUSUMS)
- Use "under capacity scheduling" to make sure that you hit the production target. This means not scheduling to full capacity, but allowing a buffer period to catch up on problems. If there aren't any problems, do continuous improvement.
- Remember takt time is derived from customer demand and available production time – so it is partly under your own control. Don't over-react to changes in customer demand.
- Stabilize production at the right level in the bill of materials. Perhaps stabilize at the MPS level, and call off via the final assembly schedule
- Give priority to regular orders. Don't let bad drive out good. Filter the erratic orders out, and make them in their own slot with lower frequency. Beware of large orders disrupting the regular schedule – split up the large order into smaller batches – and first ask the customer if the delivery requirement is really what is required.
- Use the "available to promise" logic found in most Master Scheduling packages.
- Work according to medium term forecasts rather than short-term call offs. The medium term will be more stable and probably more reliable. Test the reliability of different forecast horizons, and don't be afraid to ignore short-term forecasts.
- Gear the incentives of distributors to work towards smooth demand.

- Move to 'milk round' deliveries – whereby several small batches are delivered on a single vehicle more frequently, rather than a big batch less frequently, meaning that total number of loads remains unchanged.
- Overproduction is the greatest enemy. Do not fall into the trap of just making a few more while things seem to be going well. This causes disruption in all later stages.
- Most of all have a vision of regular, smoothed demand. Identify the barriers that are preventing this from happening, and make appropriate plans.

Further reading:

Matthias Holweg, *The 3 Day Car Challenge*, PhD Thesis, Cardiff Business School, 2002

James Fitzsimmons, *Service Management*, Third edition, McGraw Hill, New York, 2001

John Bicheno, *Cause and Effect Lean: The Essentials of Lean Manufacturing*, PICSIE Books, Buckingham, 2001.

John Bicheno, *The Quality 75*, PICSIE Books, Buckingham, 2002

Yasuhiro Monden, *Toyota Production System*, (Second edition), Chapman and Hall, London, 1994

Matthias Holweg and Frits Pil, 'Successful Build-to-Order Strategies Start with the Customer', *MIT Sloan Management Review,* Fall 2001, p74-83

Mapping, Audits and Analysis

The Value Stream Implementation Cycle

Mapping and audits are major analysis tools in Lean. Mapping is the "Meta Tool" in the Lean Toolbox because the mapping tools should guide the use of all other tools. In the section below, the maps and tools described later are underlined.

Remember that all mapping and analysis is waste unless it leads to action. Doing mapping is not doing Lean. Do not fall for Paralysis by Analysis.

What is the Aim of Mapping?

The aim is to establish priorities for Lean implementation, both short and medium term. They allow one to view the big picture, to select priorities and to avoid rushing into inappropriate sub-optimization activities. Mapping and Audits are also for idea generation – so encourage people to add notes and remarks, even cartoons. Although maps should be on display, mapping is not for decoration, it is for action – obvious, but beware of framed or laminated maps. Date all maps, and take them down after a few months. Bear in mind the four elements: Current State, Future State, Ideal State, and Action Plan.

Maps should be developed by the area's people for the area's people. Maps should be signed off by all the participating mappers, but especially by the people from the area just mapped.

Organizing

This concerns organizing for Lean implementation in general, not just for mapping. Normally this will comprise a steering committee, a Lean champion, and Lean promotion office to support the mapping activities. Desirable resources include a mapping 'war room' near the area to be mapped, pencils, erasers, and flipcharts. Clipboards. Post-it stickers and felt pens are useful – use different colors for material and information flows. Toyota likes to do most maps on A3 size sheets. Brown paper rolls and are needed for some maps. Stopwatches may be useful. There are computer packages for mapping, but if used at all should be the last stage – it is much better to allow participation around a 'messy' wall chart than a neatly produced map done by one person. It is useful to have layout diagrams if these are available. Walk the area for an overview.

Pre-Mapping Workshop

Hold a short workshop on expectations. Outline the plan. Possibly use the workshop for some initial training on mapping mechanics and wastes. Perhaps visit other areas that have already been mapped. Watch a video on mapping – there are several available. An important consideration is to define the 'system boundary' – what is to be included and what excluded. (A SIPOC diagram is useful: Suppliers, Inputs, Process, Outputs, and Customers). Take time on this one. Be guided by areas of responsibility but also natural flows of work and buffers. In perhaps half of situations it will be necessary to identify the particular value streams to be mapped using Product Family Analysis. To concentrate on the most time-consuming part of the value stream, often begin with Overall Lead time Analysis.

Get the whole team to walk the route, and then split up into sub teams to do the individual basic maps. For the Learning to See current state you may have sub teams for material flows and information flows. Mapping activities need to be explained to operators whose area is being mapped. Be honest and open.

Who Maps?

A mapping team must comprise the supervisor from the area or areas, the manager(s) of the area, possibly some operators, possibly relevant internal customers and suppliers, people from the next area to be mapped, and

When?

At the pre-mapping workshop include a discussion about when to map. Plan to map on a representative day – midweek, probably. Try to avoid peak periods or leave periods.

Which direction?

Experienced mappers like to map upstream so that they can collect customer requirements at each stage before moving on. If you find this confusing, work downstream.

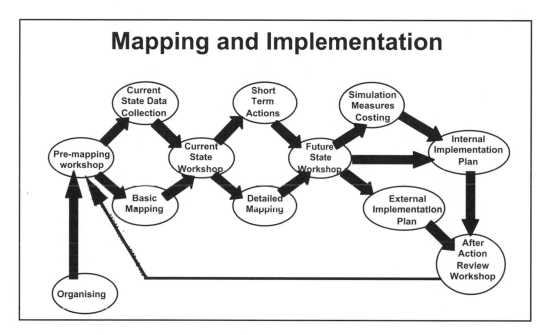

an experienced mapping facilitator (from the Lean Promotion office) or consultant. Do not delegate mapping to 'experts'. Ownership and credibility are vital. The ideal mapping team is around 7 to 9 people.

Gathering Data.

Map what you see today. Ignore the fact that 'today is not usual'. Go to 'Gemba' and collect the facts. For the majority of maps, do not sit in an office and draw the map.

Basic Mapping

Begin actual mapping. This will often comprise assembling the four basic maps – Value Stream Map, Quality Filter Map, Spaghetti Diagram, and Demand Amplification Map. Split into sub teams for perhaps 4 hours before assembling and presenting to each other. As the team walks the area, be sure to 'wear muda spectacles', and to be aware of opportunities such as 5S, standard work, pokayoke, and visual systems. Throughout, maintain a high level view – keep to the main stages. Drilling down comes later.

For value streams where there are multiple customer contact points, as in service operations, a <u>Service Blueprint</u> is better than the Learning to See map.

Current State Data Collection

Supporting information may be collected beforehand. This will often comprise takt time, working hours, operator skills, delivery performance, and supplier performance. If there are clear bottlenecks (constraints) check work time and <u>OEE.</u> Do a quick sample audit on standards and inventory record accuracy. Get the organization chart, and incorporate areas of responsibility onto the basic maps. It is useful to do a <u>manufacturing audit</u> – for example <u>Kobayashi</u> or <u>Schonberger's 16 Principles</u>. <u>Activity Sampling</u> is a very powerful tool that should always go alongside mapping.

Current State Workshop

For a small exercise this may take place on the same day as the basic mapping. Otherwise schedule a specific day as near as possible to the mapping day. Assemble the basic maps. Talk them through with people from the area. Calculate the time line, value adding ratio, and constraint utilization. List the wastes that have been spotted.

There are three aims: (a) to gain a clear 'big picture' overview appreciation, (b) to identify 'low hanging fruit' opportunities, (c) to identify areas for more detailed study.

Short Term Actions

These may be undertaken by short blitz events or other quick kill initiatives. A definite time objective must be fixed.

Detailed Mapping

Here more detailed mapping is undertaken. <u>Process activity maps</u> may be made for selected areas. Also more detail on selected aspects of information flow or scheduling. The <u>Information Value Stream Map</u> can be used in selected areas where there are clear process

flows and minimal branching resulting from decisions. Otherwise the <u>Brown Paper Map</u> can be used for selected processes. It is often useful to home in on variation of selected process or changeover times, defect rates, and demand data. In service or clerical processes, <u>Order Mapping and Tagging</u> may be useful in selected areas.

In some situations, mainly to bring home the point to management, preparing a <u>Cost Time Profile</u> may be useful.

Detailed cell design and line design is described in a separate chapter. <u>Cell layout diagrams</u> and <u>work combination charts</u> will be used.

Future State Workshop

Schedule this day specifically within days of the basic mapping. The aim is to develop (a) the next future state, (b) the action plan, and possibly (c) the ideal state. Use the guidelines of the future state questions, scheduling building blocks, and scheduling concepts mentioned at the end of this chapter and explained in greater detail in the next chapter. Draw the future state map and maybe the ideal state map. Feel free to annotate. Produce supporting diagrams and concepts, such as layouts, supermarket concepts, scheduling concepts, information flows, and people development. Try to keep all maps on display in the war room. Use the workshop as a workshop to present, to solicit ideas, and to gain buy-in.

Simulation, Measures, and Costing

Simulation may be a possibility. It can take various forms: (a) physical simulation, such as full-size cardboard modeling (b) paper simulation – whereby you work through a month's schedule on paper, or (c) more rarely computer simulation using a modeling language. It is also useful to review the measures that are in place for possible conflicts with the future state – for example a measure that encourages overproduction. Beware, for example, of OEE. Likewise review the costing system. In particular, for a future state, it is important to work through the consequences on the financial statements of inventory reductions and other changes with your accountant. See the Chapter on Lean Accounting and Measures.

Internal Implementation Plan

The internal Action Plan covering what, who, when, and where. Present it to management. Explain it to the shop floor. Use Force Field Analysis as a means of both explaining and soliciting ideas. Gantt chart the activities. Develop a plan for the next 90 days – sometimes 180 days, but never more. Develop the Master Schedule. The Route Learning Map is beginning to be used as an effective implementation and communication device. Think in terms of bite size chunks. Do a little and return to do it again, rather than a big chunk that never gets there.

External Implementation Plan

The External Action Plan, covering upstream and downstream parties. Should include the reduction of amplification. Similar comments on time.

External implementation will eventually involve the whole supply chain. For this, the Supply Chain Structure map, and 'Seeing the Whole' (extended value stream map) will become essential.

After Action Review

It is vital that this workshop is scheduled after the review period of say 90 days. All are expected to attend. It covers what was planned, what was achieved, why the difference, and what can be learned for the next cycle. Start and maintain a checklist for future mapping.

Mapping Overview

The list that follows gives an overview of the hierarchy of available maps. The stars indicate approximate frequency of use.

Pre-Mapping:
Product Family Analysis **
Overall Lead Time Mapping **
Brown Paper Overview ***
Supply Chain Structure ***

Supply Chain:
Seeing the Whole
(extended value stream mapping) **
Demand Amplification Map **
Cost Time Profile *

Value Stream:
Value Stream Map ****
Demand Amplification Map ***
Spaghetti Diagram ****
Quality Filter Map ***
Activity Sampling ***
Cost Time Profile *

Information Processing:
Order Tracking (multi branching) **
(but **** in information processors)
Information Value Stream Map
(minimal branching or options) **

Multi Customer-Contact Points (Service Maps)
Service Blueprints *
(but **** in service companies)

Detailed Activity Maps
Process Activity Maps **
Work Combination Chart***
Cell Layout ***

Implementation Maps
Route Learning Maps*

In a manufacturing company you generally move down the above list – except that supply chain mapping is often delayed because it requires the cooperation of several parties. An information intensive or pure service company would usually skip most maps in the first three categories.

Further reading:
Peter Hines and David Taylor, *Going Lean: A Guide to Implementation*, Cardiff Business School, 2000

Brown Paper Chart

A Brown Paper Chart is a high level diagram showing the main product. An example of a brow paper chart is shown below, taken from an automotive metal pressing company. It serves to clarify the overall logic of the plant. A supply chain version would show the main suppliers, service centres, supply routes, distribution routes, distribution centres, and main customers. Often products and percentages going through different channels would be shown.

The chart can become a focus in the 'war room' showing by means of frequently updated photographs, graphics, and 'post it' notes, the progress and highlights. A 'Master Schedule' can go alongside – showing the Gantt chart of progress towards implementation. The team should gather around the Master Schedule at regular (weekly?) intervals to check progress.

Product Family Analysis

Product family analysis is about breaking down the full product range into groups that can be managed together, or share a significant part of a value stream. It is the first step of value stream mapping and the basis of cellular manufacturing. There are strategic and technical considerations.

Strategic considerations

In automotive supply and some other industries it is becoming the norm to establish customer cells. This is where final assembly operations are dedicated to a particular customer. There may be a Ford cell, a Nissan cell, and a Toyota cell all on the same site, each running according to their own system. Where this is the case, the product family is pre-defined.

Even where a customer may not require dedicated cells, there may be business opportunities by creating customer cells. This is what Johnson Controls does with sequenced JIT delivery of seats into nearby car plants, or Nypro does with injection molded parts fed directly into Dell or HP. Other companies set up development

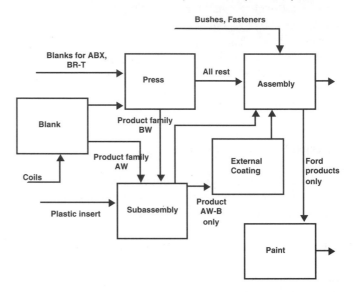

cells for ramp-up and initial improvement, and then ship the whole cell overseas when demand is established.

In other situations, take time out to think of the strategic opportunities before rushing into defining families or cells. An important consideration is the business opportunities stemming from lead time reduction by creating a cell. Home bread making may involve fair capital outlay and poor capacity utilization, but many prefer the product to supermarket purchased loaves. Thus concentrating on utilization and efficiency may involve loss of opportunity to create a new business model. For example, a cosmetics company may decide to dedicate an infrequently used line in order to reduce inventories and to be able to respond to short-term demand.

Taking this concept further, there may be opportunities to review product design – perhaps employing more expensive materials which nevertheless lead to a cut in lead time or an improved product or lower execution costs. Last, take time to review manufacturing routings – perhaps to offload a bottleneck workcentre or to simplify flows.

Since one cell will be responsible for one product family, volumes must be sufficient for this to be feasible. This may mean, on the one hand, trimming the product range or selecting out only the highest volume products, or on the other hand, changing some existing product routings to enable them to be made within the cell. This therefore may involve engineering and design. Develop the anticipated flow rate by consulting Marketing and Sales. Aim for a capacity that matches demand every week rather than every month. This may involve reducing changeover times, or permanently set up machines. An important tactical issue is the decision to move away from 'monuments' to smaller, often older retained, machines. (See sections on the Small Machine Principle and P-Q analysis.)

Overlaying all these is the question of where to begin the cell or value stream. Common routings generally apply to a greater extent downstream. Shared resources are typically found upstream. Between them there may be a supermarket.

Finally, from a control and motivational perspective contemplate the opportunities for creating a self-contained or self-managed focus factory, in line with Lean principles of simplicity, visibility, flexibility, response and low overhead. The advantages may well offset the costs of lower utilization.

Historic Note: Britain was a world leader in cellular manufacturing in the 1960s with pioneers such as Burbidge and Edwards. Some of the earliest manufacturing examples were found in Britain, although the concept has its origins with Mitrofanov in the Soviet Union during the Second World War. But, generally, cells only took off in the 1980s when the Japanese brought some of the essential ingredients into the mix: these are flexible labour, emphasis on quality and continuous improvement, attention to maintenance (or TPM) and housekeeping, and perhaps the concept of the level schedule.

Technical considerations

After thought has been given to the strategic, technical considerations may remain. The problem is how to group parts or products into cells or value streams. The

problem can be clarified by constructing a product process matrix.

There are two approaches, 'eyeball' and analytical. The eyeball involves visual inspection of the parts or the routings. Sometimes similarity of families is obvious from either part or process similarity. In the third figure two families are obvious – but there remain questions as to alternative routings or redesign involving the third process of part D.

The analytical approach may involve involve mathematical and Group Technology methods. The mathematical approach involves 'clustering algorithms' such as the Binary Ordering Algorithm that assigns weights and rearranges first rows, and then columns. The matrices below show an initial product process matrix, (with processes 1 to 7 and products A to E). The

	1	2	3	4	5	6	7
A	X		X	X		X	X
B	X					X	X
C			X	X	X		
D					X	X	X
E		X	X	X			

	1	2	3	4	5	6	7
A	X		X	X		X	X
B	X					X	X
D					X	X	X
C			X	X	X		
E		X	X	X			

	7	6	1	3	4	5	2
A	X	X	X	X	X		
B	X	X	X				
E				X	X		X
C				X	X	X	
D	X	X				X	

second matrix shows the results of the 'eyeball' approach. Note that two cells or value steams are indicated but there remains some issues in sorting out what to do with processes 3 and 4 for product A. A revised matrix as a result of applying the Binary Ordering Algorithm is shown in C.

This suggests possibly 3 cells. Note that the sequence order is not retained. Refer to the readings for detail of this and other algorithms.

Overall Lead Time Map

The aim of the Lead Time Map is simply to track, quantify and prioritize the various elements of total lead time. For a time-based competitor, it should be one of the first, if not the first, map to draw. The idea is to draw a Pareto of where time is being spent or lost. The recent '3 Day Car' project at Cardiff revealed that in European automotive of the 6 weeks needed to deliver a new car, approximately 4 weeks were spent on information processing. So, forget the factory – get after the information flows. **A very important aspect is to determine the variation in the lead time**. Try to get a histogram for each element, and overall.

Lead Time Map

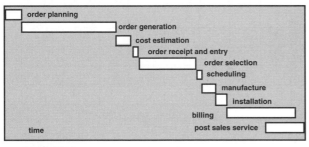

arranged as a Gantt chart

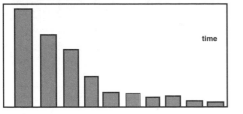

...and as a Pareto ...

The elements of overall lead time are:

- Order entry time: paperwork. The time from receipt of order to entry into the manufacturing and planning system.
- Schedule assembly time – needed to consolidate orders into balanced assembly sequences.
- Configuration time: the time from entry into the system to completion of the configuration. In assemble to order or make to order this could involve design or CAD time and configuration checks. This time will probably be zero in make to stock environments, and may be zero or near zero in repetitive operations.
- Procurement time: the time taken to procure materials and components, to kit (if done) and to bring the materials from the store to the point of use. In repetitive operations some elements of procurement time could be regarded as zero where they are done routinely or in parallel with order entry time or configuration time.
- Non-specific manufacturing time: the time taken for "variety as late as possible" manufacturing stages, where components or subassemblies are not specific to a final product or order. Note that this time element may overlap or be done in parallel with order entry time and configuration time.
- Order-specific manufacturing time: the time taken in those manufacturing stages which are order- or customer-specific. This time may be zero in make-to-stock.
- Post production move and store time: the time from completion of manufacture to the start of delivery. This time may include final packaging.
- Delivery time: this may include final configuration in the case of products that are bundled to order.

The resulting time line may be a straight line, or may have overlapping sections. Where there are overlapping sections, take the longest time line or critical path. Draw a Pareto diagram or pie chart of the total time. This of course highlights the areas of greatest opportunity for time reduction, or at least should prevent one from homing in on a relatively unimportant element. Draw a lead time distribution histogram.

An extension is to benchmark each element. The established procedure of "best demonstrated practice" aims at finding the best performer on each element, and then combining the series of best practices into an overall best practice that is superior to any individual organization.

'Seeing the Whole' Supply Chain Mapping

Seeing the Whole Mapping is very similar to Value Stream Mapping described later. Only the scope is greater – the inter-company value stream rather than the in-plant value stream. A seeing the Whole map looks just like a Value Stream Map, except that plants replace process stages. Of course some intermediate stages may be warehouses or cross-docks. Information flows are in the top half, physical flows in the bottom half. The more detailed principles will be described under Value Stream Mapping; here the special features of supply chain mapping are mentioned.

- The main benefit of Seeing the Whole mapping is to gain an understanding of the complete supply chain and to identify major co-ordination opportunities, rather than detailed kaizen implementation activities.
- To this end, assembly of the mapping team from multiple companies is easily the most difficult and important issue. It has to be seen as a mutual benefit exercise – no hidden agendas. The team will be high level, because the issues are high level. The core of the mapping team is schedulers from participating companies.
- What is a complete supply chain – how far upstream should you go? Answer: as far as possible, or pragmatically as far as cooperation from participating companies will allow. Even linking two companies is a worthwhile exercise.
- Since the focus is on the complete value stream you can afford to aggregate most in-plant stages. In general, most plants will be drawn as single process boxes or stages. An exception is where there is a mix of shared and dedicated resources

within a plant – for example a common press shop feeding a dedicated assembly line. These will often have separate scheduling systems.

- Ideally, each company in the complete supply chain will first have done an internal Learning to See map. This may not be realistic. There are plenty of opportunities to go after even if Learning to see maps have not been developed. For example, in the 3 Day Car study it was found that by far most of the 6 week delay between placing an order and receiving a new car was due to information delays along the chain. Forget the internal physical changes and work on the information flows.
- As with Value Stream maps, the main supporting maps are valuable – in particular the Demand Amplification Map, for which data should be collected alongside the Seeing the Whole map.
- The focus should be more on the information flows rather than the physical flows. Do show the physical flows along the bottom of the map, but concentrate on the information flows.
- Keep the end customer in mind throughout the exercise. Intermediate customers (other companies) are important, but the supply chain exists for the end customer. Thus waste identification and opportunities are focused on the end customer.
- A weakness of both Value Stream maps and Seeing the Whole maps is the way they deal with shared resources. (This aspect is generally ignored in *Learning to See*.) There will likely be several shared resources in a complete supply chain. The way they are scheduled is key. What other supply chains are served, and how much capacity is devoted to the particular supply chain are important questions. For instance in one supply chain studied, a mid-chain participant could originally only devote one day a week to the particular supply chain. So, could changeover be reduced or buffer (supply chain supermarket) added to allow a more frequent EPE (every product every) – and who would pay for this? A detailed understanding of the scheduling assumptions and constraints is one of the great pay-offs.
- The scheduling building blocks (see separate section) are relevant in supply chains also.
- Yet another weakness is ignoring variation – which is even more of a killer in a supply chain than in a

plant. So do consider the vulnerability of the future state chain to disruptions, breakdowns, variation on delivery times, and quality problems. Consider the · strategic location of supply chain supermarkets. Play the dice game with supply chain partners.

- CONWIP (Constant work in process – see separate section) is a powerful concept, often ignored. CONWIP in a supply chain can leapfrog several participants.

Further reading:
Dan Jones and Jim Womack, *Seeing the Whole: mapping the extended value stream*, Lean Enterprise Institute, Boston, 2002

"Learning to See" Maps

The next four mapping tools are best regarded as a set. Together they give a powerful picture of Lean status.

The "Learning to See" map has emerged as a very popular and clear way to illustrate the current and future state of a process. The method maps both material and information flows. It is quick to learn because it uses simple boxes to indicate stages, and other obvious symbols such as trucks, factories, and kanban cards. The tool is suitable for repetitive operations, especially where a single product or family is made. A powerful feature is that it 'closes the loop' from customer order to supply to manufacture ending with the delivery of the product. (This closed loop is not shown on most detailed activity charts.)

Begin with the Current State. Pick a main product. Draw a factory symbol for main Suppliers at the top left and Distribution or Customer at top right. In the top centre draw to box for Production Control. Along the centre of the page list the main stages of manufacture, one to a box. Below each stage, in the data boxes, find out and list cycle time for the chosen product, changeover time, the OEE or the percentage availability,

and the available time per week. Between the stages, show the current inventory holdings in a triangle. Then draw in the material flows. Use a broad arrow for this (the black hatch indicates push). For supply and deliveries, draw in a truck symbol and label each with the frequency of delivery.

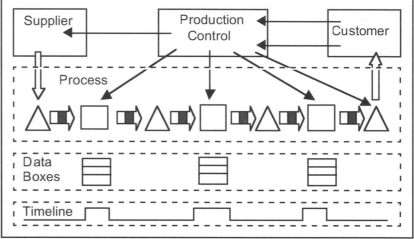

At the bottom of the page, draw a timeline line, corresponding with the production stages, to indicate the value adding time (top segments)) and non value adding time (lower segments). Although not strictly correct but nevertheless a fair approximation, calculate value adding time from the machine cycle times or unit assembly times. Calculate the non-value adding times by multiplying the inventory quantities in units (shown below the inventory triangles) by the takt time in minutes per unit.

Now find out and draw in the scheduling information. Draw narrow arrows connecting the customer with Production Control to indicate forecasts and orders. Label the frequency. You can use lightning symbols to indicate electronic links. Do the same for the Supplier. Now find out how the schedule is communicated to the factory floor. Connect Production Control to the appropriate stages by narrow arrows. An example is shown.

The point about these diagrams is that they are a clear overview that can be used for planning and participation meetings, from shop floor to top management. As a reference tool they can be placed on boards in meeting areas, and ideas can be added by Post-it stickers. Progress can be charted.

This creates the current state diagram. To create the future state and ideal state diagrams requires two steps. First, incorporate obvious short-term improvements from the four basic maps. This includes waste reductions. Show these as 'Kaizen bursts' on the diagram. The second step requires more in-depth knowledge of Lean possibilities. These are the subjects of the next two chapters. However, it is useful to break up the value steam map into pull segments or loops, often separated by supermarkets. Then use these as building blocks for layout design.

Further reading:
Mike Rother and John Shook, *Learning to See*, The Lean Enterprise Institute, Brookline, MA, 1998
Kate Mackle and John Bicheno, *Lean Mapping*, APICS Lean Manufacturing Workshop series, 2003. (CD and book). www.apics.org

Spaghetti Diagram

The Spaghetti Diagram (or String Diagram) is a long established tool for more effective layout. It tracks the waste of transport and the waste of motion. It could not be simpler. Merely get a layout diagram of the plant and trace the physical flow of the product in question on the diagram. Mark on the diagram the locations of inventory storage points. Do not forget rework loops, inspection points, and weigh points. Calculate the total length of flow. Show component delivery flow paths in another colour. Again calculate the length of travel. Wasteful movement and poor layout become clearly apparent. Do get the mapping team to walk the distance, rather than just to draw it. While the team is walking, get them to take note of variations in vertical movements – the more constant, the better.

A spaghetti diagram can also be used to map collection routes for parts, and external processing travel paths.

Many plants have, for shock-tactics purposes, worked out the equivalent annual distance traveled in terms of,

for instance, number of times around the world. Jim Womack once related the average speed of travel of an aerospace part to the speed of an ant!

The Learning to See map gives the logic of the main steps, the information flows, and the time line. The Spaghetti Diagram gives the geography. So they form a set. Strangely, this simple but powerful tool gets little or no mention in some mapping publications.

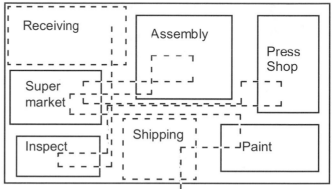

At least two flows should be traced – the product flow and the regular (or irregular) material handling routes.

Lean layout groups inventory into supermarkets from which parts are pulled. Parts should not be scattered around in many locations. Parts are delivered to the line and products collected from the line by set material handler (water spider or runner) routes. The spaghetti diagram is the prime tool for establishing the best routes.

The spaghetti diagram can also be used at the workplace level, for instance for changeover reduction analysis.

Quality Filter Mapping

Quality filter mapping aims to track the rates and sources of defects along a process route. The Quality Filter Map is a graph showing the parts per million (ppm) rate against process stage. Although this information may be collected and shown as part of a

Learning to See current state map, a quality filter map adds emphasis. Two lines should be shown, Scrap and Rework.

Note that scrap and rework should be recorded not only at points where the company records defects, but also at all operation steps. This is to ensure picking up what Juran refers to as "chronic" wastes (the underlying

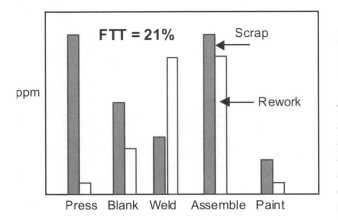

defects, reworks, or inspections that have become so routine that they are not recognized as a problem). An example is the 100% manual touch-up welds done at the end of a robotic assembly line, which enjoyed zero priority for improvement but which, upon analysis, proved to be one of the most costly quality problems in the plant.

First time through (FTT) is often calculated as part of the Quality Filter Map. FTT is expressed as a percentage:

$$\frac{100 \times (\text{parts shipped} - (\text{parts reworked} + \text{parts scrapped}))}{\text{parts shipped}}$$

Note that if parts are reworked at several workstations the FTT figure can be negative.

Quality filter mapping can highlight defects that are passed over long distances along a process route or supply chain only to be rejected beyond the point at which return for rework is not economic. Also, beware of parts that are passed onto constraint machines, thereby wasting capacity.

Beware of believing a company's official defect figures. 5 ppm at final dispatch may be the result of excellent process control, or of numerous inspections and reworks. In 1995 the story was told of a famous German car whose average time for rectification exceeded the total time required to build an entire new Toyota Carina. The final build quality of the German car was, however, superb.

Demand Amplification Mapping

This tool maps what is termed the "Forrester Effect" after Jay Forrester of MIT who first modeled the amplification of disturbances along the supply chain and illustrated the effect in supply chain games. It is also a form of the well-known run diagram used in quality management, but here shows production activities against time. Amplification happens in plant and in supply chains, but the latter has enjoyed more attention.

Amplification is the enemy of linear production and lean manufacturing, and results from batching and inventory control policies applied along the supply chain. For instance, fairly regular or linear customer demand is translated into batch orders by a retailer, then subject to further modification by a distributor adjusting safety stocks, then amplified further by a manufacturer who may have long changeovers and big batches, and then further modified by a supplier who orders in yet larger batches to get quantity discounts. The result is that, further along the chain, the pattern of demand in no way resembles the final customer demand.

An amplification map is plotted usually day-by-day across a month. Data will usually have to be obtained from purchasing, receiving dock, order entry, from completions at various stages, and from dispatch. In a supply chain, an amplification map shows orders, shipments, and inventory levels at each company in the chain over a period that matches the cumulative lead-time in the chain. It is quite a big job to get this data – but the results are often startling.

The figure shows an in-house example adapted from a real automotive first tier supplier. Orders from the automotive customer ('TDS') are reasonably regular. Final assembly tracks actual orders fairly closely. So far so good. The supporting press shop has to make in batches due to changeover. But notice that batches are uneven in size, varying by a factor of about 2. They are also unevenly spaced. Clearly things have gone awry – perhaps due to several schedules or problems with breakdowns. There is also overproduction. Inventory levels and ordering from the steel supplier are also

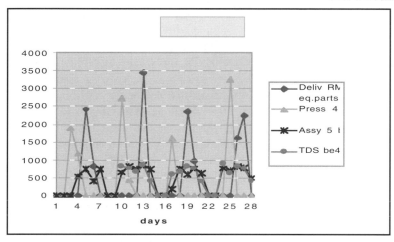

erratic. Clearly the advantages of stable, regular orders from the customers are being destroyed. Life is being made very difficult for the steel supplier – who nevertheless is picking up blame for poor service. What is going wrong, and what should be addressed?

The amplification map is a great tool for getting at the heart of scheduling issues. It is also a good evaluation tool that forms part of a periodic report to management or as as a tool for evaluating the process of Lean implementation.

The amplification issue and its possible solutions in the supply chain context are discussed in the Supply Chain chapter.

Reference:
PICSIE Books, *The Buckingham Supply Chain Game*, and *Lean Leap Game*, PICSIE Books, Buckingham, 2000.

Activity Sampling

Activity sampling is another traditional tool of the industrial engineer. It enables a quick but quantitative picture to be built up of the status of waste and opportunity for reduction. The results are frequently surprising.

Focus on an activity or machine or operator and simply take (say) 200 random observations during a shift or over a week. Categorize into value add, non value-add, or non value-add unavoidable. Further note the types on NVA and NVAU activities. Record the data using 'fence and bar' (卌). Normally an observer can focus on several, say 6, activities or people during a shift. Moreover, sampling can also be done simultaneously with other work – such as 5S audits, inventory counts, or schedule discussions. Ethically, you should inform at least the team leader that observations are being made.

200 random observations will give a reasonable picture of the use of that resource, provided they are randomly spread out across a reasonable period (say a few days). There are formulas that can be used to calculate the confidence of the observations (see any Time and Motion text) but this is often not necessary. You can pre-decide the times for observations, but it is common to just decide how many observations per hour will be taken and spread them out over the time. Record what you see at that instant, not over several seconds. Of course, avoid taking observations at regular intervals and at set points in a cycle – these are not random. In the chart shown below the observer adds the waste categories as she sees them, and the frequency of recurrence. There will always be a column for value adding activity. In the example only one process stage is being observed but it is usual to sample several steps. Each stage needs around 200 observations for confidence.

Calculate the percentage of time observed in each category. You can present as a pie chart. The potential for improvement will be apparent. Then discuss how waste can be reduced.

Take cell design and balance as an example. Activity timing will give a good indication of the times when work is actually taking place. But how much time is involved in non value adding activities such as discussions, taking breaks, reading standard work sheets, counting parts, entering data and so on? All of

Process Stage	Value Adding	Waste Type					
		Wait	Move	Inspt			
Inject	‖‖ ‖	‖‖ ‖‖ ‖	‖‖ ‖‖ ‖‖	‖			

these may be non-regular and would not be recorded in the normal activity timing. In cell design, you may find that when the cell is running it runs very efficiently, but there are frequent interruptions. There may be far more waste occurring outside of the times when the cell is running. If so, reducing the reasons for this waste should be tackled first. Occasionally, adjust the takt time to allow for unavoidable discussions or interruptions.

Cost Time Profile

A Cost Time Profile is simply a graph showing accumulated cost against accumulated time. Its beauty lies in its visual impact that, the writer can verify, often leaves senior managers stunned. Whenever value or cost is added, the graph moves upwards; a plateau indicates no value or cost being added for a period of time, for instance during delay or storage. The area under the graph represents the time that money is tied up for. The aim is to reduce the area under the graph by

reducing time and/or cost. The technique is superior to a simple Pareto analysis of cost and time accumulations because one can immediately recognize where expensive inventory is lying idle and at what stage time delays occur. An example is shown in the figure on the next page. Notice two cumulative lines, one for total cost and the other for value. The difference between these two lines represents wasteful, non value adding activities and other cost accumulations such as the cost of money being tied up in inventory. Non value adding activities include inspections, transport, clerical activities, and rework. A cost time profile can be obtained directly from the process activity map, by multiplying by the costs of the various resources. If the process activity map is recorded on a spreadsheet, the calculations for the cost time profiles are easily done. When this is done, however, note that waste may still exist in a nominally value adding operation - for instance wasteful movements in an assembly activity, so that the lower profile does not represent the ultimate aim. The vertical distance between the two lines represents some obvious wastes, but not all wastes. For example, the long plateaus also represent waste of unnecessary storage and inventory. The aim should be to gradually reduce the profile towards that shown in the bottom left hand corner of the figure.

Note that when bought in materials are added, this results in a vertical bar on the chart equal to the material cost. In practice, the time for most value adding operations is minuscule in comparison with the delay and queue times, so value adding operations also appear as a vertical jump.

So a Cost Time Profile is a graphical method to identify when and where costs accumulate. They have been used extensively in conjunction with lean manufacturing, supply chain analysis, business process reengineering and total quality. Look for long plateaus, especially later on in the process where costs have already accumulated. Attacking the long time plateaus will reduce cost, and improve responsiveness and quality.

The profiles are relevant to quality improvement because there is often a direct correlation between poor quality and wasted time. So for instance when there are delays due to rework, inspection or queuing, both costs and time accumulate. Many customers associate good quality with shorter response or delivery times. The technique has been extensively used and developed by Westinghouse who used it as part of their Baldridge award-winning performance. It is equally applicable in manufacturing or office environments.

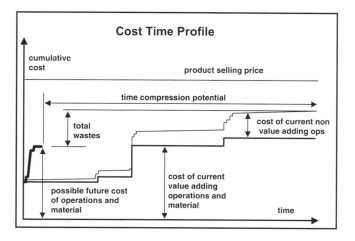

Westinghouse made extensive use of cost time profile charts, but presumably this is not what caused the break-up of the company in 1997! The company used the profiles in a hierarchical fashion. That is the profile for each sub-process or product can be combined to form a profile for a whole section that in turn can be combined into a profile for a complete plant or division. Here total costs are used, so it is necessary to multiply the unit cost profiles by the average number of units in process. All processes must be considered; value adding as well as support activities and overheads. This therefore represents a total process view of the organization, and may be used with process reengineering or Hoshin planning.

Further reading:
Jack H Fooks, *Profiles for Performance: Total Quality Methods for Reducing Cycle Time*, Addison Wesley, Reading, MA, 1993

Order Tracking

Order tracking follows through an order from receipt to dispatch. The aim is to decrease leadtime and improve customer service, and improve cash flow. Shapiro et al stress the importance of tracing the full "order management cycle" from planning to post-sales service. They state that there are typically 10 steps, some of which may overlap:

- order planning
- order generation
- cost estimation and pricing
- order receipt and entry
- order selection and prioritisation
- scheduling
- fulfilment (including procurement, manufacture, assembly, testing, shipping, installation)
- billing
- returns and claims
- post sales service

Shapiro et al suggest drawing up a matrix chart with the 10 steps forming the rows and the various departments or functions forming the columns. Trace the flow of an order, by arrows and activity boxes as it moves through the steps and departments. Identify who has prime responsibility for each step and who has a supporting role. Use the triangle symbol to indicate delays and queues. Estimate the length of these.

When drawing the sketch, use different colours or shading for physical movement of paper and for flows by computer network, telephone and fax.

Now the questioning begins. The aim is to reduce time and waste. It is essentially a creative process. Preferably the people involved in the process should be used in its analysis and improvement. Bold thinking is a requirement, not piecemeal adjustment. The title of the classic article in Harvard Business Review by Michael Hammer gives the clue: "Reengineering Work: Don't Automate, Obliterate!"; that is the type of thinking that is required. Competitive benchmarking may be useful, as may the creativity encouraged by value engineering. The same Harvard Business Review article tells how

Ford used to have 400 accounts payable clerks compared with just 7 people at Mazda.

The basic step is to examine the process chart and to split the activities into those that add immediate value for the customer and those that do not. Refer to the "7 wastes" for guidance. The concept is to achieve the added value of the product or service in as small a time as possible. Therefore try to make every value-adding step continuous with the last value-adding step, without interruptions for waiting, queuing, or for procedures that assist the company but not the customer. Stalk refers to this as the "main sequence". There are several guidelines:

- Can the non-value adding steps be eliminated, simplified, or reduced?
- Can any activities that delay a value adding activity be simplified or rescheduled?
- Are there any activities, particularly non-value adding activities, which can be done in parallel with the sequence of value adding activities?
- Can activities that have to be passed from department to department (and back!) be reorganized into a team activity? Better still, can one person do it? (What training and backup would be required?)
- Where are the bottlenecks? Can the capacity of the bottleneck be expanded? Do bottleneck operations keep working, or are they delayed for minor reasons? Are bottleneck operations delayed by non-bottleneck operations, whether value adding or not?
- What preparations can be made before the main sequence of value adding steps is initiated so as to avoid delays? (e.g. preparing the paperwork, getting machines ready.)
- Can the necessary customer variety or requirements be added at a later stage? (e.g. making a basic product or service but adding the "colour and sunroof" as late as possible.)
- If jobs are done in batches, can the batches be split so as to move on to a second activity before the whole batch is complete at the first activity?
- Can staff flexibility be improved so as to allow several tasks to be done by one person, thus cutting handing-on delays?

- What are decision-making arrangements? Can decision making power be devolved to the point of use? Can the routine decisions be recognized so that they can be dealt with on the spot? (Perhaps "expert systems" can be used.)
- Where is the best place, from a time point of view, to carry out each activity? (Can the activity be carried out at the point of use or contact, or must it really be referred elsewhere?)

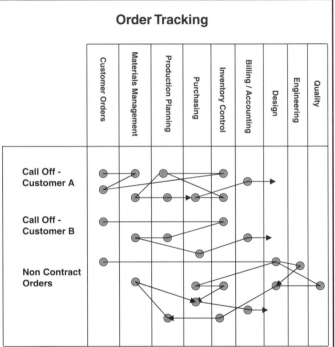

Variations
add Post-It notes to nodes (a data box or ideas)
show a time line below
label the flows with document types (paper, fax, etc.)
add supporting photographs
add rows for each activity type

- Do customers enjoy a "one stop" process? If not, why not?
- If problems do develop, what will be the delays and how can these delays be minimized?
- What availability of information will make the value adding sequence smoother or more continuous? (Is there more than one source of information, and if so can this be brought to one place? A common database perhaps?) The

established data processing principle is to capture information only once, and let everyone use the same data.

- As a second priority, can the time taken for value adding activities be reduced?

Michael Hammer has some useful non-mechanical suggestions concerning assumptions. The following is based on his "Out-of-the box thinking".

Are you assuming a specialist must do the work? (People).
Are you assuming that purchasing will pay only after receiving an invoice? (Time).
Are you assuming that record keeping must be done in the office? (Place).
Are you assuming that inventory is required for better service? (Resources).
Are you assuming that the customer should not be involved? (Customer).

Further reading:
Benson Shapiro, Kasturi Rangan, John Sviokla, "Staple Yourself to an Order", *Harvard Business Review*, July-August 1992, pp113-122
Eli Goldratt and Jeff Cox, *The Goal*, Creative Output, 1986
George Stalk and Thomas Hout, *Competing Against Time*, The Free Press, New York, 1990

Information Value Stream Map

When mapping information flows, service work or office work, where the only links with customers are the beginning and end of the process, and where relatively few departments are involved, 'Learning to See' mapping as described above can be used with little adjustment. The simplicity and clarity of Learning to See maps is a big advantage. Use the same conventions as before: Supplier in top left corner, final customer in top right corner (these will often be the same person or customer), process steps along the centre (these are the information processing steps) separated by inventory

triangles, and with time line shown along the bottom. Data boxes are also used. At the top centre of the page, the controlling office or scheduler or workflow computer system is shown – replacing the 'Production Control' box. The scheduling or ordering links between the central controller and the process steps are filled in, to complete the map.

Most symbols, such as for push, pull, inventory triangles, and people are used but additional icons can be invented for computers, letters, telephones, and so on. Current and future state maps are used as in 'Learning to See' maps.

All the questions used in the order tracking section above are relevant.

Further reading:
Don Tapping and Tom Shuker, *Value Stream Management for the Lean Office*, Productivity, New York, 2003
Peter Hines and David Taylor, *Going Lean: A Guide to Implementation*, Cardiff Business School, 2000

Service Blueprinting

Service blueprinting is particularly applicable in situations where there are multi contacts with customers – such as design interactions, and service situations such as airports and hospitals. Blueprinting is one the longest established service mapping tools and was originally proposed by Shostack. The technique has much in common with industrial engineering flowcharts, except that customer links are specifically included. The aim is to identify points at which the service may fail to satisfy customers and to identify points where value may be added for customers. A service blueprint shows time horizontally, and the hierarchy of support vertically. In drawing up a blueprint, five areas are included:

- "customer actions" are the activities (Moments of Truth) or interactions undertaken by the customer. These activities come into contact with two types of employee actions:

- "on stage" employee actions are visible to the customer and are separated in a service blueprint by a "line of interaction", drawn horizontally. Any vertical line crossing this line of interaction represents a direct contact or encounter between customer and front line employee.
- "backstage" employee actions are not visible to customers but are nevertheless in direct contact with customers (say by post or phone). These are separated from on stage activities by a "line of visibility", thus making clear what customers can see and possibly be influenced by.

A service blueprint can be read horizontally to focus on customer support activities and to answer questions such as how efficient, and how many points of contact are involved. Alternatively, a blueprint can be used to gain an overview or to understand the depth and nature of the support infrastructure, in which case it is read vertically. An immediate impression of the complexity of the service process is given by a blueprint, as are the steps that a customer faces in dealing with an organization. An illustration is shown in the figure. The power of service blueprints can be added to by including standards, pokayoke, and the Kano model, for each service activity. A service blueprint can be a

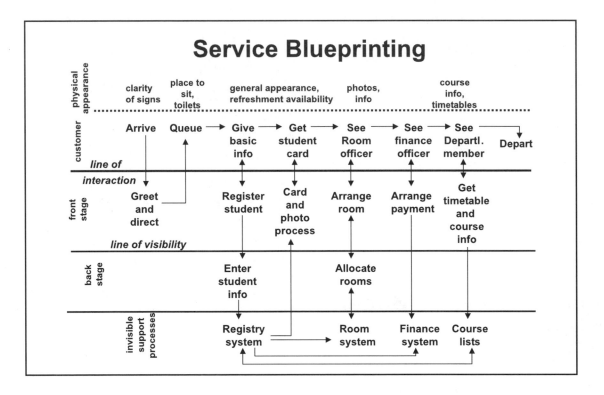

- "tangibles" are shown along the top line. These are physical evidence, signposts, appearances that customers encounter
- "support processes" are all those activities that support the front-line staff, whether visible or not. These are separated from backstage activities by a "line of internal interaction". Vertical lines crossing the line of internal interaction represent internal encounters.

particularly good device for training or standardization purposes, where photos can be added. Maintaining the up-to-date position on a computer service blueprint, possibly supported by digital photo or even video, can standardize service activities.

Think of two accompanying charts. The first is the "Spaghetti Diagram" showing the physical movements of customers and servers (shown in different colours).

The second chart lists, for each activity in the customer line, the Kano factors (Basics, Performance, Delighters), possible failsafing or pokayokes, and standard work.

Further reading:
G. Lynn Shostack, "Designing Services that Deliver", *Harvard Business Review*, Jan / Feb 1984, pp 133-139
G. Lynn Shostack, "Service Positioning Through Structural Change", *Journal of Marketing*, Vol 51, January 1987, pp 34-43
Jane Kingman Brundage, "Service Mapping : Gaining a Concrete Perspective on Service System Design", in Eberhard Scheuing and William Christopher (eds), *The Service Quality Handbook*, Amacom, New York, 1993, pages 148-163
John Bicheno, MR Gopalan and VS Mahesh, "Extending the Effectiveness of Service Mapping", *IIMB Management Review*, March 1999, pp13-24

Process Activity Mapping

The process activity map is a far more detailed map than those described above, and should be used only on sub-processes where there are particular concerns. The earlier maps generally deal with hours and minutes; the process activity map works in seconds. But, it makes no sense to concentrate on the seconds before you have sorted out the hours and days. The map is a classic tool of the industrial engineer. The difference is that now they are used not just by work study officers or I.E.'s, but supervisors and operators as well. In fact, the first preference is for operators to learn how to use this most effective tool themselves.

The process chart is the prime tool for detailed analysis of value adding and non value adding activities at the micro level.

The process chart lists every step that is involved in the manufacture of a product or the delivery of a service. Standard symbols are used to indicate "operation", "delay", "move", "store", and "inspect". (See figure.) The process chart helps identify wasteful actions, and documents the process completely. Good communication is an important reason to do this. The

systematic record helps reveal the possible sources of quality and productivity problems.

Many companies already have process charts. If they are available, beware! There are often differences between the "official" process charts and the way things actually happen in practice. Are they up to date? The team or analyst should take the time to follow through a number of products, services or customers, documenting any "horror stories" that occur. Often several actions and "rework loops", unknown to management will be discovered. But it is not the purpose of the chart to use it for "policing". Often a team will draw up a chart for their own use in improvement and should not be obliged to turn it over to management.

Constructing the Process Map

Some process maps or charts can be long and complicated. If so, first break them up into sections of responsibility or physical areas.

Then begin the detailed recording. See the figure. Preferably use a verb and a noun (e.g. select part, or verify document), and decide which of the standard categories (operation, transport / move, inspect, delay, store) the activity fits into. (Note : the difference between delay and store is that store takes place in a specific store area or warehouse, whereas delay is a result of an in-process stoppage such as waiting for a container to fill up.) You will differentiate between value adding and non-value adding operations.

Whilst compiling the process map it is good to record distance, time, inventory, and the number of operators. (If you are skilled at work study, also "rate" the speed of work, but this is a secondary benefit.) Also, record any wastes, comments, or interesting events. Many process charts are now supported with digital photographs. Whilst going around, take note of dates on inventory control cards, levels of dust, and container discipline (are containers moved in a first in first out , or a last in first out sequence?). You may encounter some carousels where parts are moved or stored automatically. If so, mark them (unobtrusively if necessary) to get an idea of the length of storage or delay.
A process map is a "snapshot" of activity at a moment

in time. Of course, workloads and inventory levels may vary over the course of a month, and hence delay times may change. Record the actual figure that you observe, but you may also ask about minimum and maximum levels. Most parts are made in batches, so try to record the average length of time to make one of the parts. Record the length of delay of a container whilst being moved.

A most useful exercise is to track one particular part, not just the type of part. However, this is often not practical due to the length of delays. So, mark a few parts and then come back and track their progress. Most manufactured parts have several branches or subassemblies flowing into the main sequence. It is a good idea to check on this first. Begin with the "main sequence". Then give attention to the major feeders, by time or cost, although it will seldom be necessary to track all feeders.

Also, you can "black box" a particular sequence of operations. There is a special symbol to indicate this. Take particular care of inspection and rework points. Why is this necessary? Can it be done earlier? What happens to reject parts ? In work study there are more detailed charting or mapping techniques available, such as the two handed flow process chart, but don't go into these unless you have identified the particular step as an important bottleneck.

Analysing the Process Map

The first step is to classify the detailed activities into value adding, non value adding, and necessary non value adding activities. See the Basic Principles chapter. Note that some prefer simply to denote activities as value adding or non-value adding, to avoid getting into long discussions about necessary. Some add green stickers to value adding steps, and red stickers for non value adding. (You will need many more red stickers than green.)

In general, the steps should then be analyzed using the 5 Whys (asking why 5 times over to get to the root cause - see the Kaizen section) and with the aid of Rudyard Kipling's "Six Honest Serving Men" (who taught me all

I knew; their names are what and why and when, and where and how and who).

Thereafter, the creative or redesign phase begins. Some "mechanical" considerations are :
- can inspection steps be moved forward or eliminated ?
- can steps be done in parallel ?
- are there obvious candidates for automation ?
- is data being duplicated ? is it effectively shared ?
- can pre-preparation be done, before the event ?
- can steps be moved to another stage? (for instance, can a supplier take over a non-core stage?)

Step	Description	Symbol	Time	Inventory	People	Machine	Notes
1	unload truck	O	8 min	4000 pieces	2	forklift	
2	place at bay	D	3 min	2000 ave	0		temp store
3	move to line	⇨	1.6 min / trip	1000 per trip	1	forklift	4 trips
4	store at line	▽	330	4000	0		
5	press	O	0.06 / piece	1	1	AZ20 press	batch of 4000
6	store in container	D	12 min	2000			

All the questions covered in the Order Tracking section are relevant here.

Selected further reading:
Diane Galloway, *Mapping Work Processes*, ASQC Quality Press, Milwaukee, 1994.

Lean Audits and Principles

In this section we review three audit procedures by Kobayashi, Schonberger and Goodman. Such self-evaluation questionnaires are useful both for identifying areas of opportunity or weakness and for guidance on implementation. Kobayashi's system is classic Japanese, concentrating on shop floor management. Schonberger's goes wider bringing in customers, benchmarking and perhaps a more Western view of employees.

Note: The European Business Excellence model has become a well-used general audit framework, but here we consider audits more specific to Lean operations.

Schonberger's Principles

Richard Schonberger, author of the excellent *Japanese Manufacturing Techniques and World Class Manufacturing: The Next Decade*, has developed 16 "Principles of World Class Manufacturing". The 16 Principles are excellent guides to Lean Operations in themselves, and a company's progress may be measured on a 1 to 5 scale for each principle. For 16 principles this means a maximum score of 80 points with "adulthood" beginning at 53 points and "maturity" at 67 points. A rating of 4 or 5 would be fairly challenging for many manufacturers.

The Principles are
1. *Team-up with Customers; Organize by Customer/ Product Family*. It is best is to be organized by (focused on) customer families (conventionally, marketing usually is; accounting and finance may be; production, staff support, and the supply chain rarely are). Next best is focus by product families— what customers buy.
2. *Capture/Use Customer, Competitive, and Best-Practice Information*. Aim: Drive your improvement efforts with external data—from customers (customer satisfaction/needs surveys), competitive products (competitive analysis), and non-competitive best practices (benchmarking studies).
3. *Continual, Rapid Improvement in Universal Customer Wants*. This is the achievement principle, measuring improvement in the eyes of customers. All customers, internal and external, want quality (Q), speedy response (S), flexibility (F), and value (V); these are universals of continuous improvement in the customer-focused organization.
4. *Whole Work Force Involvement in Change and Strategic Planning*. This principle provides a framework for empowered, self-managed teams;

"front-line" includes professionals/technicians as well as operations/clerical people.
5. *Cut to the Few Best Components, Operations, and Suppliers*. This single design principle includes both product design and design of the supply chain, which are related as follows:
   - Both call for simplification and numerical reductions
   - Reducing number of suppliers is unlikely to reach a lower limit, because new/ revised products, part numbers, operations, and outsourcing usually add new suppliers— requiring renewed efforts to simplify and reduce supply-chain breadth.
   - Diligence in holding down growth of part numbers/operations at the same time holds down additions of suppliers.
6. *Cut Total Flow Time, Flow Distance, and Startup/ Changeover Times*. This principle focuses on three core Lean concepts.
7. *Operate Close to Customers' Rate of Use or Demand*. This principle concerns scheduling and synchronization to the drumbeat of demand, takt time, monitoring schedule performance, seasonality, distribution centers/distributors, and kaizen events.
8. *Continually Train Everybody for their New Roles.*
9. *Expand Variety of Recognition, Rewards, and Pay*. This principle "closes the loop," returning value to the work force for value created through continuous improvements—necessary to keep process improvement "evergreen".
10. *Continually Reduce Variation and Mishaps*. Everybody should know and use the mostly statistical (but simple) tools of capturing variation, mishaps, and unsafe or environmentally hazardous incidents, and isolating their causes.
11. *Front-Line Teams Record and Own Process Data at the Work Place*. Effective management of quality and process improvement requires that front-line employees, not just managers and technical experts, be in charge. Ownership: to be in charge, front-liners must be collectors and owner-users of the process data. Visual management: Hidden data get less use than visual data; thus, visual management is a training topic in step 1, visual plotting of process data is a requirement in step 2.

12. *Control Root Causes and Cut Internal Transactions and Reporting.* Principle: follows the notion of *economy of control.* Controls are needed most when processes are complex, incapable, failure-prone, variable; processes that are simple, capable, rarely nonconforming thus need few formal controls. Best control is no *controls*; instead fix the processes.

13. *Align Performance Measures with Universal Customer Wants.* This principle concerns extent of use of QSFV (universal customer wants) as internal performance metrics (measures); Principle 3 is different, since it is devoted to measuring the extent of *attainments* on QSFV.

14. *Improve Present Capacity before New Equipment and Automation.* Improvement of present physical capacity (plant and equipment) via: (1) TPM (also called total *productive* maintenance); (2) simplifying operation, maintenance, setup, and process control; and (3) upgrading safety and health. Ownership: operators must acquire ownership of maintenance and safety (including safety from environmental hazards and degradation), just as they have with quality, and participate in equipment selection/improvement; maintenance/safety people must be teachers/ facilitators, just as quality people had to become under total quality management.

15. *Seek Simple, Movable, Scalable, Low-cost, Focused Equipment.* The ideal capacity for a family of high-volume standard products is a dedicated team with dedicated, minimal-setup capacity, run like a largely self-contained business unit. For low-volume, high-variety products, the ideal is a dedicated team with flexible skills and flexible, quick-change capacity; example: a March snow-storm kept most Ford Romeo, MI, Engine Plant associates home, but the Niche Line ran because it takes just a single, small team to build engines on that line. In either case, facilities should be as movable as possible—buildings equipped with solid floors, few impediments, all utilities available everywhere, rectangular shape; standardized equipment, often on wheels; modular tanks and piping, etc.

16. *Promote, Market, and Sell Every Improvement.* The organization delivers QSFV so impressively that its customers are attached and remain.

Schonberger's Principles and comments are reproduced with kind permission from Richard Schonberger. Schonberger & Associates, Inc. offer a benchmarking service based on these principles. Address: 177 107th Ave. N.E., #2101Bellevue, WA 98004, Phone & fax: 425-467-1143. www.wcm-wcp.com

Kobayashi's 20 Keys

Iwao Kobayashi's concept of the "20 Keys" has gained increasing acceptance as both a manufacturing audit and an implementation guide to lean manufacturing at shop floor level. The keys relate to 20 concepts fundamental to lean operations, the majority of which are to be found in sections throughout this book. Kobayashi's concept is especially useful because:

- Guidance is given on the order of implementation of the keys
- A five point scale is provided for each key as an aid to internal evaluation, going from level 1 beginner to level 5 ideal (certainly beyond "world class")
- Links between the keys are established. For instance, in order to reach higher level in the production scheduling key, actions are required in all other 19 keys. It is not possible therefore to reach higher levels in most of the keys without substantial progress in all keys.
- As an evaluation method, comparisons can be made with other organisations, although this applies to Schonberger and Fisher as well.

The sense of the 20 keys is given below showing the links to other sections in this book, and some comments on the range of characteristics required.

Note (1): For the full rating scale, from level 1 to level 5 for each key, as well as many useful tips, the full 285 page book is recommended.
Note (2): Some Western managers and critics of lean manufacturing feel that Kobayashi's ideas on operators (for instance keys 3, 4, 6, 7, 10, 15) are much too regimented and that Western workers cannot be expected to become automatons. Lean enthusiasts tend to discount such views, saying that this represents a misunderstanding, and that standards and discipline are fundamental to continuing improvement.

1.   Clean and Tidy (see section on 5S).
2.   Participative management style (or top-down bottom-up management) (see the section on Hoshin). From disorganised to interactive, cross-functional involvement at all levels.
3.   Teamworking on improvement. (See section on Continual Improvement).
4.   Overproduction, reduced inventory and reduced leadtime. (see Muda and Time Based Competitiveness).
5.   Changeover Reduction (see section of same title).
6.   Continuous improvement at the workplace (see Gemba, Improvement). Kobayashi calls this "manufacturing value analysis".
7.   "Zero monitoring" (see Flexible manpower lines, Cell balancing).
8.   Process, cellular manufacturing (see Cells, Kanban).
9.   Maintenance (see TPM).
10. Disciplined, rhythmic working (see cell balance, and heijunka).
11. Defects (see Quality, pokayoke). From inspectors being responsible for defect detection, to process control, prevention, operator responsibility, and pokayoke.
12. Supplier Partnership (see Supplier Development, Supplier Associations).
13. Waste Identification and elimination (see Wastes, Mapping).
14. Worker empowerment and training (see People).
15. Cross-functional working, multiskilling. (see People).
16. Scheduling (see Flow, Pull, Regularity).
17. Efficiency (see Kaizen costing and performance measurement).
18. Technology and microprocessors. (see Thinking Small).
19. Conserving energy and materials (see Wastes).
20. Appropriate Site Technology and Concurrent Engineering (see New Product Introduction).

According to Kobayashi, keys 1 to 4 are the basics, the starting point. These lead on to keys 5 to 20 which work together as a set. However key 4 is critical to time, key 11 to quality, and keys 6 and 19 to cost. Each of these latter 4 keys requires development in all the other keys to become fully effective. Kobayashi also uses the "bean sprout analogy" which is that, in a field of bean sprouts no one sprout can grow much ahead of the others or else it will blow down. Similarly in Lean, development must take place in areas approximately equally.

It is interesting to note the similarity with the views of Dan Jones. Dan states that the foundation of Lean Thinking is 5S, Shop Floor Teams, 7 Quality Tools, and PDCA (keys 1, 3, 11, 6), which support production smoothing, demand smoothing, JIT, and Jidoka (keys 10, 16, 5), which in turn are held on place by waste elimination and TPM (keys 13, 9), and capped by policy deployment (key 2).

The Ford Production System (FPS) audit tools also once adopted the 'lowest score principle, as above. So if you fail on one you fail on all. This scoring procedure has apparently now been abandoned as being too tough and de-motivating.

Some companies, for example Arvin Meritor, use the 20 Keys not only as an audit tool but also as a main platform for development. Their sites are continually striving to reach the next key stage in each category. In this regard Kobayashi's book is very useful.

Rapid Plant Assessment

R Eugene Goodman has developed a useful plant assessment tool that is aimed at more effective benchmarking and assessment of supplier plants. So when you go on a plant tour, have your team assess the visit immediately afterwards using the Goodman methodology. It can be used in your own plant, but that was not the original idea.

The assessment comprises a matrix of 11 categories,each rated from poor to best in class, and 20 questions that assist the evaluation of each category. The 11 categories cover the points below, with references to material in this book.
•   Customer satisfaction. (You can get a good idea by asking the employees and looking out for visual evidence such as graphs.)

- Safety, Environment, Cleanliness, Order. Essentially evidence of 5S.
- Visual management. A core Lean concept
- Scheduling. Look out for single pacemakers, overproduction, heijunka.
- Flow and Space. The waste of movement and spaghetti. Evidence of cells and pull
- Inventory. How much? Overproduction evidence?
- Teamwork and Motivation. Evidence of policy deployment, blitz, kaizen, see the continuous improvement section.
- Condition and Maintenance of tools and equipment. TPM and 5S.
- Management of Complexity and Variety. Difficult to assess but see the essential Paretos and NewProduct introduction sections.
- Supply Chain integration. Get an impression by questioning on supplier partnership and amplification.
- Commitment to Quality. Look out for rework, SPC, Six Sigma, and continuous improvement initiatives.

The 20 questions are a useful supporting set.

If you plan to visit another plant or a supplier, it is a good idea to use this tool. Download a copy for a few dollars from the Harvard Business Review website. Reprint R0205H.

Further reading on Audits and Assessment:
Richard Schonberger, *World Class Manufacturing: The Next Decade*, Free Press, New York, 1996, Chapter 2
Iwao Kobayashi, *20 Keys to Workplace Improvement*, Revised Edition, Productivity Press, Portland, OR, 1995
Dino Petrarolo, "The 20 Keys to Workplace Improvement", *Industrial Management* (US), Jan-Feb 1998, pp 22-28
R Eugene Goodman, 'Read a Plant - Fast', *Harvard Business Review*, May 2002, pp 105-113

Route Learning Maps

A Route Learning Map is an increasingly used tool for transformation and change. It fits well between strategy and policy deployment. Made famous by Sears, in creating buy-in for a corporate turnaround, the tool has recently been used in several Lean transformations. It is a fun tool for change and discussion.

The concept is simple. A cartoon-type diagram is produced on a large A0 sheet. It shows a curving road. The road represents the road traveled by the company or the site, sometimes since its inception. The destination is the future. Imagine a car traveling along the road. Billboards, buildings, signs, and statues are shown alongside the road, depicting the history of the organization. One billboard may show a graph of sales growth, another the growth of assets. Buildings and statues depict landmark events. A merger might be shown by another road joining the main road. Bridges, representing important hurdles, may be crossed. Old and current photos of technology or the plant may be used. Developments in the wider environment – competitors, competitive products, and the economy are shown in appropriate locations. Opportunities are depicted by, perhaps, cartoons of potential customers. There will often be cartoons of encounters or 'legendary' events. Basically there are few rules for constructing the map. Just fun.

Once the map is produced appropriate managers talk it through in small groups – say six at a time. "This is where we have come from, and this is where we are going. These are the threats. These are the opportunities. This is what we aim to do." Discussion is encouraged. In some companies, following discussion, copies of the map are put on display and people encouraged to add their own notes and drawings.

The map or cartoon will often be produced in a participative way. It begins with a middle or senior manager with some knowledge of the past and the desired future. This provides the outline. Make the best use of creative artists in the organization. Encourage humour. Also encourage ideas and participation. The idea is to produce a diagram with wide appeal and interest, which is easy to appreciate.

Although not calling it a route learning map, and not employing much participation, Jaguar depicts its vision as a series of pictures and diagrams as the starting point for its policy deployment process. Celestica has used it enthusiastically.

Further reading:
A J Rucci, S P Kirn, R T Quinn, 'The Employee-Customer-Profit Chain at Sears', *Harvard Business Review*, January / February 1998, pp83-97

Creating the Future State

Creating the Future State from the current state maps is a considerable challenge. It is relatively easy to take waste out of current systems whilst retaining their essential characteristics, but it is another issue to completely envision a full Lean system. That is why many Lean implementations founder. To do a successful transformation requires fairly in-depth knowledge of important lean principles and tools. You cannot create a true Lean vision without having good insights into Lean layout and Lean scheduling. There are no quick and easy short-cuts. The future state is addressed in the next two related chapters. Layout and cell design provides the physical framework. Thereafter, Six Building Blocks and Ten Scheduling concepts are presented.

Although *Learning to See* advocates moving from Current State to Future State incrementally, there is a strong argument for starting with the Ideal State or vision and working backwards. There appears to be many companies that have put much effort into Current State analysis and then just 'got stuck'! The next two sections help with the vision.

Creating the Future State (1)

Layout, Cell and Line Design

Lean Plant Layout

This section deals with general plant layout for Lean. Cell and workstation design is dealt with in a separate section.

- If you are fortunate enough to have a green field situation, try to get the length / breadth ratio correct. Schonberger suggests 60:40 for flexibility and flow.
- Remember the plant builds in waste for many years.
- Take the opportunity to question the value stream map and inter-facility spaghetti diagram. Should processes be relocated (outside or in) or downsized. Think radical – plant re-layout is a rare opportunity, not to be missed.
- Try to avoid a plant which is too big – and unfocused. A few hundred people (400?) are about the maximum for Lean effectiveness.
- Think of the possibility of several smaller focused plants, each serving a particular customer under a true JIT system. Johnson Controls and Nypro are outstanding examples.
- Alternatively, can the plant be broken up into small focused self-contained factories, preferably end-to-end, each with its own order entry, production control, dispatch, meeting areas, and so on? An outstanding example is Freudenberg-NOK.
- Can you have suppliers on site? Ford Amazon and Smart Car are trying this. Toyota city is a bigger case. Encourage suppliers to downsize or right-size facilities.

- Achieving overall flow from one end to the other, with no backtracking, is OK. But better is to have multiple access points around the outer walls, with multiple loading docks, which can feed directly into and out of cells. Maximize the number of external doors, like Dell.
- For some operations a central material handling spine is good. Cells can be arranged on either side of the spine. This spine layout is ideal where you have short-lifetime cells and a changing product line
- The grouping of inventory into supermarkets is critical for Lean. Supermarkets provide the basic framework. They should be stable, whilst cells come and go. Try to have a few supermarkets, rather than inventory all over the place or in one central warehouse.
- Break up the value steam map into pull segments or loops, often separated by supermarkets. Then use these as building blocks for layout design.
- Avoid one big warehouse – especially an automated warehouse or automatic storage and retrieval system. There will always be a temptation to fill it. If you have an AS/RS already, set in place a plan to reduce usage then close it down.
- Establish a series of specific 'waterspider' routes – with material handlers making regular circuits. This powerful concept paces the work and flows information regularly via pull systems.
- Avoid long lines and conveyors. People will have to go around them for years. Try for compact cells.
- Think three dimensions. Can deliveries be made from below or above? For example, can plastic be fed into injection molding machines from the floor below thereby allowing a high state of cleanliness and separation of operators and forklifts?
- Don't get hooked on using old facilities. Better to demolish and move. Costs will quickly be recovered. Like Dell. Many plants grow in a haphazard way, locating new work in any available space. They pay the price over many years.

- Locate design and engineering areas close to manufacturing. Make them share common break areas. Even better make engineers walk past production areas to get to their work area.
- Locate production control in the middle of the plant floor. If possible, managers' offices also. Don't make supervisors' offices too comfortable.
- Foster communication and visibility in the office by open plan layout.

Cell Design

The main stages follow. Stages 1 to 8 are each discussed in greater detail in separate sections.

1. Product Family Identification. This fundamental stage breaks the plant into lines and cells. These may be obvious, as in automotive customer product cells, or less obvious requiring matrix analysis. The intention is to determine what products should be made in each cell or line.
2. Value stream mapping is a standard early step. The intention is to gain a picture of the overall flow and to see if the value stream should be broken up into stages or sub cells. This is particularly important in the case of shared resources or convergent operations where capacity needs to be checked and the issues of dedicated resources considered. However, where there are established cells this step may be delayed or omitted. Just go straight in after the waste.
3. Strategic issues need to be considered. What is the objective of the cell? Is it efficiency (minimization of cost), or reduced leadtime, or flexibility, or a combination? Take the opportunity to ask if strategic advantage can be gained by adopting another approach. For example, if you can gain big advantage through reduced leadtime then perhaps cost is not that important. (An example is a "cell" to process photographic film in one hour locally – it costs more, but some customers are willing to pay for speed and convenience.) Rajan Suri has pointed out that there are two approaches to cells – the technical and the managerial. The former involve calculations and waste elimination and the latter involves understanding the market and where

competitive advantage lies. Look at the wider opportunities – for example using stainless rather than mild steel, and rationalizing on bar stock. Going wider, is there a case for splitting the product line into stable base demand (perhaps overseas?) and more responsive local cells. Or, thinking in terms of running the cell during ramp-up, but then having reached maturity, relocating to a low wage country.

4. Plant layout and supermarkets form the skeleton for cells. Cells may come and go, but supermarkets should remain in place for longer. Carrying raw material inventory in multiple locations around the plant is generally a bad idea. The material handler needs to establish the rhythm of delivery. The basic layout of the cell should be considered at this stage. U shape, line, or S shape? The length of the line or cell depends on inter-station buffer inventory. For one product, nil is desirable. But for mixed model lines with highly variable times and variation in mix, some inventory may have to be kept in buffer locations – perhaps between every (say) three stations
5. Activity timings and activity sampling are side-by-side activities. Separate machine jobs / time from operator tasks / time. An operator can tend several machines, so it is waste for an operator to stand idle while a machine runs. Timings need to be taken for each work element – note the work elements should first be studied and broken down into value adding (VA), and non value adding (NVA such as waiting, walking, moving parts). Ford adds another category - non value adding unavoidable (NVAU such as taking readings, changeover, adjusting). Video at least 10 time observations. Take actual times with no allowance for personal rest and delay. Simultaneously or separately conduct an activity sample, making a minimum of 200 observations at random intervals. This must be done for each work element, except NVA – so it involves a lot of observations! Record the number of VA, NVA, and NVAU observations but record each under suitable categories. Note that some cycle times recorded as VA are likely to include elements of waste. The timings are relevant to cycle times, but the activity sample is relevant to how operators spend their day – including

discussing, unofficial breaks, visiting toilet, assisting, and unoccupied. Note that cell operators should not have to fetch and deliver parts used in the cell. This waste activity should be grouped together in a single runner or material handler working between several cells and the supermarket.

6. Then calculate takt time, or weighted takt time in the case of multiple products. Often use projected takt time, on a future volume. The cell cycle time is a time slightly below takt time – a typical figure is 95% of takt time. (In build to order operations, you should allow for some things to go wrong.) This is the figure that is used for balance later. It allows for variation. It does not allow for toilet and other breaks that should be taken in planned intervals. Note that some difficult stations may have a greater allowance.

7. At this point check for constraints or bottlenecks. This would be a stage where cycle time is near to or exceeds takt time or where there is an off-line activity – for instance sending parts to a subcontractor for plating. An in-cell activity exceeding takt would probably need an additional shift and before and after buffers. A tight constraint needs to run near-continuously to avoid having to run for an additional shift. In this case the resource must be protected by a time buffer (x hours of stock) and be prioritized to ensure continuous operation. In both cases, consider a Drum Buffer Rope arrangement whereby work is fed into the cell at a rate in accordance with the bottleneck. The process is still located in the cell. An out-of-cell process step can be managed by having exit and entry buffers at that stage, but running the cell according to one-piece flow before and after the stage. That is, feeding into the outbound buffer one at a time, and withdrawing from the inbound buffer one at a time.

8. A paper kaizen involves re-sketching the cell, and reducing or removing all NVA and NVAU activities. It is a preliminary design and balance. You should also include an estimate of the standard (minimum) inventory. Design for one-piece flow – this is crucial – and minimal inventory between workstations.

9. Now combine the paper kaizen exercise with the activity sample to get an idea of the 'optimal' or theoretical operations. Divide the sum of the corrected VA and NVAU times (each multiplied by 1 – NVA proportion) from activity sampling to give the theoretical minimum times.

10. Divide this by the takt time to give the minimum number of operators. Round up for greater than about 0.25 – but round down below this to allow for the learning effect.

11. Calculate the reference cost over a week. Include operator and inventory savings. Separately estimate space and quality savings. This is a 'wake up' call to management. It is also for assessing whether the cell should be relocated overseas, compared with current costs. (Often no!)

12. A cardboard simulation is a good idea for important cells. It is optional, but helps with fine-tuning and operator buy in. Simulate the operation of the cell full scale by using the minimum operators and proposed new layout.

13. Cell layout is the detailed re-layout. Certainly use a scale drawing – often CAD. Pay attention to machine access. A good principle is to design the layout as if one operator were to run the cell. Use gravity feeds. The material handler should deliver all parts to the cell and remove completed products – the cell operators should not do this. The material handler should work a regular, standard circuit.

14. Now balance the work between the operators against the cell cycle time. Part of this step (and the last two steps) is to decide the operator working directions and allocations. Options are working in the same direction as product flow, in the opposite direction, or using 'rabbit chase' with two or more operators. A widely held guideline is to use one (the most experienced) operator in the first and last operations of a U shape cell. Balancing refers to allocating the timed work elements between operators against the target takt time. Ford uses magnetic strips with a width corresponding to the work element time. Operators in consultation with the team leader and sometimes an industrial engineer arrange the strips on the board. This is called a Yamazumi Board at Ford and a NUMMI Board at GM (after the joint Toyota GM venture in California). Some tasks are inherently more variable or difficult. More allowance should be given for these tasks. Some companies rank the assembly stations into three categories – red,

requiring a highly trained operator; blue, requiring mid range skills; and green, requiring basic skills. These colours can be shown along the base of the balance board. It is good practice whilst doing a cell balance exercise to do a '+1' and '-1' exercise. That is to balance the cell for one more operator and for one less operator. This means that if the takt time changes, adjustment can be made at short notice. Or alternatively the cell can run with one more or one less operator with reduced or additional time respectively to gain the same output.

15. The detailed workstation layout and ergonomics is then finalized. Of course, this step would have been

evolving all the way though. Operators should stand, not sit, except for accurate work and hand assembly. Maximize visibility, safety, and communication. Avoid the need to bend or reach. Use standard laws of ergonomics. See the last section of this chapter. A word on automation: Lean is not anti-automation in cells, but is cautious about it. Good reasons for automation are quality and 'dull, dirty, dangerous' or 'hot heavy hazardous'. A bad reason is to save people – for two reasons. First, robots don't improve. Don't lock in waste. Automation is not as flexible as people. The Toyota view is that automating to allow machines to run unattended is good. So is auto-eject. But material handling is another story.

16. Preparing two standard work charts – the Work Combination Chart and the Cell Layout chart, completes the design. The best people to prepare these are the cell operators working in conjunction with industrial engineers. The work combination chart is a Gantt-type chart showing the sequence of activities and times that each operator follows. See the figure. Note that movement activities are not recorded but shown as wavy lines connecting the activities. The cell layout chart shows the geography or plan view of the cell, the routes that each operator follows in the work sequence, and very importantly the locations and quantities of the standard inventories. You will notice that the example shows operators moving back and forth. This is not desirable if operators can walk around the cell in a circle, either in the direction of material flow, or in a direction opposite to flow. However, this can also be inefficient involving more waits but less movement.

17. Then design the pull system or Heijunka that regulates the flow into and out of the cell. This will include mixed model, pitch, and 'runner' considerations. The runner is vital because he or she regulates the flow, delivering parts and removing products. This is discussed in the next chapter.

18. Finally consider the wider organizational arrangements. The cell should be as self contained as possible – a 'mini business'.

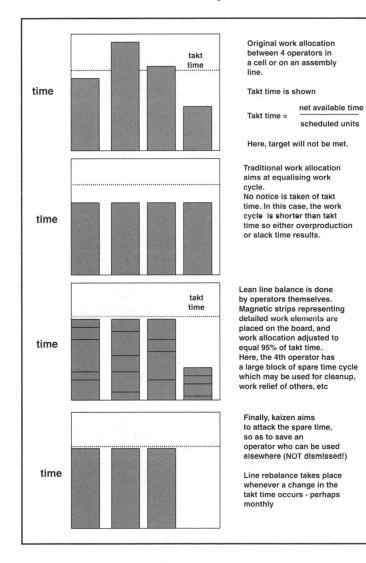

Original work allocation between 4 operators in a cell or on an assembly line.

Takt time is shown

$$Takt\ time = \frac{net\ available\ time}{scheduled\ units}$$

Here, target will not be met.

Traditional work allocation aims at equalising work cycle. No notice is taken of takt time. In this case, the work cycle is shorter than takt time so either overproduction or slack time results.

Lean line balance is done by operators themselves. Magnetic strips representing detailed work elements are placed on the board, and work allocation adjusted to equal 95% of takt time. Here, the 4th operator has a large block of spare time cycle which may be used for cleanup, work relief of others, etc

Finally, kaizen aims to attack the spare time, so as to save an operator who can be used elsewhere (NOT dismissed!)

Line rebalance takes place whenever a change in the takt time occurs - perhaps monthly

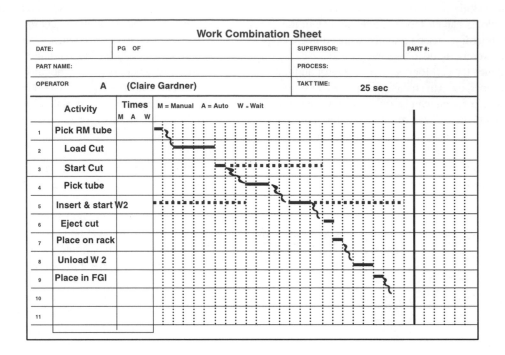

Work Combination Sheet

DATE:	PG OF		SUPERVISOR:	PART #:
PART NAME:			PROCESS:	
OPERATOR A (Claire Gardner)			TAKT TIME: 25 sec	

M = Manual   A = Auto   W = Wait

	Activity	Times M A W	
1	Pick RM tube		
2	Load Cut		
3	Start Cut		
4	Pick tube		
5	Insert & start W2		
6	Eject cut		
7	Place on rack		
8	Unload W 2		
9	Place in FGI		
10			
11			

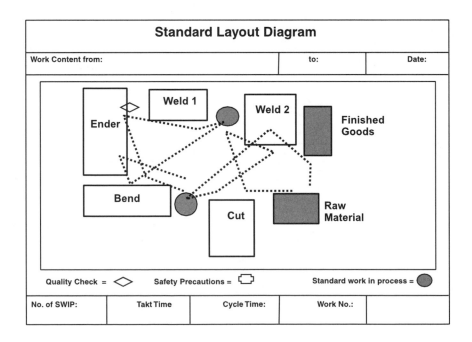

Standard Layout Diagram

Work Content from:		to:	Date:

Ender

Weld 1

Weld 2

Finished Goods

Bend

Cut

Raw Material

Quality Check = ◇   Safety Precautions = ▢   Standard work in process = ●

No. of SWIP:	Takt Time	Cycle Time:	Work No.:	

Balancing complex mixed model lines is illustrated in the next figure, which shows a line balance board for a mixed model line with two products. Time is on the vertical axis. First, takt time is established. Then the target cycle time is set below the takt time to allow for general operator variation. A third line is the operator target times. These individual station times allow for relative complexity and uncertainty at each workstation. In the example, operator B has a much more difficult or variable task than the other operators. In the Green Zone activity times for the common elements are assembled. These activities are done for every product. Of course the Green Zone is variable for each workstation, so the zone limits are approximate. In the Red Zone the work elements unique to each product are accumulated. In some cases, for instance A, a total product assembly time can exceed the operator target time, so long as the weighted average time, reflecting the product mix, does not exceed the target time.

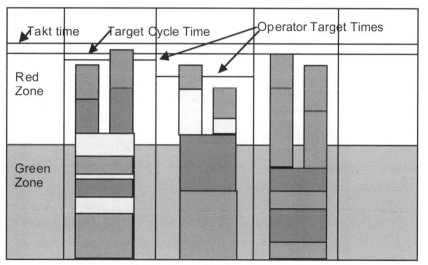

Moving Lines and Pulse Lines

Henry Ford's original line was a 'pulse' line – in other words cars spent time at a fixed location before moving on to the next fixed location. This principle is now being rediscovered for a variety of large, slow moving, complex items such as aircraft engines, wings, aircraft and vehicle maintenance, remanufacturing, large transformers, electrical switching gear, earthmoving equipment, and ship and boat sections. Moreover, the principles may be applicable in areas as diverse as hospitals, construction, even education. The Lean principles of (relatively) fast, flexible flow fully apply. As with much of Lean, a big issue is believing that a moving line is possible in the first place – traditional ways (batch and queue, project management, complex scheduling, bottlenecks etc.) have been in place for decades.

As Henry Ford found a century ago, such lines are a revolution in productivity when compared with static build. As well as huge productivity and time gains, there is invariably a big reduction in space, a big improvement in quality (through improved standardization and visibility), and big gains in training and apprenticeship. Historically, the American railroads were built with a type of moving line system, progressing 50 miles per day, and today track maintenance is just beginning to adopt moving line concepts.

Further reading:
Nancy Hyer and Urban Wemmerlöv, *Reorganizing the Factory: Competing Through Cellular Manufacturing*, Productivity Press, 2002. This massive tome of almost 800 pages is probably the prime reference on cells in general. Please give us a 100 page version!
Mike Rother and Rick Harris, *Creating Continuous Flow*, Lean Enterprise Institute, Boston, 2001.
Kevin Duggan, *Creating Mixed Model Value Streams*, Productivity, 2002

A pulse line is used where station cycle times are long – say several days, and a moving line is used for shorter station cycle times – say several hours. A moving line moves very slowly (perhaps in mm per minute) but continuously using a track or conveyor. One or several products are on the moving line at a time, depending on complexity. A pulse line uses a platform, such as 'hovercraft' cushion, to move between fixed stations at a regular takt time. Typically a small number of items are on the pulse line at a time.

Pulse or moving lines may be fed by supporting cells from which parts are pulled, or automotive style using a broadcast schedule to synchronize several lines.

The steps to set up a pulse or moving line are broadly the same as those used for a cell. Many of the steps are similar to the previous section. A few differences are given below.

The Pulse Line
Integrating Fast, Flexible Flow

- Visible, synchronised, progress
- Problem and Response boards (PDCA)
- Standard footprints for everything
- C parts kept on Wheeled Trolleys & kanban
- Time Buffer in last bay
- Levelled or Balanced work (predictable)
- Green area reserved for products only
- A CONWIP System
- Pulse line moves every X days
- Rapid & focused Training & Development
- 5S: only what is needed
- Tool and part shadow boards for each bay
- Standard Work elements for each day, each bay
- Lineside Daily Scheduling Board (Heijunka?)

first determine the number of operators as for cells, but bearing in mind simultaneous operations, then balance the operators' work against the takt time. In pulse lines determine the number of operators per station – this will depend on simultaneous operations as well as technical considerations. In both cases, earlier stations could be more fully loaded whilst later stations are more lightly loaded to retain catch-up capability. Make allowance for uncertainty and complexity.

5. Establish standard locations and footprints for tools and parts. Each station should have its own shadow board. This is one of the great advantages of such lines, so pay attention to waste-free ergonomic micro-layouts. Get operators to participate in developing their own part and equipment handling systems. Keep frequently used tools and parts line-side. Get a 5S system established. Over time, work on rationalizing tools and parts.

6. Establish pull systems for required parts. Try to pull as much as possible. Use the runners, repeaters, strangers / ABC classification system (see separate section). Establish priority kanban systems and supermarkets for supporting cells feeding the line. A and B parts should be stored on specifically designed wheeled racks, and moved to the exact location just-in-time.

1. Establish the product families. A line can be used for a class of products, like helicopters, even though there may be considerable customization between individual units, but not for mixed products such as helicopters and aircraft.
2. Calculate takt time. This will determine the number of stations in a pulse line, and the total time in a moving line.
3. Develop standard work packages. Even in high variety lines there will be much fully standard work, and some semi-standard as for example in maintenance. Identify, time, and document. These are the essential 'Lego bricks' for such lines.
4. Accumulate and determine the standard work packages against the takt time. In moving lines,

7. Establish a progress signaling system. Visibility is another great advantage of lines, so capitalize on this aspect. In a moving line signaling is typically by marks on the floor corresponding to time and a light system so operators can report and display completions. In a pulse line, each days standard work elements are loaded via cards on a Heijunka-

like board, and turned around when complete. In both types, it is necessary to pre-consider contingencies resulting in delays – transfer to next day or station (this has limited possibility in a moving line because downstream work location layouts will have been balanced), floating labour, stop the line, work overtime (not desirable?). Develop a board on which unforeseen problems are displayed, and display an action sequence – perhaps like a TPM red card system.

8. Establish the planning system. For mixed model or variable time lines such as maintenance, the work packages in each cycle may vary. The work packages and manning will then have to be pre-planned subject to the constraint of the takt time. This planning is probably best done by a Heijunka-like manual capacity board that loads up the individual standard work elements.

Big and exciting opportunities lie in this concept being applied in maintenance, hospitals, and construction. 100 Years after Henry Ford, we are only just beginning.

Virtual Cells

Sometimes it is not possible to create a cell in one area due to size or environmental conditions such as a clean room. Stages may have to be separated. In this case a virtual cell may be a possibility. Instead of two areas with say four similar machines each being managed as a process job shop, consider retaining the layout but changing to four virtual cells of two different machines each, managed as four distinct lines or cells. The advantage is vastly reduced lead time and reduced scheduling complexity, against the penalty of greater transport and the need for cross training.

Operators identify with the line rather than with the process job shop. In the simple case cited, each operator would have to have the skills to run both types of machine and would move from one area to the other 'flowing' the product one piece at a time as far as possible. The old way would involve batch and queue; the new way would frequently involve setting up both machines as a flow line, albeit in separate locations.

Applications are in low volume high-tech manufacture, and in 'metal-bashing' (say involving blanking and pressing) where lead time and low inventories are of the essence. It may be that the virtual cell runs as a virtual cell for part of the week only.

Paper Kaizen and Theoretical Minimum Times

A Paper Kaizen is an activity done in a group as a theoretical or planning exercise to remove waste and make improvements prior to a situation before trying it out for real at Gemba. As such it could be seen as the P in the PDCA cycle. It is normally followed up by an exercise at Gemba – for example a cardboard simulation or actual implementation on the factory floor.

Paper kaizens are usually undertaken with either the four basic mapping tools (current state, spaghetti, demand amplification, and quality filter maps) or on a more detailed level with activity times, possibly activity sampling and a layout relating to a cell.

In a cell-based paper kaizen, begin with a calculation of takt time and target cell cycle time – say 95% of takt. Then calculate the theoretical number of operators by sum of the activity times / target cell cycle time. Note: exclude machine cycles, assuming that machines once started can finish their cycles unattended. Attempt to reduce the number of operators by accumulating times against, but not exceeding, the target cycle time for each operator. (Begin a new column of activities when times exceed the cycle time.) This is done by reducing walk times, changing the layout, and removing as many non value-adding activities as possible. Also consider the possibility of auto eject and gravity feeds. Remember to think in three dimensions – can inventory or tools be stored on racks?

A cell-based paper kaizen should end with three preliminary outputs:
- A new layout diagram showing operator movements and standard inventory
- A work balance chart or sketch
- A work combination sheet

Usually you will end the paper kaizen activity with a fraction of an operator left over – like 2.4 operators. The next stage is to try in out for real or full size to try and reduce the 0.4.

If you have used activity sampling you should extend your paper kaizen to take out as much of the extra wastes discovered as part of the sampling. For instance, you may find that by more efficient organization or communication you can extend the effective working time per day. This would increase the takt time and possibly reduce the number of operators.

It may be that activity sampling reveals waste in the actual operation cycles – apart from walking and waiting most of which would be eliminated. For instance, connecting a hose may involve adjustment and checking. If this is found, the various activity times can be reduced by an appropriate percentage.

Ergonomics

Good ergonomics – of both products and processes – should be essential for any manufacturer – Lean or otherwise. What makes Lean Ergonomics an extension of conventional ergonomics? This brief section does not deal with ergonomics per sé (there are many excellent texts available), but comments on the Lean perspective on Ergonomics.

- Working to Takt or Rhythm. A regular rhythm can assist good blood circulation. By contrast, with 'static' effort (for instance where a moderate rate of work persists for 1 minute or more, or slight effort lasts for 5 minutes or more – (Kroemer and Grandjean 1997) flow of blood can be obstructed.
- Lean favors standing rather than sitting (except for intricate work) – for flexibility to move between workstations, but also for posture and to help avoid lower back problems. Ergonomists recommend a combination with a predominance of sitting. Certainly standing or sitting without movement is poor practice. Sitting can lock-in an operator and inhibit movement. A good compromise is to have standing and moving operators but also frequent breaks with comfortable chairs in team areas. This fits in with 'standard work rate or stop' philosophy discussed under balancing. Some sitting can be accommodated in lines and cells – as per Toyota's 'Raku Raku' seats which swing inside a car to allow a sitting operator to assemble. Some cell workstations are amenable to the best of all – allowing the operator to sit or stand.
- There is an inverse relationship between force exerted and duration of muscular contraction (See Kroemer and Grandjean, p 11). Toyota has developed an ergonomic evaluation system based on this relationship – a maximum force for each particular duration. Exceeding the limit calls for workstation redesign.
- The best workstations (both sitting and standing) allow for height adjustment both for the height of the operator and the type of work (higher for accurate, lower for heavier). Seats should be adjustable for height and backrest inclination. Look up the recommended heights of seats, work surfaces, and inspection surfaces for your own operators in an ergonomic text. See readings.
- 5S. Take the opportunity to do 'Ergonomic 5S', not just 5S. Shadow boards for tools and parts need to be correctly located ergonomically. Try to maintain a natural posture at all times. The 5S principle of avoiding personal toolboxes can make sense both ergonomically (located at correct height and reach) and for standardization reasons. Every course on 5S should at least say a few words on work heights and ergonomic workstation layout, lifting, lighting, controls, vibration and noise. Visibility principles should extend to ergonomics – for example seeing the progress of a moving line clearly marked by lights or time markings on the floor. Can a tool shuttle be used on a line to keep pace with the line?
- TPM and Quality related gauges, dials and displays should also be designed using ergonomic principles. Operating ranges should be colour marked so normal conditions can be seen at a glance, lubrication levels made visible without bending, needle orientation aligned on dials, etc. (see Kroemer and Grandjean, chapter 8).

- Make use of visual warning devices. An example is colored stickers placed on all containers to indicate if they are human movable, human movable with care, or only machine movable.

Further reading:

K. Kroemer and E. Grandjean, *Fitting the Task to the Human*, 5th edn., Taylor ad Francis, London, 1997
Jan Dul and Bernard Weerdmeester, *Ergonomics for Beginners*, Second edition, Taylor and Francis, 2001

Creating the Future State (2)

Constructing a Pull System
Six Building Blocks and Ten Lean Scheduling Concepts

In this section the intention is to provide a set of building blocks and scheduling concepts that can be slotted together Lego style to construct almost any pull system. The six building blocks provide (together with layout) the skeleton; the concepts are the circulation system. To this must be added eyes and brain (vision, strategy), the nervous system (Hoshin for deployment, and measurement system), and the muscular system (for quality and improvement), and the digestive system (to give energy and to get rid of waste). The total system gives fast, flexible flowing human action. The ten concepts follow on from the six building blocks.

These blocks follow from either the Goldratt section or cell principles. The idea is that the blocks can be combined to make up any factory.

Block 1: A is a constraint or bottleneck feeding B a non-constraint.

Q: Where should buffer be placed? Ans: In front of A, (to ensure that it is able to keep working) but not in front of B (which can easily catch up). Beware, however, if B is sufficiently starved it may become the constraint.

Q: How much buffer in front of A? Ans: Sufficient to ensure time coverage for frequent upstream disruption, but not for unusual events. May also include replenishment time for parts on a pull system, plus safety stock.

Block 2: B is a non-constraint feeding A that is a constraint or bottleneck

Q: Where should buffer be placed? Ans: As before in front of A, not in front of B

Block 3: A is a constraint; B and C are non-constraints

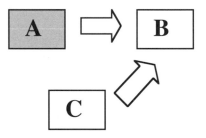

Q: Where to place buffer inventory? Ans: In front of A and not in front of B on line A to B, as before. But also in front of B on line C to B. Why? Because after the product has passed the valuable constraint, it should be delayed as little as possible, for instance waiting for a part from non-constraint C. Think of an assembly line making cars – you would not want to delay the main line whilst waiting for a minor part. So definitely between C and B if it is a low cost item. However, if it is an expensive part a buffer in front of B would be too costly, so a synchronisation must be arranged.

Block 4: A is a process with relatively long changeover, feeding two or more lines or cells, with little or no changeover.

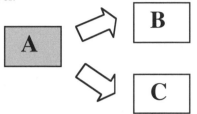

Q: Where to place an inventory 'supermarket'? Ans: B and C probably would like to work whenever required. If so, a supermarket must be placed between A and B-C. If B and C work only periodically and one at a time, a supermarket can be avoided if A can be synchronised. Also, a supermarket will be needed in front of A so it can work on either part when called upon by B or C. Q: How does A know what to work on? Ans: You need a priority kanban (or accumulation kanban) system that indicates when buffers in front of B and C get too low. The target batch size is discussed in a section below.

Block 5: Two or more processes feeding a single constrained process.

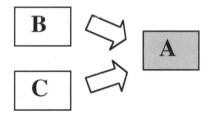

Q: How much buffer in front of A? Ans: As with Block 1, sufficient to protect it from disruption. But you also need to know if both B and C are required to make a part at A, or if they are separate. The former requires a buffer of each, the latter requires a synchronised scheduling (pull) system, building inventory of B whilst A works on C, and vice versa. The priority (pull) system for B and C needs to be arranged accordingly.

Block 6: A, B, C, D are sequential operations.

Q: What are relevant questions here? Ans: First, is there a constraint or near constraint in relation to overall takt time? If yes, split into pull loops, separated by supermarkets. Second, can the process be flowed, especially one-piece flow or pitch-time flowed. (Pitch flow means you have one piece flow, but can alternate different products every pitch increment – in other words is changeover time + time to make pitch quantity less than pitch time?) If it can be flowed, then the processes can be treated as one cell and controlled by one pull signal, possibly with a supermarket or buffer only in front of A and after D.

The Ten Scheduling Concepts: Overview

Demand Smoothing
Takt and Pitch Time
The Pacemaker
Supermarkets
Runners Repeaters and Strangers
Mixed Model Scheduling
Kanban and Pull
Lean batch sizing and 'every product every' (EPE)
Material handling routes (or 'Runner' or 'Waterspider')
Heijunka for levelling and capacity management.

These ten concepts form a set which, together with the building blocks, enable most plants having any sort of repetitive production, and many with less regular flows, to implement a successful Lean scheduling system in a value stream.

The starting points are demand smoothing and takt and pitch. These are discussed in the Preparing for Flow chapter. The smoother the demand, the more stable the production, and the easier it will be to implement. Smoothing the demand also enables supermarket inventories (raw material, work in process and finished goods) to be reduced. The takt time is the drumbeat, and the pitch time is the repeating increment with which containers are moved and the material handler circulates.

The Pacemaker concept is for production to be scheduled at one single point, with other stages either being pulled or flowing in a first-in-first out sequence to the final stage. One pacemaker has the effect of synchronising the plant's value stream.

Kanban and other pull systems enable the co-ordination and synchronisation of flows as governed by the pacemaker. Pull systems are robust. They help avoid overproduction and help highlight problems.

Establishing the schedule at the pacemaker is aided by two concepts: Runners Repeaters and Strangers (RRS), and Mixed Model scheduling. Runner products often enjoy dedicated facilities. Repeaters should be scheduled at regular intervals. Strangers should be fitted around the repeaters. Mixed model scheduling is about running the smallest possible repeating batch size down a line. One piece flow is the ideal. Mixed model production allows inventories to be reduced and cells to be balanced around the mixed model sequence. Most of all, mixed model allows regularity of flow - that is making and moving in one repeating sequence all day rather than at several rates throughout the day.

Lean batch sizing considerations are necessary for stages involving longer changeover operations. This batch sizing needs to be governed by the pacemaker so that synchronisation is maintained, and inventories kept low.

The whole process is held together by the material handler or runner. This person has a regular route, circulating around the plant every pitch increment or round multiple of a pitch increment. On every lap the material handler collects up kanbans, picks needed parts from the supermarket, delivers the requirements from the last lap, and is on the lookout for any deviations. The material handler moves the parts and products and the operators make and assemble. These are separate functions.

Finally, levelling at the pacemaker is aided by the Heijunka system. This planning and execution system, first establishes work for each pitch increment throughout the day, then authorizes the work to begin on time but not too early, and is also a problem detection tool.

Apart from demand smoothing and takt, (discussed in the Preparing for Flow section) the remaining eight tools are described in greater detail below.

The Pacemaker

The single pacemaker is the stage around which the whole value stream within the plant is scheduled. The pacemaker is the heart and the material handler is the circulation. Having one pacemaker avoids amplification problems (see the mapping section) and creates synchronisation.

The pacemaker need not be a constraint or bottleneck, though often is. It is usual to select a process well downstream as the pacemaker, so that upstream operations can be pulled. After the pacemaker, you would like flow to be first in first out (FIFO) or to go into a finished goods supermarket.

A pacemaker relies on as smooth a demand as possible. Also, the pacemaker will operate at or near the pitch increment as the drumbeat - typical would be 95% of the pitch time to allow for a little variation. This is really 'undercapacity scheduling'. It is common to use a Heijunka box at the pacemaker as the actual scheduling mechanism.

Supermarkets and FIFO Lanes

Lean aims at flow - the ideal being one piece flow. Flow should take place between supermarkets. Traditionally, there are large amounts of inventory before and after workstations - some of it waiting to move, some waiting for the next operation, some of it buffer. It is hard to tell. This is bad practice. Supermarket areas should be grouped together to enable the material handler to visit on his or her regular routes. It is called a supermarket because that is where the material handler 'goes shopping' for parts.

With reference to value stream maps, often supermarkets are established at the boundary between loops of pull - say between a press and a group of cells, or where two value streams converge or diverge, or where two CONWIP loops meet.

It is permissable to have work in process inventory between workstations only when it is under visible kanban control (or CONWIP or drum buffer rope - see later). All other inventory should be located in relatively few supermarkets.

Some practitioners make a distinction between various types of inventory held in the supermarket. That is, they keep ordinary WIP inventory separate from safety stock (needed to cater for uncertain demand), and buffer stock (needed to cater for process uncertainties such as quality problems or breakdowns). Although this causes a little more inventory to be held, it is good practice because it helps highlight the causes of problems.

The finished goods supermarket is sometimes called the 'wall of shame' to indicate that demand management and schedule stability still has somewhere to go. Finished goods supermarkets need to regard the inventory dynamically. Use a clear marker system which shows if there is too much inventory in circulation. You can use a marker for each container or location of a part in the supermarket, and then remove the marker the first time the container is moved. If the container never moves for a month (say) the marker will remain, indicating excessive inventory.

FIFO Lanes are also good Lean supermarket practice, even though they take up a bit more space. They help avoid date senstive inventory problems and are good for visibility and housekeeping. Simply, inventory is removed from one end and brought in at the other. Monitoring is easy via dates or colour coding according to the day of arrival.

A (by now hopefully) obvious point: do not use an automatic storage and retrieval system as a supermarket. They encourage more inventory, prevent visibility, and have slow response for a material handler or runner. And they may break down. However a small AS/RS does have a role for consumables and slow response parts, if space and security are issues.

Runners, Repeaters and Strangers (RRS)

Runners, Repeaters and Strangers is a powerful idea for lean scheduling, thought to have originated in Lucas Industries during the late 1980s.

A "runner" is a product or product family having sufficient volume to justify dedicated facilities or manufacturing cells. This does not mean that such facilities need to be utilised all the time, merely that it is economic or strategically justifiable to operate such facilities on an as-and-when basis, and not to share them with other products.

A "repeater" is a product or product family with intermediate volume, where dedicated facilities are not justifiable. Repeaters should be scheduled at regular slots. Even though the quantity may vary, the slot time should remain approximately constant. This brings advantages of order and discipline. For instance, maintenance and tooling know that a particular job requiring a particular die is needed each Tuesday morning, suppliers get used to the regular order, setup resources are made ready, the forklift truck may be standing by, and so on. Regularity is the key: try for once per day at the same time; if this is not possible then (say) Monday, Wednesday, Friday at the same times; if this is not possible then (say) every week at the same time, and so on.

A "stranger" is a product or family with a low or intermittent volume. Strangers should be fitted into the schedule around the regular repeater slots. They have lowest priority.

So in constructing the production plan or schedule, begin by doing a Pareto analysis to split the products into runner, repeater, and stranger categories. Then runners are of little concern so long as there is adequate capacity. They enjoy their own resources. Repeaters form the backbone of the schedule and should be slotted in at regular intervals as often as capacity will allow, maximising flow and minimising inventories. Make transfer batches smaller than production batches. Then fit the strangers around the repeaters.

This is much like the way we run our lives. We have runners, for example heartbeat that goes on all the time, and we don't plan for these. But you may be conscious of keeping your heart in good condition through exercise. Then repeaters: we sleep every night perhaps not for the same length of time but every night. You know, without being told, not to telephone your friends at 3 a.m. Likewise you have breakfast every day. You use the opportunity to talk to the family, because they are all there without having to arrange a special meeting. What you don't do, even though it may appear more efficient, is to have one big breakfast lasting three whole days at the beginning of the month (one "setup"). You organise your food inventories around these regular habits. Then strangers: you do different things each day, but these different activities are slotted in around the regular activities.

Quality Guru, Phil Crosby talks about running your business "like ballet, not hockey". In ballet you rehearse, adjust and do it the same for each performance. In hockey, each game is different. Runners, repeaters, and strangers allow ballet style management. Too often, it is hockey style - we collapse exhausted in our chair at the end of the week, feeling satisfied but having solved the same old problem for the 500th time.

The entries in the cells indicate the broad options. The table is not intended to be applied to every company but is a broad guideline. Each company should develop its own matrix. An A class repeater is likely to be a candidate for tight kanban (that is,

	Runners	Repeaters	Strangers
A	Tight kanban	Tight kanban?	MRP / forecast
B	Loose kanban?	Loose kanban	MRP
C	2 bin / ROP	2 bin	2 bin / 'go see'

kanban with small safety stock). A class strangers are probably candidates for MRP or some forecast-based system as lack of repetition makes kanban less feasible. B class repeaters are probably candidates for kanban with more safety stock. Generally C class items should be managed by a simple procedure such as a two-bin system or reorder point system – perhaps periodic review for runners and continuous review for strangers.

A further dimension is lead-time, shown in the table below.

Here, VMI is vendor managed inventory and signal kanban is a launch activated signal system such as used for Ford engines or Johnson controls seats.

RRS and ABC Classification

A useful way to think of Lean scheduling and pull options is the next table.

	Runners	Repeaters	Strangers
A long LT	Loose kanban	MRP	MRP
A short LT	Tight kanban	Tight kanban	Signal kanban
B long LT	Loose kanban	Loose kanban	MRP
B short LT	Tight kanban	Tight kanban	Signal kanban
C long LT	2 bin / ROP	2 bin	2 bin
C short LT	VMI	VMI	Go see

The columns are runners, repeaters and strangers – see the last section. The rows are the standard A, B, C inventory classification. A items are expensive, B intermediate, C are low cost commodity items.

Note that there should always be efforts to convert strangers into repeaters and repeaters into runners, thereby reducing and eventually eliminating the need for MRP.

Mixed Model Scheduling

Mixed model scheduling means scheduling ABC, ABC, ABC..... in a repeating sequence rather than in three large batches. There are several reasons for this: it is a powerful aid to cell balancing, it reduces WIP inventory and sometimes finished goods inventory, it may lead to better customer service, and (the big one) it results in a constant rate of flow all day rather than in different rates for different products. In practical terms, mixed model often means one (small) container of A, followed by a container of B, a container of C, then back to a container of A, and so on, rather than 10 containers of A, followed by 10 of B, and so on.

Mixed model scheduling is related to Lean batch sizing in as far as each tries to achieve more frequent EPE - 'every product every'.

In assembly operations with no changeover, mixed model operations should pose no problem. Where there are short changeovers, you can calculate the minimum feasible batch by changeover time + batch size x assembly time = batch size x takt time. This will give the desirable minimum number of a product that has to be kept together in a mixed model run sequence - say AAAA,BB,CC, D.

Mixed model sequences are, of course, derived from product mix demand. So if you have two products, A with 66% demand, and B with 33%, then the best mixed model sequence is AABAABAAB. You work out the best sequence from the nearest lowest common denominator. Thus if demand for A, B and C is in the ratio 10, 5, 2 the lowest denominator is 2 and the approximate ratios are 5, 2, 1 translating to ABABACAA followed by ABABABACA.

In a Heijunka box the mix model sequence is placed in the pitch increments. Some companies use standard pitch increments, and vary the length of the work day, others derive the pitch increment directly from takt. Either way, first, the mixed model batch size or container size decides the pitch increment, and second, the number of pitch increments and the product mix decides the mixed model sequence. Thus if there are 48 10-minute pitch increments in the heijunka and the lowest common denominator demand mix is 6A, 3B, 2C, 1D then the day would be divided into 4 12-pitch increment repeating slots, each of ABABACABACAD.

Kanban

Kanban is just one form of pull mechanism. Some others are CONWIP, Drum Buffer Rope, 2-bin, faxban, and audio-based call. Remember also that pull is the fourth of Womack and Jones' Lean principles. That is deliberate – there is a lot to do before introducing kanban – reducing demand amplification, reducing changeover, creating more stable work through standard work, reducing the defect rate, and reducing disruptions through breakdowns. Do all of these first!

Kanban is an effective way to reduce muda (waste), mura (unevenness) and to avoid muri (unreasonableness).

Kanban is the classic signalling device for production pull systems. Nevertheless there remain uncertainties about types and quantities. A basic classification is:

- Production Kanbans
    - Production
        - Product
        - Capacity or Generic
    - Signal or Triangle
- Move or Withdrawal Kanbans
    - In plant
    - Supplier

Production Kanbans

Single Card Kanban

Traditional kanban is suitable in all stable manufacturing environments where there is repetitive production. In practice, the single card kanban category is by far the most popular type. It is easy to understand, easy to see, and reasonably easy to install. Single card kanban means that a single card (or pull signal) operates between each pair of workstations. Although there may be several single-card kanbans in a loop between a pair of workstations, each kanban is the authorisation to both make a part or container of parts and to move it to a specified location. Two major categories are product kanban and generic kanban.

Product Kanban

Product kanban is the simplest form of pull system. With this type, whenever a product is used it is simply replaced. If there is no call, there is no authorisation so there is no production. In practice, the variations of this type include kanban squares (a vacant square is the authorisation to fill the square with another similar part), cards (which are returned to the feeding workstation to authorise it to make a replacement quantity as specified on the card), and other variations such as "faxban" or "e-ban" (which operate in exactly the same way as cards, except that the pull signals are electronic not physical).

Product Kanban with Multiple Products

(a) Sequential Operations

In sequential operations having several different products, product kanban can be used between stations provided there are not too many products. Here, one partly completed product of each type is placed as buffer between each workstation. If product A is called for at the end of a line, triggers are activated sequentially along the line to make a replacement A. Other products do not move until they are called for. This system allows a quick response build from a limited selection of products, but has the penalty of holding intermediate buffers of part completed products of each type. Hence this system becomes impractical for more than a handful of products. The generic kanban type should then be used, as explained below.

(b) Assemble to Order Operations

A variation that is employed in several assemble-to-order operations (for instance, personal computer "make to order") involves simply having shelves with at least one or two of all parts and subassemblies surrounding the final assembly area. When an order comes

in, it is simply configured from the appropriate shelves. This then creates a blank space on the shelf that is the signal for subassembly areas to replace that subassembly. Subassembly areas are themselves arranged into cells that pull parts from the shelf, and hence back to the store. In this way, literally millions of different configurations can be made under a pull system.

(c) Product Kanban with Synchronised Operations

Where there are several legs in a bill of material or assembly structure, synchronisation can be achieved by variations of so-called "golf ball" kanban. Here, as the main build progresses, signals are sent to areas producing supporting assemblies to warn them to prepare the appropriate assemblies "just in time" to meet up with the main build as it progresses along the line. Different colour "golf balls" are moved (often blown by air or sent electronically) to the subassembly stations to signal them to prepare the exact required subassembly. This form of kanban can be used internally (say to prepare different windscreens or coloured bumpers) to go onto particular cars, or externally (for instance when sent to external seat suppliers to prepare the exact sequence of seats to meet up with a particular sequence of cars).

(d) Emergency Kanban

Emergency kanban is a "special event" kanban that is inserted in kanban loops to compensate for unusual circumstances. Such kanban cards are of a different colour so that they may be distinguished easily. Such kanbans automatically go to the head of the queue so their requirements are dealt with as soon as possible. Having produced the additional quantity, emergency kanbans are withdrawn.

A variation is additional kanbans that are inserted to meet seasonal demand or to compensate for transport disruption, such as rail disruption or poor weather. These temporary cards are also withdrawn as soon as possible.

Generic Kanban

Generic (or "capacity") Kanban authorise feeding workcentres to make a part, but do not specify what part is to be made. The part to be made is specified via a manifest or a "broadcast" system. It is therefore the preferable pull system where there are a large number of products, all of which have similar routings and fairly similar time requirements at each workstation. Generic kanban has less WIP than product kanban, but the response time is slower.

Signal Kanban

Where there is changeover, a signal (or triangle or priority) kanban is used. As parts are withdrawn, so kanbans are hung on the board under the appropriate product column. (See page 116). A target batch size is calculated for each product (see Batch Sizing), and the target is marked on the board. When a sufficient number of kanbans has accumulated to reach the target, a batch is made. This gives a visible, up-to-date warning of an impending changeover. In normal circumstances the batch is made when the target level is reached. If these are problems kanbans may accumulate beyond the target level. This would indicate higher priority. Normally, a batch is made to cover all the kanbans in the product column. In very slack periods, a smaller batch may be made to cover only the cards on the board.

Dual Card Kanban

Dual card kanban, long established at Toyota, and increasingly elsewhere, uses both production and move kanban cards. Production (or signal) kanbans stay at a particular workcentre and alternate from Kanban board to finished goods container. The workcentre operator uses them. Conveyance kanbans stay between a particular pair of workstations and alternate between move card mailbox and full container (with conveyance card attached). The material handler uses them.

A material handler collects up the conveyance kanbans from the mailbox (usually as part of his regular runner route – see also section on Takt and Pitch time) and takes them to the appropriate feeder workstation. There, the material handler detaches the production (or signal) kanban from the full container, and attaches the conveyance kanban to the container. The production kanbans

are returned to the kanban board of the workstation. When works starts on the batch, as authorised by the production kanban, the operator detaches the conveyance kanban from the container and hangs it on the mailbox for the upstream conveyance.

The dual card and signal kanban systems, working together, mean that the move quantity does not have to equal the make quantity. This is good for linking several operations using a pacemaker or Heijunka system. Also, production kanbans have very short lead times because they stay at the workcentre. This means quick response and lower inventory.

Move Kanbans

In the single card system, these are simply kanbans that trigger parts delivery to the line, either from an internal supermarket or from an external supplier. In the dual card system, move kanbans work with production kanbans or signal kanbans as above.

The Ford System

Ford calls their kanban system SMART (for Synchronous Material Availability Request Ticket). There are several variants:
- SMART cards are for slow moving, small or inexpensive parts. These are collected by the material handler on his regular route and returned to the SMART office where they are scanned by bar-code reader. Flashing lights indicate to the material handler the priority for replenishment. This is a 'loose kanban' or slow response system.
- SMART call is for fast moving or heavy or expensive parts or where space is limited on the line. The operator presses a button lineside when a re-order point is reached. This is a 'tight kanban' or fast response system.
- E SMART gives pull signals directly from the line to external suppliers. Such parts bypass the warehouse / supermarket.
- SMART squares painted on the floor indicate the exact stopping point for the front wheel of a forklift or tugger vehicle, to optimise unloading.

Other Forms of Kanban

A kanban carousel is a storage rack on wheels that is rotated. The back is filled while the front is being used. Good for kit parts. A post on a trolley has an adjustable height indicator that can be used to adjust the pull quantity. (Both from Arvin Meritor). Sequenced in line storage (SILS) is a sloping gravity feed rack on wheels for mixed model heavy parts moved between next-door supplier and consumer. A slowly rotating two-tier table stores parts below and has packing operations on top. The table rotates at takt time around a group of assemblers. There are load and unload stations. Some automotive plants use a shuttle that travels along with a car over a set of workstations, for custom components such as seats.

Rules of Kanban

Downstream operations come to withdraw parts from upstream operations.
Make only the exact quantity indicated on the kanban.
Demands are placed on upstream operations by means of cards or other signals.
Only active parts are allowed at the workplace. Active parts should have specific locations.
Authorisation to produce is by card (or signal) only.
Each kanban card circulates between a particular pair of workstations only.
Quality at Source is a requirement. Only good items are sent downstream.
The number of kanbans should be reduced as problems decrease.

Numbers of Kanban Cards

In line with Lean Manufacturing, the correct answer to the question of the number of kanban cards should generally be "less than last time!" The well-known water and rocks analogy applies. That is, reduce the inventory levels by removing a kanban (or by reducing the kanban quantity) and "expose the rocks". Note that the philosophy of gradually reducing inventory by removing kanbans is "win-win" approach: either nothing will happen in which case you have "won" because you have found that you can run a little tighter or you "hit a rock" in which case you have also "won"

because you have hit not just any old rock, but the most pressing rock or constraint. This is what Toyota has done for decades.

The general rule on kanbans is therefore to start "loose", with a generous amount of safety stock, and to move towards "tight kanban" gradually, but steadily. Probably in the majority of cases the number of kanbans is calculated on a safe assumption of having comfortably sufficient inventory in the replenishment loop. However, Ohno warned about an excessive number kanbans – thereby loosing the responsive 'feel' of a pull system. If you really want to use a formula, try what follows:

Calculating the Number of Cards

In general, kanban works like the traditional two-bin system. In the two-bin system the reorder point ROP is calculated thus

$$ROP = D \times LT + SS$$

where D = demand rate during the lead-time LT between placing and order and receiving delivery, and SS is the safety stock. This familiar formula is the basis for all kanban calculations. If the container or stillage quantity is Q, then the number of kanbans is simply $N = (D \times LT + SS) / Q$ where N should be rounded up. This assumes that the Kanban card is sent as soon as the first part is removed from the container.

It is often better to think of a safety lead time instead of a safety stock. The safety lead time (ST) is a time buffer making allowance for the unplanned stoppages. In this case the formula is $N = (D \times (LT + ST))/N$.

1. Number of Cards where there is Changeover

Leadtime must include changeover + batch run time + queue time + delivery time. In Lean we often think of the EPE cycle (Every product every – see batch sizing section). The EPE cycle is the interval in days between running a product. It would not include delivery time or safety time. The delivery time would frequently be linked with the material handling (or waterspider) cycle or pitch time, and is in effect the response safety time between the point of consumption and the changeover operation. The formula then becomes

$$N = (D \times (EPE + \text{delivery time} + \text{safety time}))/Q$$

Demand for A is 30 parts per day and A is run three times per day, with a 1 hour delivery cycle. 2 hours is the safety time. The container quantity is 5 and the operation works an 8 hour day. Then N = (30 x (0.33 + 1/8 + 2/8))/5 = 4.25 kanbans. Of these, the safety lead time accounts for (30 x 2/8)/5 = 1.5 kanbans, so you would have to select 4 or 5 kanbans in the loop. Often these would be 'Triangle' kanbans to indicate that a changeover operation is part of the loop.

The batch size is 30/3 = 10, equivalent to 2 kanbans, which would be the trigger point on the kanban board next to the changeover operation.

2. Number of Cards for Assembly Operations or from Suppliers

In repetitive assembly operations where there is no changeover, the demand is expressed in units per day, and the lead time LT is the time required to go through all the necessary steps between "placing the order" (hanging the kanban on the board) and receiving it. This would normally include the usual lead time elements of run + wait + move. Note that run time should be the time to fill the container, wait time should include both pre- and post-waiting for movement and waiting on the kanban board or mailbox before the order is actioned. Where parts are obtained from an external supplier, the lead-time would be the expected lead-time for delivery as used in any inventory calculation. Demand and lead-time should always be expressed in compatible units; say demand per week and lead-time in weeks. Then use N=(D x (LT+ST))/N.

Safety lead time should also be allowed. This would reflect the any uncertainties in delivery, quality, breakdown or other disruption. Note two points. First, the principle of moving from "loose" to "tight" pull and second, the fact that safety stock has usually already been somewhat allowed for in the rounding up calculation to calculate the number of cards.

A Final Note on Kanban

In the preceding sections, traditional kanban has been explained. The weakness of traditional kanban is that it assumes repetitive production (even where generic kanban is used) and also a fairly level schedule. Where the schedule is not level, quite significant buffer inventories between the various stages may be idle for lengthy periods, waiting to be pulled. This is of course "muda". Further complications are routings that may vary significantly between products, and variation in processing times resulting in unbalanced lines and temporary "bottlenecks". In such circumstances traditional kanban systems can sometimes have more inventory than MRP push systems. Some variations have been developed to overcome these limitations. These are covered in the next sections.

Notice also that the number of kanbans depends on demand. This means that when demand changes, the number of kanbans should change. In an unstable environment there could be quite a bit of adding and subtracting kanbans. When takt changes, kanbans will often have to change. This means the schedulers have to be vigilant. Some have suggested that an MRP system be used to generate the required number of kanbans. This does not sound like generally good advice to the writer. Apart from sounding like a reversion to job cards, the philosophy of MRP is inherently that of the job shop rather than the flow shop. MRP is fine for planning, but not for execution.

CONWIP

CONWIP or "constant work in progress" (Hopp and Spearman, see next chapter) links the last process with the first by a multi-stage signal system. Cards do not operate between each pair of workstations as in traditional kanban, but instead cards follow the product or batch through all stages in a section. As a product or batch is completed at the last process, the card is sent to the first process thereby authorising the start of a new batch. Alternatively, whenever work is completed at the end of a route, an equivalent amount of work is let in at the beginning of the route. The amount of work is calculated in terms of (say) the beginning process. A CONWIP loop may be an assembly line, a cell, or a whole factory. Where cards are used, CONWIP cards are not product specific. They authorise the start of production of a batch or product of whatever type is required. In this sense they are like generic or capacity kanbans.

CONWIP is a beautifully simple but robust system because inventory automatically accumulates in front of temporary bottlenecks, which is just where it is required. For variable operations, a shifting product mix, and where there are maintenance problems, CONWIP is an attractive system. Moreover, it frequently requires less inventory than stage by stage kanban. There is a similarity with the OPT type "drum, buffer, rope" which links bottleneck workcentre to gateway workcentre and places a "time buffer" in front of the bottleneck. However, with CONWIP the bottleneck does not have to be identified (indeed it may shift) and the time buffer does not need to be calculated.

To establish a CONWIP loop start with 'loose' inventory and tighten. Inventory, of course, reflects lead time so required lead time multiplied by takt time is an upper bound.

CONWIP loops can be established between supermarkets with several loops making up a full value chain. Where parts are used in two different end items, for instance, one CONWIP loop can be set up for components, and two loops can be set up for the end items.

A further extension allows two categories of priority. Normally first in first out (FIFO) is used, but jobs having "hot" CONWIP cards are allowed to jump the queue at the first operation or at buffers set up between CONWIP lines.

Why bother with kanban when there is CONWIP? Because, where production stages are well balanced, it is easier to pick up problems faster with kanban. Kanban is a tighter material control system. However, kanban requires strict operating conditions and higher linearity of flow. Of course it is possible to use both kanban and CONWIP simultaneously; CONWIP to control the main flow and kanban to control parts delivery to the line.

POLCA

CONWIP and kanban work well where there are fixed lines and routings. Where cells and flow lines can be created this is by far the best thing to do. However, a job shop or a changing network of routings presents another challenge. The use of a computer-based APS comes to mind. POLCA or "paired cell overlapping loops of cards with authorisation" (Suri, 1998) is a push-pull system that allows different routings and job-shop type operations.

Many job shops suffer from the problem of having a long and constantly shifting list of jobs at each workstation. Schedule adherence is a big issue where, for instance, an operator has two widely separated jobs on his list with only a minor changeover between them. It 'makes sense' locally to do the two jobs one after the other. The problem is that a downstream workstation may be delayed. The situation is made much more complex when there are shifting priorities and breakdowns. Even daily runs on an APS system and strict schedule adherence do not help.

POLCA offers a possible solution. There are two important concepts. First, a job should not be started too early, because it clogs up the plant and adds to the leadtime. Second, a job should not start on any machine before it has a good chance of progressing through the next machine without much delay.

The first objective is achieved by using a finite scheduling-type system to determine earliest release dates. This determines the time before which jobs may not start, NOT when they are due to start. A job card is issued showing the routing. This card travels with the job from start to finish. The second objective is addressed by issuing a number of POLCA cards to each pair of machines or workstations. A POLCA card stays with the job as the job progresses through both workstations in the pair. To begin work at any workstation the job card must be available, and a POLCA card for the present and next workstation. The POLCA card is returned to the beginning of the first workstation when the job is completed at the second workstation. At workstation A there must be a POLCA card for A-B available. At workstation B there must be a card for B-C available.

POLCA card A-B is returned to the front of A when the job is completed at B. POLCA card B-C is returned to the front of B when the job is completed at C. And so on. If C experiences a problem B can work on jobs that feed other workcentres (say D, E, F) but not C. The final workstation on the job card works on a due date basis.

This arrangement ensures minute to minute signalling of the appropriate jobs that can be worked on to more or less ensure flow. Continuous push is not possible. The number of POLCA cards determines how much inventory there will be in each pair of loops. The system is not foolproof; in as far as it is possible for a job to be delayed considerably so a maximum wait may be specified.

POLCA is a fairly complex system compared with traditional kanban, and should not be used where there is linear repetitive production. Both CONWIP and POLCA can handle non-linear demands and changeover operations. POLCA could be considered where routings are irregular or repeat only at infrequent intervals.

Further reading:
Yashiro Monden, *Toyota Production System*, Second Edition, Chapman & Hall, London, 1994
William Sandras, *Just in Time: Making it Happen*, Oliver Wight, 1989
Wallace Hopp and Mark Spearman, *Factory Physics*, (Second edition), McGraw Hill, Boston, 2000
Rajan Suri, *Quick Response Manufacturing*, Productivity Press, Portland OR, 1998
James Krupp, 'Integrating Kanban and MRP to reduce Lead Time', *Production and Inventory Management*, Third/Fourth Quarter, 2002

Batch Sizing

This section gives an introduction to batch sizing and scheduling in situations where changeover remains a significant factor. Of course, one should still continue to attack changeover times, since any reduction improves the flow and allows reduced batch size.

First, a few words on the economic batch quantity. From a lean perspective, this approach should be totally rejected. Major criticisms include:

* no account is taken of takt time or flow rate
* classic "batch and queue" thinking
* changeover cost has to be given as a cost per changeover, whereas changeover teams are usually a fixed resource
* inventory-holding costs are often understated
* capacity is assumed to be infinite, and
* demand is constant and uniform - a lean ideal, but sometimes not a practical one.

The general Theory of Constraints batch sizing guideline is to increase batch sizes on capacity constrained machines, whilst reducing batch sizes on non-constrained machines. If changeover teams are available they should be used to carry out more changeovers on non-constrained machines, with corresponding reduction in batch sizes, so that such machines become fully utilised doing either changeover or running. The resulting reduction in WIP can be used to justify employing more resources on changeover. As a general guideline, this makes good sense, and is compatible with lean thinking.

Minimum Batch Quantity with Changeover

The minimum practical batch quantity when there is changeover is sometimes governed by the external changeover time. In other words, unless the batch is greater than this minimum, the machine will be idle waiting for external changeover operations. This is a reminder that it is not just internal changeover operations that govern batch size. Effort may have to be put into minimising external operations also.

Batch Sizing with Takt Time and Changeover

The basic case is where the batch size is determined in relation to takt time and changeover time. Here the batch size is determined from the "cycle quantity" which in turn gives the batch size. The optimal, or minimum, cycle quantity occurs when the cycle of changeover times + run times exactly balances the rate of demand or takt time. In other words:

changeover time + run time x batch size = takt time x batch size

or

$$\text{cycle quantity} = \frac{\Sigma \text{ (changeover time)}}{\text{(overall takt time - unit run time)}}$$

where

$$\text{overall takt time} = \frac{60}{\Sigma \text{ (total demand per hour)}}$$

$$\text{cycle quantity} = \frac{\Sigma \text{ (changeover time)}}{\text{(takt time – weighted ave run time)}}$$

and

batch size of a product = cycle quantity * product proportion

Example: There are 3 products A,B,C. Changeover time is 30 minutes each for all products. Run time on the machine is 5 minutes for all products. Demand rate, or (takt time) is 1 every 20 minutes for A, and 1 every 40 minutes for B and C (i.e. the mix is 2:1:1)

> Demand per hour is 3 A, 1.5 B, and 1.5 C or a total of 6.
> Overall takt time = 60 / 6 = 10 minutes
> Cycle quantity = (3 * 30) / (10 - 5) = 90 / 5 = 18
> Batch size of A is 18 * 0.5 = 9, batch size of B and C = 18 * .25 = 4.5 or 5

Note also that this assumes batch production is 2A, B, C and not A,B,A,C. The latter is of course more in line with lean manufacturing mixed model production. So if mixed model is desired there will have to be one more changeover per cycle. Overall takt time remains the same, but

> cycle quantity = (4 * 30) / (10 - 5) = 120 / 5 = 24

> and each batch size becomes 24 * .25 = 6

or 6A, changeover, 6B, changeover, 6A, changeover, 6C, changeover

Batch Sizing with Constrained Capacity, Changeover, and Pareto Demand

A situation found in literally thousands of companies is where a variety of products of differing quantities have to be scheduled through an operation where there remain fairly substantial changeover times. Almost invariably capacity is an issue. Also invariably the product quantities are not uniform- there is a mix of "repeaters" and "strangers" often forming a strong Pareto distribution of demand. This situation is found in press shops, in textile converters, in chemical plants, and in injection operations, to name but a few.

As always one should attack changeover times and work to improve OEE. Also there should be the ongoing consideration as to product contribution and product line rationalisation. This is assumed. The issue remains how to determine batch quantities. This section gives an introduction to the remaining batch-sizing issues assuming that there is one constrained machine through which a whole portfolio of products must be routed. If there is more than one machine, begin by allocating products to machines.

Every Product Every (EPE) Batch Sizing

The EPE concept is an important Lean idea that establishes a regular repeating cycle. A Lean ideal is to run every product every day. This would be excellent for service and inventory. EPE regularity has big advantages for standard work, quality, predictability, suppliers, changeover time, and regular time for improvement. "A good Lean schedule is a boring schedule" is a good maxim. So is the question "Do you run your factory ballet style or football style?" Ballet is regular and predictable. Football is enjoyable but every game is different. An EPE cycle is often referred to as a 'campaign'.

The basis of batch EPE is to make the batch as small as possible by doing as many changeovers as possible in the available time. But changeover time itself must be challenged continually.

Time available for changeovers = Total available time – Total run time

Number of batches = Time for changeovers / changeover time

Example: ACME makes 6 products A,B,C, D, E, F in a press shop. All changeovers take 30 minutes. Demand for the products mean than total daily actual run time is 3, 2, 0.5, 0.5, 0.5, 0.5 hours respectively. Net available working time per day (after breaks, routine maintenance, team meetings) is 8 hours per day.

Then total run time per week = 7 hours
Total changeover time for all products = 3 hours

Is an EPE of 1 day possible? No. (Time required is 7+3 = 10 hours)
Is an EPE of 2 days possible?
Time required = 7 + 7 = 14 hours for run + 3 for c/over = 17 hours
Time available = 8 + 8 = 16 hours. (Not possible)
Is an EPE of 3 days possible?
Time required = 3 x 7 + 3 = 24
Time available = 3 x 8 = 24
So, an EPE of 3 days is just feasible, and would be the Leanest solution. This would mean batch sizes (or run lengths) of 9, 6, 1.5, 1.5, 1.5, 1.5 hours. But perhaps 3 days is not a nice round number because this would mean this week would not be the same as next, and there is a risk of overtime is there is any stoppage. Try a 4 day EPE.
Time required = 4 x 7 + 3 = 31 hours
Time available = 4 x 8 = 32 hours
So, an EPE of 4 days would mean 1 hour free per week for contingency. Not a bad solution.
A 5 day EPE
Time required = 5 x 7 + 3 = 38 hours
Time available = 5 x 8 = 40 hours
This would mean 2 hours free per week. These 2 hours could be used to do an extra changeover on 4 extra days a week for the big runner product A. 5 days is also a nice round number, leading to this week looking just like next week. This could lead to the following schedule (in run hours for each product).

The sequence would be c-MA-c-MB-TB-c-TA-WA-c-WB-c-WC-ThC-c-ThA-c-ThD-FD-c-FA-c-FE-c-FF (where MA is Monday run A). As can be seen it is reasonably complex.

	A	B	C	D	E	F	C/ov	Total
Mon	3	4					1 hr	8 hrs
Tues	3	4.5					0.5	8
Wed	3	1	0.5				1	8
Thur	3		2	0.5			1	8
Fri	3			2	2.5	2.5	1.5	8
Total	15	10	2.5	2.5	2.5	2.5	5	40 hrs

Deriving the Target Changeover Time

An alternative is to calculate the target changeover time that will allow an EPE of (say) one day. In the above example there are 7 hours of run time per day, leaving 1 hour for changeover. 6 changeovers are required for an EPE of 1 day, so the target changeover time is 10 minutes. For a 2 day EPE it is 20 minutes per changeover. This is a very useful calculation since changeover times below 10 minutes will not yield further inventory or lead time reductions, but will give more free time for other improvement activities. But, can this be used?

Signal Kanban, EPE, Batch Sizing and Heijunka

In many environments having worked out the minimum EPE as above, a signal kanban system is set up and the schedule determined by pull signal from a downstream pacemaker. Signal (also known as triangle) kanbans accumulate on a board next to the changeover operation. When kanbans equal to the EPE batch quantity have accumulated, this is the signal to make the batch.

Take the previous example of 6 products. Assume the container quantity is 30 minutes of production for each product. A feasible EPE of 3 days would mean a production run of 9 hours or 18 kanbans of 30 minutes each. Similarly B would have 12, C to F would have 3 kanbans each. Normally the downstream operations (a cell?) would pull from the supermarket (located after the changeover operation) in containers rather than strict one-piece flow. The proportions of products A through F are 6:4:1:1:1:1 and a possible mixed model sequence is

ABAC ABAD ABE ABF

It is possible to repeat this sequence every day with each letter representing a container of 30 minutes of

run line indicates the target batch size, determined from the EPE calculation above, expressed in number of kanbans above the base card. When the accumulated kanbans reach the run line, a batch sufficient to cover all the outstanding kanbans in the column, is made. All the triangle kanbans for that product batch are set aside and another signal card – say a diamond - is hung on the board to indicate that the product is currently being run. This is the case for product F. B is the next product due to be run. Any signal kanbans that have accumulated beyond the run line are also run. Normally there would be some safety kanbans for each product (refer to the earlier section on number of kanbans) so it is possible that there may be

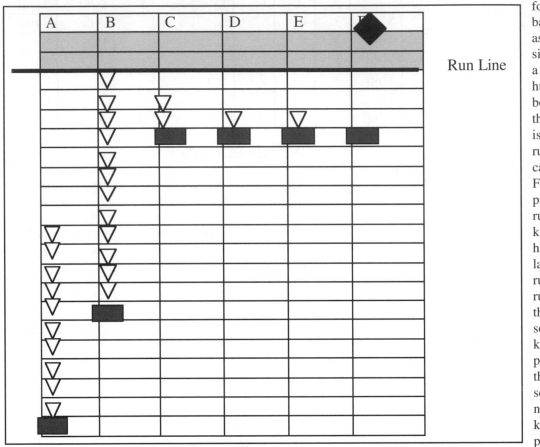

Run Line

products. In Heijunka systems, this mixed model sequence could be loaded into the Heijunka box in half hour pitch increments. The signal kanban board next to the changeover operation would, however, have to reflect the feasible 3 day EPE. It would look as shown above.

Triangle signal kanbans accumulate on the board as containers are pulled from the supermarket. The dark bar in each column represents the base card. Above that the kanbans accumulate from bottom to top. Base cards allow easy adjustment when takt times change. The dark

kanbans in excess of the target quantity on the board. The row above the run line is frequently coloured in red or yellow to indicate that safety stock is being consumed.

The board is of course dynamic, visible and up-to-date and reflects changing priorities. A warning of the batch to be made can be clearly seen. In the example, B is due for manufacture and C is likely to be next. With such a board, a detailed schedule for the changeover is not required – it merely responds to the downstream pacemaker.

Batch Sizing Toyota Style

The above EPE calculation assumes that 6 products are to be run on the press. But a prior question is, how many presses should you have in the first place? A Toyota approach is to begin with a seemingly arbitrary 90/10 split between run time and setup time. This approach is based on long experience. It is non optimal, but a good general solution.

This method has the great virtue of keeping the pressure on changeover times. If changeover times slip, it will not be possible to complete the week's work. So, this method must be accompanied by changeover time monitoring.

Why 90/10? Consider a series of products moving through two stages; say a blanking line and a press line. Changeovers are involved. As batch sizes come down, total lead-time comes down because the split batches can be moved to the next stage sooner. However, there is a limit to this. Eventually changeover times come to dominate, and lead time increases. The point is that queuing and simulation studies show that for a utilisation factor of around 85%, lead-time is minimised at around a 90/10 ratio. A utilisation of 90% (or OEE) is achievable at better companies. At utilisation factors of 50%, however, a 97/3 ratio may be better. Is this why Toyota uses 90/10? We don't know.

An Improvement?

The concept here is to find the batch sizes that will allow the greatest amount of flow together with the lowest overall inventory levels. Consider this: a company makes 3 products A, B and C which go through one machine on which changeover has been reduced to 30 minutes. Demand is in the ratio 4:1:1. The company has made fair progress towards lean and currently produces according to a "mixed model" schedule of 40 A, 10 B, 10 C, 40 A, 10 B, 10 C. Can flow be improved, and inventory cut without a further reduction in changeover? Yes! This approach involves cutting the batch size of the high demand products whilst simultaneously increasing batch sizes of low demand products.

First, begin by arranging products in Pareto fashion from high demand to low demand.

Second, determine against demonstrated changeover and run times and OEE, the feasible EPE as above. Third, examine this EPE against the realities of the plant and decide by how much the minimum cycle time should be rounded up to make a convenient EPE.

Now commence the "trade off" process. In general, any product having a demand (or changeover time) greater than 4 times another product should be "traded" by halving the batch quantity of the higher demand product and doubling the batch quantity of the lower demand product, thereby retaining (or approximately retaining) the total overall changeover time. The extra or spare capacity can be used for cases where changeover times differ and for marginal cases. Finally, having determined the batch sizes, the last step is to arrange the products in a mixed model sequence. Begin with the high demand products and space them as evenly as possible.

Further reading:
Yasuhiro Monden, *Toyota Production System*, (Second edition), Chapman and Hall, London, 1994

Material Handling Route (Runner or Waterspider)

A regular set route for a material handler is a powerful regularity concept. If the pacemaker is the heartbeat, the material handler is the circulation system lifeblood. Material handling is waste, of course, but instead of waste being spread out amongst many operators, group up all this waste into a single material handler and make that person a vital part of flow.

The material handler should follow a set route, collecting kanbans, picking parts at the supermarket and delivering parts to the line. He or she starts and ends at the pacemaker or heijunka box, thereby initiating the next round of activity as the heijunka card is issued. Regularity gives confidence to those being served. The material handler working with the pacemaker essentially levels the rate of production. The route should be carefully worked out in a standard time, just a little less than the pitch increment or a whole number of pitch increments.

The material handler is also on the lookout for problems. He will know of any shortage or stoppage along his whole section of the value stream. He should notify problems to supervision.

A little and often is the maxim of the material handler - hence the term waterspider, skitting across the pond.

Heijunka

Heijunka is the classic method of Lean scheduling in a repetitive environment. It simultaneously achieves a level schedule or pacing, visibility of schedule, and early problem highlighting. It is usually used at the pacemaker process, and as such controls and paces the whole plant. Moreover it can be used as a form of '10 minute MRP' synchronization tool. It can be used for production scheduling, for warehouse order picking, and in the office. Finally, it encourages schedules to be developed and controlled by supervisors at the Gemba.

Simply, Heijunka is a post-box system for kanban cards that authorizes production in pitch increment-sized time slots. (See separate section on takt and pitch time.) A typical pitch increment is between 10 and 30 minutes. The box is loaded at the cell level by supervisors or team leaders. It is in effect a manual finite scheduler. As with kanban, a Heijunka system is always visible and up to date. You can see at a glance how far behind schedule you are.

A Heijunka Box has columns from left to right for each pitch increment, and rows for each product or family. For each pitch increment – except break increments – a Heijunka card is placed in one of the product rows to authorize production of one pitch increment's amount of work. A pitch increment normally fills a (small) container of parts, so deviations, when planned work is not completed, are clearly apparent. The cell is authorized, kanban style, to produce only that amount at the specific time – not before. Alternatively, a material handler is authorized to collect only that specific quantity at that time – not before. Therefore, loading up the Heijunka

box levels the schedule and withdrawing the cards paces production during the shift. Should any item fail to be ready for collection, or the cell is unable to start work, this is immediately apparent. The worst case of undetected cell failure is one pitch increment.

Heijunka is the pacemaker of the material handling system. A regular material handling route should be regarded as an integral part of Heijunka. The resulting regularity of flow of materials and of information is a major advantage. The material handler (or 'waterspider' or 'runner') starts and ends his regular cycle and the Heijunka box – perhaps every pitch increment, or certainly at a constant number of pitch increments. During the regular cycle, the material handler collects kanbans, picks parts, and delivers parts from the previous cycle. A constant route is followed. The material handlers may also collect finished products or issue the Heijunka card to the beginning of the cell. Stability of the schedule is required for successful Heijunka. You would like to maintain a pitch increment and mixed model schedule as long as possible. Frequent line or cell rebalance leads to lower productivity. Toyota frequently maintains the same takt time for several months. On the other hand, Unipart uses Heijunka for daily warehouse pick lists that are always different. They use standard 12 or 24 minute pick cycles, and load up orders to fill a pitch increment, depending on location and size.

Where Heijunka is used with a finished goods store, the material handler takes the Heijunka card for the slot as authorization to withdraw from finished goods. He detaches the production kanban on the container and sends it to authorize making the next batch. The production kanban is later attached to the completed container of parts, which is placed in finished goods. The used Heijunka card is placed in a box to be used tomorrow.

If demand cannot be met as per the Heijunka schedule, (i.e. there has been a stoppage), the material handler draws on buffer stock but raises a flag to show that he has done so. At the end of the shift, the buffer must be replaced. Some users differentiate between buffer stock to cope with line stoppages, and safety stock to cope with customer surges in demand.

Mixed model scheduling is inherent in Heijunka. The Heijunka box is loaded mixed-model fashion – not AAAAAABBBCCC but ABACABACABAC. See the section on Mixed Model.

Heijunka is not a tool for the job shop or for highly variable production. Having said that, Dell Computer uses a 'sort of' Heijunka (but not called that), by loading up work into two hour increments which are issued to the factory floor. It can be adopted for maintenance and long cycles.

A basic issue is whether to maintain a constant pitch time increment and derive the batch or pitch quantity as the takt time changes or to maintain a standard container quantity and derive the pitch increment as the takt time changes. The former seems most popular, leading to stability of material handling routes and rate of work. In this case, when the takt changes the container quantity should change and the number of pitch increments changes to meet the demand. You may end the shift with idle time or overtime. In a warehouse you simply accumulate the required number of picks to fill the slot. On the other hand, if you change the pitch increment as the takt time changes, rebalancing is required and material handling routes may have to change to fit in with the new pitch increment. Container sizes, however, remain constant.

Where there are very long work cycles or takt time such as with large item (Refer for example to the section on the Pulse Line), the pitch increment can be made a fraction of the pitch time – normally a convenient time increment such as 30 minutes or 1 hour. This is referred to as "Mini Pitch" or "Inverse Pitch". The Heijunka is then built around 30 minute standard blocks of work. The great advantages of levelling and pacing remain.

Heijunka cards may also be 'piggybacked' to achieve the effect of a 'broadcast' sheet as found in automotive plants. In this case a slot may contain several cards, each of which goes to a separate subassembly thereby synchronizing several streams automatically. This avoids having a separate schedule for each.

Heijunka should be regarded as the final Lean tool. Why? – because so much must be in place for it to be a real success – cell design, mixed model, low defect levels, kanban loops and discipline, changeover reduction, and operator flexibility and authority. But Heijunka is the real 'cherry on the top' – it is the ultimate tool for stability, productivity, and quality.

Kamishabi

The Kamishabi (Come e she bai) board is a useful variation on Heijunka used for scheduling routine activities of operators. Like Heijunka it is visible, kept at the workplace and loaded by the operators.

A Kamishabi board is simply a T Card display board with a column for each day of the week. The cards have a different colour for front and back. Activities that are supposed to be done day by day are written on cards and placed in slots under the appropriate day. When the activity is completed the card is turned around, so the colour for 'complete' shows. Anyone walking past can see what activities have been done and what is still due.

Activities shown on cards include TPM activities, 5S activities, training, meetings, and any other regular planned activity. Operators themselves are responsible for planning and completion.

Often the cards will have specific time durations and instructions. Some boards have specific times of the day for activities to be carried out. Others adopt a colour coding system for area or priority. Simple and effective.

Inventory Issues

Inventory Cost

The topic of inventory cost and value is important in lean operations because both involve deviation from traditional thinking. The traditional view of inventory carrying cost is that it includes capital cost (the cost of capital or the opportunity cost of capital) and holding cost (costs of the store or warehouse, including space occupied, wages, damage, obsolescence, and material handling equipment in the store). Some of these costs are regarded as fixed or overhead by some companies, but nevertheless are directly attributable to inventory and should be included. So, typical figures would be a capital cost of 10% p.a. and a holding cost of 15% p.a. leading to an inventory carrying cost of 25% p.a.

However, the "lean" view goes beyond this. In most plants inventory actually involves far more cost: inventory takes up space on the factory floor (which not only costs space but also prevents compact layouts which in turn means more material handling and decreased effectiveness of communication); it may involve activities such as cycle counting and record keeping, the costs of backflushing activities and other reporting to the MRP system; it may also involve defect detection costs which tend to rise with larger batches (if each batch is inspected and an error detected the whole batch must be reworked, if a smaller batch the rework quantity falls). All this is waste, or muda. Very significantly, large batches of inventory work against regular flow (the ideal of making some of each part every day), which in turn can have an impact on finished goods stocks and on customer service. Small batches, by contrast, enable production at the customer's rate of demand thereby simultaneously decreasing finished goods holdings and improving customer service. So, what is the real carrying cost of inventory? All we really know is that it is much higher than the carrying cost. How about 50% to 80% p.a.?

Safety Stocks and Time Profiles

Traditionally, safety stock is held as a buffer against uncertainty. In MRP and reorder point systems, inventory is re-ordered when the level dips below the reorder level. Safety stock is held in case demand exceeds that expected during the re-order period. When inventory levels are high, as occurs in batch production immediately following the run, there is minimal risk of stockout. There is only risk during the short period when inventory is low. On the other hand when frequent small batches are being made, there is greater exposure to the risk of stockout. Perhaps therefore more safety stock should be held in this latter case. But not all stockouts will result in lost sales; in some cases customers expect to wait. In other cases a stockout can be

catastrophic, resulting in the loss of a customer and future transactions concerning many other products.

In the Drum Buffer Rope (DBR) system (See Goldratt) safety time rather than safety stock is held. This is more efficient. In front of a constraint, some of each product does not have to be held – merely a quantity of the next product to be made to cover for possible stoppages.

Whether using the DBR system or not, it is a good idea to monitor regularly the time profile of important buffers – raw material, in front of constraints, and finished goods. An inventory profile shows hours of inventory against products ranked by the lead time remaining before each product is due to be sold. A healthy profile does not have products in buffer that are due for sale a long time in the future. These would indicate either overproduction or inappropriately early launch. On the other side of the profile there may be inventory that is already past its due sales date. This also indicates a schedule failure. So reduce the spread of the profile and centre it on an appropriate lead time.

This approach has much in common with the Six Sigma methodology of measuring the variation, and then reducing the variation and shifting the average.

See also the note on Throughput Dollar Days and Inventory Dollar Days in the Measures section.

The Near Future

Radio Frequency identification (RFID), both passive and active, is about to revolutionise inventory management particularly in supply chains. The promise is for greatly improved inventory accuracy and demand analysis, leading to leaner inventories with improved service.

Theory of Constraints and Factory Physics

This section deals with the remarkable contributions of Eli Goldratt on Theory of Constraints and with Hopp and Spearman's seminal work on Factory Physics. Both Goldratt and Hopp and Spearman are physicists turned production experts who have derived their theories from first principles.

Sometimes the Goldratt ideas have been seen as being in conflict to Lean operations. In fact, there is remarkable synergy. Possibly the only real conflict is in the use of OPT, black-box type, software rather than JIT style visual control. (OPT was the computer based finite scheduling package originally developed by Goldratt. But even then Toyota apparently uses finite scheduling software for new products.) In particular the Theory of Constraints (TOC) principles, which have developed from OPT, have been used by many successful lean organisations, even though they do not use the software.

Likewise, Hopp and Spearman's Laws of Factory Physics are fundamental statements that should be understood by every Lean practitioner. Their CONWIP system has gained a large following. A limitation of Factory Physics is that the classic book is a little too mathematical for some practitioners; this should not be a turn off – just ignore the maths and soak up the wisdom.

In an excellent paper, Moore and Schienkopf explain the synergy between TOC and Lean. TOC is able to identify the constraints that Lean is then able to target for waste reduction. Both are logical and pragmatic. Both share the goal of flow and throughput. TOC is better at identifying that handful of potential improvements that will make a real difference. Lean has a battery of useful tools and an attractive philosophy. Lean's mapping techniques enable one to understand the system and its dependencies more clearly. TOC helps to identify and quantify the opportunities without taking the "leap of faith" sometimes associated with some lean implementations. Both encourage pull rather than push. But in some circumstances, for example where demand is erratic, the "drum buffer rope" may be more effective than kanban.

Throughput, Inventory, Operating Expense

Goldratt advocates the use of Throughput ("the rate at which the system generates money through sales"), Inventory ("the money invested in purchasing things that it intends to sell"), and Operating Expense ("the money that the system spends to turn inventory into throughput") as the most appropriate measures for the flow of material. We should note some important differences with more conventional usage of these words. Throughput is the volume of sales in money terms, not units. Products only become 'throughput' when sold. Some constraint or bottleneck, either internal or external governs this. Inventory is the basic cost of materials used and excludes value added for work in progress. Again, building inventory is of no use unless it is sold, so its value should not be recorded until it is sold. And Operating Expense makes no distinction between direct and indirect costs, which is seen as a meaningless distinction. The aim, of course, is to move throughput up, and inventory and operating expense down. Any investment should be judged on these criteria alone. This cuts decision making to the bone.

All three have an impact on the essential financials of business (cash flow, profit, and return on investment), but in varying degrees.

Goldratt says throughput is the first priority, then inventory, then operating expense. Why so? Because throughput has an immediate positive impact on the three financials, whereas one can afford to *increase* inventory and operating expense provided throughput improves. Decreasing inventory has a one-off effect on cash, and can reduce leadtime but unless one is careful reducing inventory may reduce throughput. Likewise operating expense, but with the possibility of removing inherent skills of the business. Note that many businesses, when faced with a crisis, adopt just the opposite priorities – first cut people, then inventories, then perhaps try to improve throughput.

Dependent Events and Statistical Fluctuations

Goldratt believes that pure, uninterrupted flow in manufacturing is rare if not impossible. This is because of what he terms "statistical fluctuation" - the minor changes in process speed, operator performance, quality of parts, and so on. Average flow rates are not good enough to calculate throughput. Goldratt has a dice game to illustrate this. Each round, five operators roll a dice that represents their possible production capacity in that time period. The average of each dice roll is 3.5, so one might expect that the average production over say 20 rounds would average 3.5 units per round. In fact, this does not happen because intermediate workers are from time to time starved of parts due to the rolls of previous operators. Try it. These are dependent events. Even with very large buffer inventories between operators, part shortages sometimes develop. JIT, according to Goldratt, aims at attacking statistical fluctuation so as to enable flow - so it does. But Goldratt believes that this is both very difficult and a waste of resources - which should be better directed at bottlenecks. Hence the TOC rules in the next section.

This may sound like conflict. In fact, one should take the best of both. Yes, try to reduce statistical fluctuation,

but also be aware of dependent events and bottlenecks. Also, Lean tends to ignore variation (just look at *Learning to See*) that may prove a disaster. Remember, that TOC is particularly applicable in batch environments that are moving towards flow manufacturing. The more you reduce changeover times, the more you smooth demand, the more you reduce variation, the more you tackle waste, the better. Irrespective of TOC, Lean or whatever.

Constraints, Bottlenecks and Non-Bottlenecks: The Synchronous Rules

In this and the next section, the rules and 'laws' of Goldratt and of Hopp and Spearman are given. Together they make a powerful set.

A constraint is something that prevents an enterprise from making more money, or perhaps in the case of a non-profit enterprise, something that prevents it from growing or from serving its customers better. There are four types of constraint: physical (a "bottleneck" in a plant is an example, although strictly a bottleneck is something that actually limits making more money), logistical (say, response time), managerial (policy, rules), and behavioural (the activities of particular employees).

In plant scheduling, however, it is constraints that determine the throughput of the plant. For many this is a whole new, radical idea. Note that what is being said is that there is generally only one constraint, like the weakest link in a chain. A "balanced" plant should not be the concern of management, but rather the continuing identification, exposure, and elimination of a series of constraints. Eventually outside constraints may be the determining factor. Examples are a market constraint or a behavioural constraint. Whilst working on the alleviation of the constraint, the schedule should be organised around this constraint. The principles (often referred to as the TOC or Synchronous principles) are as follows. (Note that here the word 'bottleneck' is used, but it is often a constraint rather than a bottleneck)

1. *Balance flow, not capacity*. For too long, according to Goldratt, the emphasis has been on trying to equate the capacity of the workcentres through which a product passes during manufacture. This is futile, because there will inevitably be faster and slower processes. So, instead, effort should be made to achieve a continuous flow of materials. This means, for example, eliminating unnecessary queues of work in front of non-bottleneck workcentres, and by splitting batches so that products can be moved ahead to the next workstation without waiting for the whole batch to be complete.

2. *The utilisation of a non-bottleneck is determined not by its own capacity but by some other constraint in the system*. A non-bottleneck should not be used all the time or overproduction will result, and therefore the capacity and utilisation of non-bottlenecks is mostly irrelevant. (Traditional accountants have choked on this one!) It is the bottlenecks that should govern flow.

3. *Utilisation and Activation are not synonymous*. This emphasises the point that a non-bottleneck machine should not be "activated" all the time because overproduction will result. Activation is only effective if the machine is producing at a balanced rate; and this is called utilisation. Notice that this differs from the conventional definition of utilisation, which ignores capacity of the bottleneck.

4. *An hour lost at a bottleneck is an hour lost for the whole system*. Since a bottleneck governs the amount of throughput in a factory, if the bottleneck stops it is equivalent to stopping the entire factory. The implications of this for maintenance, scheduling, safety stocks, and selection of equipment are profound! If you think about this, it also has deeply significant implications for cost accounting.

5. *An hour saved at a non-bottleneck is merely a mirage*. In effect it is worthless. This also has implications for the areas mentioned in point 4.

6. *Bottlenecks govern both throughput and inventory in the system*. A plant's output is the same as the bottleneck's output, and inventory should only be let into a factory at a rate that the bottleneck is capable of handling.

7. *The transfer batch may not, and many times should not, equal the process batch*. A transfer batch is the amount of work in process inventory that is moved along between workstations. Goldratt is saying that this quantity should not necessarily equal the production batch quantity that is made all together. Instead batch splitting should be adopted to maintain flow and minimise inventory cost. This applies particularly to products that have been already processed on bottleneck machines - they are then too valuable to have to wait for the whole batch to be complete. Note that MRP makes an assumption at odds with this principle, in assuming that batches will always be kept together.

8. *The process batch should be variable, not fixed*. The optimal schedule cannot, or should not, be constrained by the artificial requirement that a product must be made in one large batch. It will often be preferable to split batches into sub-batches. On bottleneck machines, batches should be made as large as possible between setup (changeover) operations (thereby minimising setup time) but on non-bottlenecks, batches should be made as small as possible by setting up machines as often as possible so as to use all the time available. What is being suggested is the fairly radical view that batches not being processed on bottlenecks should be split, and the machine re-set up for other product batches, to such an extent that the non-bottlenecks become near-bottlenecks.

9. *Lead times are the result of a schedule, and cannot be predetermined*. Here Goldratt disagrees with the use of standard pre-specified lead times such as one usually finds in MRP.

10. *Schedules should be assembled by looking at all constraints simultaneously*. In a typical factory, some products will be constrained by production capacity, others by marketing, and yet others perhaps by management inaction. It is important to know which constraints are affecting performance in any part of an enterprise. If, for example, you have a production constraint, it would be foolish to expend more effort on marketing.

The thought that a constraint governs throughput of a plant has massive implications for investment, costing, and continuous improvement. Essentially, an investment that only affects a non-constraint is waste. Likewise, continuous improvement efforts. Recall that decisions should be based upon the impact on throughput, inventory, and operating expense.

Costing has also had a shake-up. "Throughput accounting" uses the equation Revenue - direct materials - operating expenses = Profit. Here, there is no "variable overhead", direct labour is not subtracted when calculating throughput and is treated as a fixed (or temporarily fixed) cost, and inventories are not revalued on their path through the plant. Therefore, throughput accounting is simpler and more meaningful.

The Laws of Factory Physics

Hopp and Spearman have developed and mathematically proven a series of fundamental relationships in manufacturing. They term these the 'Laws of Factory Physics'. The Laws are of prime importance to a deeper understanding of scheduling. The dice games (see earlier section) are a fun way to experience some of these basic laws. Here, some of Hopp and Spearman's Laws are summarised in relation to the dice games. Of course, the dice game has exaggerated variability, but nevertheless illustrates the principles.

- *In steady state, all plants will release work at an average rate that is strictly less than average capacity. The dice game has an average capacity of 3.5.* Over 20 rounds, the game inevitably produces less than 70 units. Goldratt calls this statistical fluctuations and dependent events – each workstation is dependent on earlier workstations.
- *Little's 'Law'. Work in Process = Throughput x Lead Time.* (Derived by John Little, and the basis of Factory Physics.) This relationship applies to a machine, a line or a factory. So if throughput is 100 units per week and lead time is 2 weeks, then WIP is 200. Although this 'obvious' relationship is strictly only a good approximation, it is useful because it gives the 'gist' for a host of situations. Thus (a) reducing lead time implies reducing WIP or increasing

throughput, or some combination, (b) it gives a way of estimating leadtime from WIP and throughput that are generally easier to determine, (c) it gives a way of estimating utilization (an important part of OEE, but difficult to determine). If you know the throughput of a machine in jobs per hour and the cycle time in hours, you get the theoretical WIP at the machine in fractions of a piece. This is the utilization. (e.g. 10 jobs per hour, cycle time 2 minutes or 0.033 hour, utilization is 33%).

- *In an unconstrained system, inventory builds relentlessly.* (Not a Law of Factory Physics as such.) The longer you play the game, the greater the amount of WIP (and the longer the lead time).
- *Accumulation of inventory is not necessarily an indication of a bottleneck (or constraint).* (Not a Law of Factory Physics.) In the dice game, all stations are equally balanced, but accumulations build and decline, sometimes quite steeply, at particular workstations.
- *Increasing variability always degrades the performance of a production system.* This can be illustrated by re-playing the game but requiring re-rolls for dice throws of 1 and 6, then another game requiring re-rolls for throws of 1, 2, 5, and 6. Average capacity is retained at 3.5 but throughput steadily increases.
- *In a line where releases are independent of completions, variability early in a routing increases cycle time more than equivalent variability later in the routing.* A dice game can restrict variation to between 4 and 5 in later workstations. In the next game, reverse the variation restrictions. The former has greater output. The implication is to make improvements and standardisation starting downstream.
- *In a stable system, over the long run, the rate out of a system will equal the rate in, less any yield loss plus any parts production within the system.* If the dice game is played long enough, output will stabilize at an average of 3.5 pieces – but it takes a very long time, and huge quantities of inventory.

- *If a workstation increases utilization without making any other changes, average WIP and lead time will increase in a highly non-linear fashion.* Another demonstration is to increase utilization by increasing the WIP levels – say start with 6 pieces, not 4 (a 50% increase). Output in no way increases by 50%. This is predicted by queuing theory, but also by everyone's experience of highway driving – adding a few cars makes not difference at low levels of utilization, but eventually adding a few cars leads to jams. (This phenomenon is the fatal flaw in MRP that assumes constant lead time at any level of utilization below 100%. Queuing theory predicts sharply increasing waits above a utilization of around 70% or 80% depending on variation.) See figure.

more of these three ways. Clearly a dice game where everyone rolls a constant number needs no buffers.

For Lean (and Six Sigma), the implications of these Laws are profound. Variation is the enemy. Planning and control systems must recognise the Laws. Execution systems must be adaptive.

Further reading
Wallace Hopp and Mark Spearman, *Factory Physics*, (Second edition), McGrawHill, 2000

Drum, Buffer, Rope

According to the Goldratt philosophy, the Drum, Buffer, and Rope principle should govern all plants. The drum is the beat of the constraint that determines the throughput. A time buffer protects the drum. (This is a buffer representing so many hours of the next items to be processed, rather than a number of items, and determined by the probability of failure upstream of the drum). And the imaginary rope links the drum with the gateway or entrance work-centres, like a long-distance kanban. The rate of entry of work into the system is thereby synchronised with the drum-processing rate; if the drum should stop, no more work is let into the system.

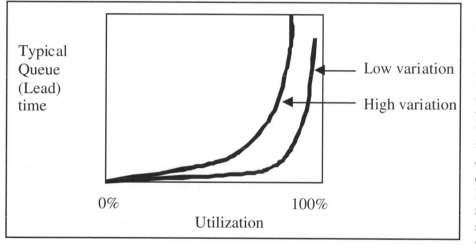

This suggests that the schedule should be built around the drum. Forward schedule on the drum, and backward schedule on non-constraints. Then combine with the synchronous rules. This is not necessarily a simple thing to do. See the section on the Lean building blocks.

- *Cycle times over a segment of a routing are roughly proportional to the transfer batch sizes used over that segment, providing there is no waiting for a conveyance device.* This Law is a variation on Goldratt's view that transfer batches should not be the same as and generally should be less than process batches.
- *Variability in a production system will be buffered by some combination of inventory, capacity or time.* In other words if you do not attack variation, it will attack you in one or

Monitor inventory at the drum. Keep a profile of inventory at the time buffer and check on how long it will be before each item is turned into cash (not finished goods!). The process sequence at the drum should be heavily influenced by how fast items will be turned into cash. Likewise, items arriving at the time buffer should not arrive too early. In fact, the time buffer should be where the manufacturing manager should go every day, and ask just these questions. To establish the true constraint, it is a good idea to sample the inventory in hours of work at each workcentre every day. Consistently more inventory at one workstation is strong evidence of the constraint, as is a fairly consistent lower level of inventories downstream of the constraint.

Goldratt used a hiking analogy in his book *The Goal* to illustrate Drum Buffer Rope, Dependent Events and Statistical Fluctuations. Initially fat Herbie, carrying a heavy pack, brings up the rear and is left behind on the trail. The others beat him to the campsite. But what is important is not when the first hiker gets to camp, but when the last hiker, who also carries vital equipment, arrives. So the hikers decide to put Herbie towards the front, since those following can easily catch up any time that Herbie loses. They also offload his pack as much as possible. Herbie, of course, is the bottleneck. Then the hikers go one step further. A rope is attached from Herbie to the person in the lead on the trail to prevent him getting too far ahead. But the rope also has some slack to allow for fluctuations. By the way, because of fluctuations and dependent events, this system works best if the slowest walker is significantly slower than the others.

The Theory of Constraints Improvement Cycle

Theory of Constraints (TOC) and the related Thinking Process (TP) was and is being developed by Eli Goldratt as an extension to his classic work *The Goal*. Goldratt claims wide applicability for TOC, not limited to manufacturing management. At the heart of TOC is the realisation that if a company had no constraints it would make an infinite profit. Most companies have a very small number of true constraints. From this follows Goldratt's five step TOC process of ongoing improvement.

The TOC Improvement Cycle has similarities to PDCA, but is more focused. It is an exceptionally powerful cycle for Lean, but often ignored by Lean practitioners.

1. Identify the constraint or constraints.

2. Decide how to "exploit" the constraint. A constraint is precious, so don't waste it. Make sure you keep it going, protect it with a time buffer, seek alternative routings, don't process defectives on it, make it quality capable, ensure it has good maintenance attention, ensure that only parts for which there is a confirmed market in the near future are made on it. Here the batch size should be maximised consistent with demand requirements. Have supermarkets that facilitate flow into and from the constraint.

3. "Subordinate" all other resources to the constraint. This means giving priority to the constraint over all other resources and policies. For example policies with regard to overtime and meetings may have to change. Measures may have to change. Make everyone aware of the constraint's importance. For instance move inventory as fast as possible after processing on the constraint, reduce changeover time on non-constraints so as to reduce batch size and improve flow to the constraint, make sure that the constraint is not delayed by a non-constraint (a non constraint can become a constraint if it is mismanaged). The right batch size at a non-constraint is derived from doing the maximum number of changeovers that time will allow – in other words minimize the batch size and maximise flow.

4. "Elevate" the constraint. Break it, but only after doing steps 2 and 3. Buy an additional machine or work overtime on the constraint. If it were a true bottleneck, this would be worthwhile. Beware, however. It is seldom necessary to break a constraint because this is only necessary where the constraint is a bottleneck. Knowing the constraint is often a valuable piece of information around which planning and control can take place. If you break the constraint, it will move – possibly to a hard-to-determine location.

5. Finally, if the constraint has been broken, go to step 1. Otherwise continue. Be careful that you do not make inertia the new constraint, by doing nothing.

Hutchins makes the useful point that there are five stages for each of these five steps. They are (1) gaining consensus on the problem (2) gain consensus on the direction of the solution (3) gain consensus on the benefits of the solution (4) overcome reservations, and (5) make it happen.

Further reading:

H. William Dettner, *Goldratt's Theory of Constraints: A Systems Approach to Continuous Improvement*, ASQC Quality Press, Milwaukee WI, 1997

Lisa Scheinkopf, *Thinking for a Change: Putting the TOC Thinking Processes to Use*, St. Lucie, APICS, Boca Raton, 1999

Eli Goldratt, *The Theory of Constraints*, North River Press, New York, 1990.

Robert E Stein, *The Theory of Constraints: Applications in Quality and Manufacturing*, (Second edition, Revised and expanded), Marcel Dekker, New York, 1997

Wallace Hopp and Mark Spearman, *Factory Physics* (second edition) McGraw Hill, Boston, 2000

Eric Noreen, Debra Smith and James Mackey, *The Theory of Constraints and its Implications for Management Accounting*, North River Press, Great Barrington, MA, 1995

Ted Hutchin, *Constraint Management in Manufacturing*, Taylor and Francis, 2002

Richard Moore and Lisa Schienkopf, *Theory of Constraints and Lean Manufacturing Friends or Foes?* Chesapeake Consulting Inc., 1998 (Supplied by Goldratt Institute).

Web site: www.goldratt.com

Quality

The goal of Perfection, the last of the Five Lean Principles, covers quality, delivery, flexibility, and safety. The Toyota Temple of Lean has two pillars, JIT and Jidoka (Jidoka being closely associated with quality, especially pokayoke). The two pillars are mutually supportive. For instance, improving quality improves Just in Time performance through less disruption and smoother flow. And improving JIT improves quality. Reduced batch sizes allow faster detection and less rework. Pull systems could be regarded as a quality tool. Layout influences quality through improved communication. Postponement reduces variation. Jidoka is a major way of exposing waste and improving quality through surfacing problems.

A Framework for Lean Quality

Perfection in Quality should be approached in each of three ways, according to Hinckley.

- The second approach is through a reduction of **variation**. Quality is one of a family of five inter-related concepts which together make up a foundation stone for Lean stability. The others are standard work, TPM, 5S, and visibility.
- The third approach is though the prevention and reduction of **mistakes**. The prevention, detection and elimination of errors and mistakes forms part of Jidoka, one of the pillars of the Lean temple.

For each of these three approaches, complexity, variation and mistakes, there are five possible sources of problems – man, machine, material, methods, and information, as was pointed out by Shingo. (The fifth 'M' – Mother Nature – may also be a source of problems, but this aspect can be included in the earlier categories.) Hinckley recommends using a 3x5 table (for complexity, variation, mistakes and men, machine, material, method, information) as an overview. In this section, tools relevant to each approach will be discussed. Hinckley makes the point that as variation is tackled via SPC and six sigma, and complexity via design simplification, the relative fraction of defects due to mistakes increases. For that reason Pokayoke is increasingly important.

Hinckley states that the most effective order to tackle quality problems is first to address the product, then the process, and finally the related tools and equipment. Within each category, first simplify, then mistake proof, then convert adjustments to settings (i.e. one stop rather than fiddling back and forth), and finally to control variation.

	Product	Process
Complexity	GT, DFM, DFSS, QCC tools, Kano model	DFM, Layout, SOPS, 5S, SMED, Mapping
Variation	Six Sigma, Shainin tools	Six Sigma, visibility, SPC, TPM, 7 quality tools, 5S, SOPS, Shainin tools, Successive inspection
Mistakes	Pokayoke, DFM	Pokayoke, 5S, SOPS, visibility

- The first approach is through a reduction in **complexity** in product design and in process design.

COMPLEXITY

'Complexity' refers to both product and process. Product complexity refers to both the number of components and the difficulty of assembly. Process complexity refers to both the number of operations and the difficulty of each operation. Hinckley, following on from Boothroyd and Dewhurst, has shown that product defect rates are strongly related to assembly complexity.

Product Complexity

Quality Control of Complexity (QCC)

Hinckley has developed a method called Quality Control of Complexity. The frequency of mistakes increases with increasing assembly complexity. The QCC method begins by constructing a tree diagram for assembling a product. Then the time required to complete the assembly is estimated from a set of tables covering alignment, orientation, size, thickness, insertion directions, insertion conditions, fasteners, fastening process, and handling. Alternative designs can then be evaluated based on the ratio of times to the power 1.3 (a value which has been found to be widely applicable). The results can be dramatic both for quality and for cost – perhaps a 50% reduction over the full lifetime. The power and simplicity of this technique should not be ignored.

Design for Six Sigma (DFSS)

DFSS uses a defined set of steps called IDDOV (Identify, Define, Develop, Optimise, Verify) similar to the DMAIC steps in Six Sigma. It also uses a similar project organisation with Champions, Master Black Belts, Black Belts, and Green Belts. DFSS is discussed in more detail in the New Product Introduction chapter.

The Identify and Define stages aim to clarify the customer and his or her needs. Typical tools are the Kano model and Quality Function Deployment.

The Develop stage involves brainstorming and identification of alternatives, and their evaluation. Techniques include TRIZ, Pugh analysis (Concept Screening), and FMEA (Failure modes and effect analysis).

The Optimise stage uses the Taguchi methodology for design optimisation and then for tolerance optimisation. In particular, parameter design uses a design of experiments approach to reduce overall variation by identifying and concentrating on the vital few critical parameters. The difference from standard six sigma is that here the concentration is on prevention and maximisation of benefit, rather than on detection and reduction of effects. Likewise tolerance optimisation concentrates on the vital few tolerances.

Finally, the verify stage involves looking at the capability of the manufacturing process, and examining how the product will perform in the field by conducting experiments on prototypes and pilot tests. Capability studies, SPC and pokayoke are all relevant.

Notice that, as with Six Sigma, a lot of attention is given at the front end. It is appropriate to take care at early stages to define the customer, the purpose, the environment, and the usage.

Group Technology (G.T.)

Group Technology is a set of procedures aimed at simplifying products without compromising customer choice. It identifies similarities in function to reduce product and process proliferation. Thus a part designer would not start from a blank CAD screen, but would first search a database for products with similar functions. Similarly, for instance in selecting fastenings, she would make the selection from a pre-defined set rather than from an unlimited choice. The impact on part proliferation, on inventory, on manufacturing routings, and of course on quality can be dramatic.

Various GT coding and classification systems exist to assist both product designers and process designers. A part is described by stringing together a set of digits that cover for example material, usage, shape, size, machining, and forming. For cell design, particularly for complex machining cells, GT may be an early port of call to examine alternative methods and routings. Generalised classification systems can be complex, but frequently companies develop their own much more simple version which serves adequately.

Design for Assembly

Design for assembly, design for manufacture, and more generally DFx, are a key set of techniques for Lean processing simplicity. They impact time, cost, inventory, and quality. Design for manufacture is discussed in the Design and New Product Introduction section of this book.

Process Complexity

Process complexity may be independent from product complexity. A range of tools can reduce process complexity. The tools include.
- Part presentation
- Dividing work into tasks that can be completed in one or two minutes
- Using standard operating procedures
- 5S
- Simplified material flows and layout
- TPM
- SMED
- Visual controls

VARIATION

A principal approach for the reduction of variation is Six Sigma. But foundation tools for the limitation of variation include TPM, 5S, Standard work and changeover reduction. Tools for the control of variation include SPC and Pre Control.

Before starting out on a sophisticated six sigma programme, a Lean company should ensure that they have made reasonable progress with 5S, visibility and standard work and, in many environments, with TPM. This is akin to sending in the public health engineers before the medical specialists. The medics will have point impact, but it is unlikely to be sustained. The public health engineer working to achieve clean water and pollution from sewage is likely to have far greater and lasting impact. Then the medics take over to do their valuable work. This is not to say that a 5S program needs to be fully implemented – it a question of the 'low hanging fruit'.

Statistical Process Control (SPC) is a good technique for variation monitoring and control, provided that its limitations are recognised. SPC is concerned with monitoring the process, not the product. If the process is good, and capable, then the products that are produced by the process will be good. However, SPC is probably not reliable for monitoring or controlling at levels of five or six sigma – below perhaps 1000 parts per million (0.1%).

MISTAKES

The toolbox for the control of mistakes comprises 5S, Standard operating procedures, pokayoke, self inspection and successive inspection.

Self Inspection and Successive Inspection. Self inspection is where an operator performs an inspection immediately after the manufacturing step is made. Successive inspection is where the next operator checks the previous step or steps. Such inspections are sometimes ridiculed because they are error prone, waste time (because every part is checked rather than a sample), and are usually unsophisticated. But do not be misled – these types of inspection are worthy of consideration because they provide immediate or short-term feedback and (in the case of successive checks) are capable of a high degree of reliability. For instance, if an inspection has 90% reliability, 100 out of 1000 defects would remain after the first inspection, 10 would remain after the second, and 1 (or 0.1%) after the third. This is a higher reliability and often faster than SPC. They do involve non value adding time, however.

Of course self inspection and successive inspection require good motivation and participation. This can be a failing. Relevant points are discussed in the People and Sustainability chapter.

Note: Shingo distinguished these types of inspection from 'judgement' inspection and acceptance sampling that involves both longer delay and increased risk of error.

Six Sigma

In recent years Lean and Six Sigma have begun to compete, but in more enlightened companies to be seen as partners. Phrases such as 'Lean Sigma', 'Lean Six Sigma' have emerged. This is both good news and bad news. Good news because Lean has often tended to ignore variation, and is less strong at detailed problem

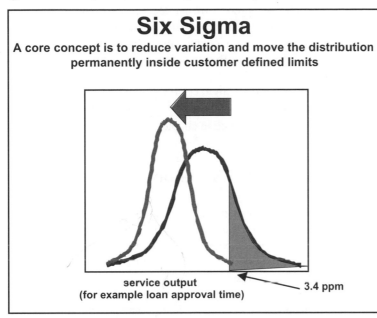

Six Sigma

A core concept is to reduce variation and move the distribution permanently inside customer defined limits

service output
(for example loan approval time)

3.4 ppm

solving (as opposed to problem surfacing). Together they make for a powerful combination. But also bad if each is defined too narrowly – as the first section of this chapter sets out there are complexity, variation, and mistake issues in a comprehensive approach to quality. Narrowly defined Six Sigma is not much about complexity or mistakes, and may downplay the role of foundation Lean techniques.

The term "six sigma" derives from the spread of the normal distribution (plus and minus 3 standard deviations or 3 sigma indicating the control limits). If specification limits can be set and the process spread limited such that the distance from the process centre line to the nearest specification limit is six standard deviations, then a highly capable process will have been achieved. Even if the process were to shift by 1.5 sigma, the risk of producing defects would still be

limited to 3.4 parts per million. (There would still be 1.5 standard deviations from the control limit to the nearest specification limit – So "six sigma performance" means close to perfection.

Whether or not a process can achieve 3.4 defects per million, is in a sense not the point. The point is the rigorous process that moves one towards the goal. It is probably true that today most manufacturing firms are achieving 3 or 4 sigma performance (6210 ppm is 4 sigma), and most service firms achieve around 2 sigma (309,000 ppm). So Six Sigma is better thought of as a structured problem solving methodology rather than to do with product quality.

Six Sigma is concerned not only with reducing the number of defects but also with reducing the variation or spread. Part (or product) variation and Process variation are both of concern. In the figure opposite loan approval time is the attribute most important to the customer. Six Sigma would aim not only to reduce the number of applications that are not dealt with in the specified time, but also to reduce the spread of approval times. Thereafter the target time could be reduced to form a new goal.

A starting point for Six Sigma is the belief in process. An organisation is characterised by processes, frequently cross-functional. The SIPOC model makes clear that a process has suppliers, inputs, the process itself, outputs, and customers. It is useful to go through these systematically. Six Sigma has a specific methodology: Define, Measure, Analyse, Improve, Control (DMAIC) - in essence similar to the Deming or Shewart Plan Do Check Act cycle. Six Sigma progresses on a 'project by project basis', and is process oriented. These projects are generally fairly narrow and have definite begin and end points. It takes customer requirements into account at an early stage. A strong feature of Six Sigma is its bias towards data – measuring the variation of the process, and trying to both narrow the variation and to shift it within customer

requirements – with 3.4 parts per million being the (frequently unattained) Six Sigma goal. Another feature is its strong financial bias – the benefits of every project are expected to show up in the financials, and are certainly costed. (Many a Six Sigma Black Belt will say that Six Sigma is not about defect reduction, but about making or saving money.)

Six Sigma is strongly based on statistics. Insistence on hard data is indeed a great strength. But Shingo warns, "When I first heard about inductive statistics in 1951, I firmly believed it to be the best technique around, and it took me 26 years to break completely free of its spell". Shingo's journey away from a statistics-based approach to quality should be required reading for every black belt and helps explain Toyota's lack of enthusiasm for Six Sigma (see below).

GE's version of Six Sigma revolves around six key principles. These are:

Critical to Quality. The starting point is the customer, and those attributes most important to the customer must be determined.
Defect. A defect is anything that fails to deliver exactly what the customer requires.
Process Capability. Processes must be made capable of delivering customer requirements.
Variation. As experienced by the customer. What the customer sees and feels.
Stable Operations. The aim is to ensure consistent, predictable processes to improve the customer's experience.
Design for Six Sigma. Design must meet customer needs and process capability.

Six Sigma is driven by people qualified in the methodology. A useful innovation has been to recognise Six Sigma expertise by judo-type belts. A black belt typically requires four weeks of training held over four months and requires practical results. The four weeks correspond to Measure, Analyse, Improve, Control in the DMAIC cycle. Black belts often work full time on Six Sigma projects and typically aim at savings exceeding $200k per year. Master black belts are more experienced black belts who act as mentors. There are also Six Sigma "Champions" who define the WHAT (a

very important role, requiring cross functional and cross process knowledge), whereas Black Belts are concerned with the HOW. Some companies retain their Black Belts for between two and three years, and thereafter move them into line management positions or Champion positions. Green belts go through less rigorous training. Some companies, for instance Allied Signal / Honeywell have set goals of 90% of the workforce becoming green belts within 5 years. In a Six Sigma project there is typically a process owner, team leaders, a black belt, perhaps several green belts, and team members. Implementation and human issues are considered to be as important as the six sigma tools themselves.

Design for Six Sigma (DFSS) addresses design of product issues. This aspect is discussed in the New Product Introduction chapter.

Lean and Six Sigma

It may be argued that Lean and Six Sigma both have strong Deming connections. Deming placed emphasis on two main themes during his life – removal of waste and reduction of variation (Deming, 1982). Waste reduction is central to Lean, and variation reduction is central to Six Sigma. Several large multinational manufacturing companies, for example Ford and Honeywell, have had separate Lean and Six Sigma programmes. Inevitably, these two powerful and widely used approaches have clashed and merged with titles to indicate this fact. The authors have identified Lean Sigma, Fit Sigma, Six Sigma plus, Power Lean, Lean Six Sigma, and Quick Sigma. Some of these are trademarked. There are likely to be others.

Integrating Lean and Six Sigma

The integration of Lean and Six Sigma has become fashionable. To cite but a few examples:
The TBM institute have made bold claims for their programmes by declaring "*LeanSigma utilizes Six Sigma and Lean principles to reduce both defects and lead time with the speed of kaizen.*" (Dean & Smith, 2000) But they also recognised key issues with Lean

implementation such as: The difference in the speed of "kaizens" and Six Sigma projects, and the new roles of Black belts and Greenbelts. Effectively they have added to the Six Sigma practitioners' roles aspects of Lean principles, Values stream mapping and Kaizen methodology. Their internal case studies suggest that Lean Sigma projects produce results 2-3 times faster than normal Six Sigma projects.

Mike Wader (2000), of the Air Academy Associates, suggests that many world class companies are now following Maytag's lead and implementing top down between Lean and Six Sigma that occurs when the two programmes are run independently.

Drickhamer (2002) discusses how the adoption of Lean techniques prior to the application of Six Sigma projects can provide real benefits, removing the elitist strain from Six Sigma through teamwork whilst tackling the low hanging fruit with Lean. This has a double benefit of removing much of the process noise that is the bug bear of Six Sigma projects. In two key insights he notes firstly from the Six Sigma perspective on blitz events, *"The Solution to many complex and long-standing*

Area	Lean	Six Sigma
Objectives	Reduce Waste	Reduce Variation
	Improve Value	Shift distribution inside customer requirements
Framework	5 Principles (not always followed)	DMAIC (always followed)
Focus	Value Stream	Project / Process
Improvement	Many small improvements, a few 'low kaizens'.	A small number of larger projects - $0.25m cut-off? One at a time
	Everywhere, simultaneous	
Typical Goals	Cost, Quality, Delivery, Lead time	Improved Sigma Level (Attempt Six Sigma 3.4 DPMO)
	Financials often not quantified. Vague?	Money saving
People Involved in improvement	Team led by (perhaps) Lean expert. Often wide involvement on different levels.	Black Belts supported by Green Belts
Time Horizon	Long term. Continuous, but also short term Kaizen	Short term. Project by project.
Tools	Often simple but complex to integrate	Sometimes complex statistical
Typical early steps	Map the value stream	Collect data on process variation
Impact	Can be large, system-wide	Individual projects may have large savings
Problem root Causes	Via 5 whys (weak)	Via e.g. DOE (strong)

Lean Sigma programmes where again Lean is used to remove the waste and non-value adding activities whilst Six Sigma is used to control the variation within the value adding portion of the process, combining their tools and data sets to produce a comprehensive improvement programme. One of the key reasons he notes for integration is to avoid the battle for funding *problems can't be resolved using intuitive methods in less than a week"* and secondly from the Lean perspective *"If you go and make everything a Six Sigma problem, you are going to constipate your system and waste a lot of resources"*.

With this background, a comparative table is shown.

Cases of Lean with Six Sigma

To learn specific lessons from using Lean and Six Sigma together, six cases are given. All are from companies that have well established Lean and Six Sigma programmes. In all cases the exact roles for Lean and Six Sigma are yet to be resolved.

Company A

Company A is a medium size automotive parts manufacturer. It has many years of experience of Lean of a fairly substantial nature. Kaizen teams have been established for several years and address problems thrown up either internally or externally. Teams know about value stream mapping, takt time, the 7 tools of quality, the 7 wastes, and OEE. Cells are long established. There are some kanban systems in place and changeover reduction exercises have been held. Standard operations are quite well documented. The company had held numerous Kaizen Blitz events. They have been supported by the equivalent of a Lean Promotion Office. For several years, the reject rate for solenoid valves in a cell has been high – around 150,000 ppm. The kaizen team in the area has had several attempts at the problem – including mapping the process, cause and effect diagrams, run diagrams, histograms, and some attempts at 5 why analysis. Some progress has been made over the years but the reject rate remained stubbornly high.

A Six Sigma Black belt program was initiated. The first black belt trainee took on the solenoid defect problem as his Six Sigma project. The MSA (Measurement System Analysis) had been carried out previously during the installation of the equipment but was still repeated for this project. An MSA study is a series of statistical tests that are designed to measure the proportion of measurement system error compared to the natural variation in the samples being measured. It is often also called a gauge R&R (Repeatability and Reproducibility) study. In this project the test equipment carried out 8 tests in its test cycle, which for customer confidence were carried out on 100% of the assembled product. Of these 8 tests 3 passed the MSA study comfortably, and 3 passed to a level where they could be considered usable for categorising production (though not for process improvement). Of the two that failed one of these was

for the second most important element identified by the Pareto analysis. This meant the test equipment could be incorrectly categorising these products as good/bad product. However, in the process of gathering MSA data it became apparent that the spring force measurement test was producing negative spring force measurements – a result which is physically impossible. As spring force was the top cause of rejects for this product, it was quickly established that all these failures were due to the observed negative values. This enabled the team to call in the machine supplier who on being shown the results traced and corrected a software bug. Once this bug had been corrected spring force was immediately eliminated as a failure mode, instantly reducing the observed reject rate by 46% to 81,000 ppm.

Company B

Company B is an electronic equipment manufacturer with several years of Lean experience but no Lean promotion office. Though supplier connections, senior management have 'bought into' Six Sigma and several black belts have been trained over the last three years and claim many thousands of pounds of saving. Following some successes a black belt was allocated a changeover reduction project. The project began with the black belt recording changeover times, which were of the order of 30 minutes, over a period of three weeks. This enabled him to draw a distribution of changeover times that turned out to be multi-modal. The root causes of the multi modes were then sought.

This approach is markedly different from the conventional Lean approach to changeover reduction which relies on the SMED methodology. Typically, a video is made of the changeover, internal, external and waste activities are identified, internal activities are shifted to external as far as possible, engineering changes made, and the changeover standardized. A team from the area does this and the whole exercise takes a few days. So, why use Six Sigma? Answer: A combination of ignorance of SMED, an unwillingness to share the plaudits, but mainly faith in the familiar.

The interesting point was that the Six Sigma way did reveal things that the SMED approach could easily have missed – including differences between shifts (and who the best operators are), differences in pre-settings, procedural, reporting and recording differences, and differences in the post changeover activities to bring production up to full speed. The downside of the Six Sigma way was that, arguably, the changeover itself took longer and sustainability is more of an issue. In summary, although this cannot be verified, the Six Sigma project resulted in a more consistent but longer changeover time than would have been achieved through SMED. The right way is surely to do SMED first, possibly followed by a Six Sigma project.

Company C

Company C is an aerospace manufacturer. The company has been 'dabbling' in Lean, mainly though the insistence of customers and the Lean Aerospace initiative, and in Six Sigma due to contacts with GE and others. The Six Sigma project involved improving the performance of an assembly operation. By 'performance' is meant variation in dimensional accuracy, strength and to a lesser extent in assembly time. As with company C, the black belt began by building a database of performance data. Apparently important input variables include quantity of sealant used, temperature, setting time, and material thickness. Aerospace is an industry where there are supposed to be strict standards of consistency in order to meet, for example, FAA requirements. Possibly because of this, the assumption was made that the operations were being carried out from a stable base. Part way through the study, at a meeting held with a kaizen engineer, the question of standard operations was raised. The black belt and kaizen engineer decided to investigate. They found significant differences in the methods being used. This was due to several factors: 5S discipline was weak, standard work was too broad, and there were inconsistencies between operators and between shifts. The Six Sigma project was halted whilst 5S and standard work was improved. When the project was re-started a shift in the data had occurred, and in addition was found to be much less variable. Thus a chance question redirected the work. Of course, in Lean, standard work, and associated 5S is supposed to be a foundation stone. The stone was missing.

Company D

Company D is an earthmoving equipment manufacturer. The parent company has had a Lean initiative for a decade. As part of the initiative, product simplification has been attempted through a part classification and coding (G.T.) procedure. The GT programme was initiated by production engineers and has been running with little impact for several years. Certainly GT requires cooperation between design, marketing, engineering, purchasing, manufacturing, and production to be a success. There was little impact beyond the engineering function. Lean has had its champions in the company, apparently, but never at top levels.

The company began a Six Sigma initiative two years ago, which was enthusiastically supported by top management. The Master Black Belt reported directly to Director level. After some successful Six Sigma projects, the GT project was chosen for the next Six Sigma project. A black belt was selected. Interestingly, the black belt did not have a background in production engineering and, to begin, knew nothing about part classification and coding. In a matter of weeks, GT became high profile. All relevant departments became involved. Although it is as yet early days, GT is at last having an impact. Product part counts have begun to decline. Inventory is down. Purchasing is reviewing contracts. Design procedures have been reviewed and the 'clean sheet of paper' approach has been finally scrapped. Marketing, in cooperation with engineering, has begun to work with customers on product modification. The 'bottom line' is that the project has begun to yield big savings. Six Sigma has been given the credit.

The point is, is it the Six Sigma methodology that has yielded the benefit or is it the fact that Six Sigma has had the support of top management? Probably both, but without doubt the support of top management has been a key factor.

Company E

Company E is a very large automotive components manufacturer, previously owned by one of the 'big three' automotive companies. The group has had a significant level of commitment to both Lean and Six Sigma for at least five years, and before that to 'world class' practices for well over a decade. At present Lean and Six Sigma are two distinct areas that have worked pretty much separately. The author had the opportunity to sit in on a high level meeting where the projects for the year were being decided. There were presentations on several improvement initiatives including Six Sigma, Lean, and IT.

Six Sigma has an established method for project selection called cross impact analysis. It involves allocating scores to projects based on their perceived customer impact. It is a judgmental process and real customers are not consulted. Data is collected, where possible, using the SIPOC process. Six Sigma also uses brainstorming at top levels, conducted by master black belts, which attempts to break down a problem into sub-projects – this is also called Y=f (X) or 'big Y' analysis. A constraint is that each project should aim at savings of at least $250,000

There is no agreed way for Lean to identify projects but the Lean manager had adopted an approach combining policy deployment with value stream mapping. Policy deployment begins with top management goals rather than with customers. The Lean manager had taken the stated goals (the 'whats' and 'whys') and deployed them down one level to get into the 'hows' and 'whos'. He supported his proposals with reference to current state value stream maps, including quantitative data. A weakness, however, was that the projected benefits were not quantified in terms of dollar savings. It was clear, by the projects that were selected, and by subsequent interviews, which approach had had the greatest impact. It was the Lean presentation. Of course, one might argue that the impact was as much to do with personality as with methodology. But in that company at least, the question has been answered.

Company F
This is the same company as company A. As mentioned, several kaizen events have been held. As the company has trained more black belts and green belts, these people have been included in blitz events. There has been a noticeable improvement in the rigor of data collection and analysis. The use of 'Minitab' software is standard in such events. Data analysis has sometimes resulted in a 'Gee Whiz' reaction as the facts and root causes have been teased out. The opinion has been widely expressed that the blitz events, and improvement in general, has improved markedly irrespective of whether there has been a formal black belt project in place.

<u>Conclusions from the Cases</u>

From the cases, the following points may be made:
1. Build on a firm foundation. Without standard work and 5S there is likely to be much 'noise' to detract from Six Sigma project performance.
2. Take waste out first, especially 'low hanging' waste. There seems no point in a time consuming analysis if quick wins can be made.
3. Six Sigma can add a powerful dimension in traditional Lean areas, especially for more complex issues. Although Lean methods are useful for basic projects, Six Sigma is capable of more in-depth analysis where there are complex interactions.
4. The rigor of Six Sigma training is likely to benefit many Lean improvement initiatives by simply giving team members added skill in data interpretation and analysis – even without the more sophisticated statistical tools and tests.
5. Lean has much to say to Six Sigma during Six Sigma projects. This includes involvement and focus via value stream analysis and deployment, but also several Lean concepts such as waste identification, SMED, pull, supplier development, postponement, cell design, and so forth.
6. Begin and end many Six Sigma projects with Lean. Move from a firm foundation created by standard work and 5S, progress to the Six Sigma project, and 'hold the gains' by standard work, visibility, and a 'kaizen culture'.
7. Value stream mapping and policy deployment are powerful ways to direct improvement initiatives, both for Lean and Six Sigma projects.
8. Organizational politics are (often?) more important than the approach used.

Toyota and Six Sigma

The classic Lean Company is Toyota. But, thus far, Toyota appears not to have employed Six Sigma in any way. Why? Frankly, the author does not know but has held informal discussions with a number of Toyota staff. There appear to be at least six reasons, possibly more. These are:

1. The preference for pokayoke. See the earlier Shingo quote. That spirit seems to persist at Toyota where there are reported to be between 5 and 10 pokayoke devices for each process step!

2. The idea that problems and defects need to 'surfaced' immediately, not studied at length. TPS is packed with concepts that are designed to highlight problems as soon as possible. The systems include line stop, andon board, music when a machine stops, Heijunka (which can highlight non attainment of schedule within minutes), and of course a wide awareness of 'muda'. The thought seems to be to 'enforce' short term and continuous problem solving. Moreover, when problems are identified, the '5 whys' are employed to try to get to the root cause.

3. A worry about the elitism of Six Sigma, especially the 'black belt' image. The TPS way is for everyone to be involved in improvement, and hence a great reluctance to identify specialist problem solvers – however good. This is also reflected in policy deployment.

4. A 'Systems Approach'. Although Six Sigma would claim to use a systems approach, Toyota certainly uses it through value stream mapping and policy deployment. Hence, it avoids the sub-optimisation that is a risk in Six Sigma projects.

5. A belief that many quality problems lie in design.

6. Toyota has a significant improvement organization in place, that undoubetedly extends the Six Sigma master black belt / black belt / green belt organization. Refer to the Improvement section of the book.

Acknowledgement:
The author would like to acknowledge the significant contribution of Brian Johns, MSc in Lean Operations and Six Sigma Master Black Belt, to this section.

Further reading:
Keki Bhote, *The Ultimate Six Sigma*, AmaCom, New York, 2002
Paul Pande, et al, *The Six Sigma Way*, McGraw Hill, New York, 2000
Michael George, Michael, *Lean Six Sigma*, McGraw Hill, New York, 2000
See Six Sigma Forum magazine, published by ASQ

B Dean B. & B Smith B, (2000), 'From the Business Office to the Shop floor: LeanSigma™', *Managing Times*, Q3, TBM Institute; 2000
Mike Wader, 'The Lean Sigma Approach', *Manufacturing Digest*, Fall 2000
Ron Basu, 'Six Sigma to Fit Sigma', *IIE Solutions*; July 2001
David Drickhamer, 'Where Lean Meets Six Sigma', *Industry Week*, 1 May 2002
International Quality & Productivity Center, *Proceedings Lean Six Sigma Conference*, London.
Kaufman Consulting Group White Paper, *Implementing Lean Manufacturing*, 2001
C Martin Hinckley, *Make No Mistake*, Productivity Press, Portland, 2001

Mistake-proofing (Pokayoke)

The late Shigeo Shingo did not invent mistake-proofing ("pokayoke" in Japanese, literally mistake proofing), but developed and classified the concept, particularly in manufacturing. Recently mistake-proofing in services has developed. Shingo's book *Zero Quality Control: Source Inspection and the Pokayoke System* is the classic work. More lately C Martin Hinckley has made a significant new contribution through his work *Make No Mistake!*

A mistake-proofing device is a simple, often inexpensive, device that literally prevents defects from being made. The characteristics of a mistake-proofing device are that it undertakes 100% automatic inspection (a true pokayoke would not rely on human memory or action), and either stops or gives warning when a defect is discovered. Note that a pokayoke is not a control device like a thermostat or toilet control valve that takes action every time, but rather a device that senses abnormalities and takes action only when an abnormality is identified.

Shingo distinguishes between "mistakes" (which are inevitable) and "defects" (which result when a mistake reaches a customer). The aim of pokayoke is to design devices that prevent mistakes becoming defects. Shingo also saw quality control as a hierarchy of effectiveness from "judgement inspection" (where inspectors inspect), to "informative inspection" where information is used to control the process as in SPC, and "source inspection" which aims at checking operating conditions "before the fact". Good pokayokes fall into this last category.

According to Shingo there are three types of mistake-proofing device: "contact", "fixed value", and "motion step". This means that there are six categories, as shown in the next figure with service examples.

Pokayoke Types		
	Control	**Warning**
Contact	Parking height bars Armrests on seats	Staff mirrors Shop entrance bell
Fixed Value	French fry scoop Pre-dosed medication	Trays with indentations
Motion Step	Airline lavatory doors	Spellcheckers Beepers on ATMs

after: Failsafe Services :
Richard Chase and Douglas Stewart, OMA Conference, 1993

The contact type makes contact with every product or has a physical shape that inhibits mistakes. An example is a fixed diameter hole through which all products must fall; an oversize product does not fall through and a defect is registered. The fixed value method is a design that makes it clear when a part is missing or not used. An example is an "egg tray" used for the supply of parts. Sometimes this type can be combined with the contact type, where parts not only have to be present in the egg tray but also are automatically correctly aligned. The motion step type automatically ensures that the correct numbers of steps have been taken. For example, an operator is required to step on a pressure-sensitive pad during every assembly cycle, or a medicine bottle has a press-down-and-turn feature for safety. Other examples are a checklist, or a correct sequence for switches that do not work unless the order is correct.

Shingo further developed failsafe classification by saying that there are five areas (in manufacturing) that have potential for mistake-proofing: the operator (Me), the Material, the Machine, the Method, and the Information (4 M plus I). An alternative is the process control model comprising input, process, output, feedback, and result. All are candidates for mistake-proofing. According to Grout, areas where pokayoke should be considered include areas where worker vigilance is required, where mispositioning is likely, where SPC is difficult, where external failure costs dramatically exceed internal failure costs, and in mixed model and JIT production.

Shingo says that pokayoke should be thought of as having both a short action cycle (where immediate shut down or warning is given), but also a long action cycle where the reasons for the defect occurring in the first place are investigated. John Grout makes the useful point that one drawback of pokayoke devices is that potentially valuable information about process variance may be lost, thereby inhibiting improvement.

Hinckley has developed an excellent approach to mistake proofing. He has developed a classification scheme comprising five categories of mistake (defective material, information, misadjustment, omission, and selection errors). The last four have several sub-categories. For each category, typical mistake proofing solutions have been developed. Thus, having identified the type of mistake, one can look through the set of possible solutions and adapt or select the most suitable one.

Hinckley quotes Hirano in listing the five most useful mistake-proofing devices. They are
- Guide pins, to assure that parts can only be assembled in the correct way
- Limit switches, that sense the presence or absence of a part

- Mistake-proofing jigs, detect defects immediately upstream of the process ensuring that only the correct parts reach the process.
- Counters, that verify that the correct number of parts or steps have been taken
- Checklists, that reminds operators to do certain actions

Further reading:

Shigeo Shingo, *Zero Quality Control: Source Inspection and the Pokayoke System*, Productivity Press, 1986
C Martin Hinckley, *Make No Mistake*, Productivity Press, Portland, 2001
An impressive web site with numerous examples and pictures is at:
http://www.cox.smu.edu/jgrout/poke-yoke.html

Bringing Lean and Six Sigma Together

Martin Hinckley's useful framework for comprehensive quality improvement has been extended, below, by two more columns and used as a framework for suggesting the most effective approach.

Combining Lean and Six Sigma

	Men/People	Machine	Method	Material/Product	Measures	Mother Nature
Variation	Lean (teams involvement, policy deployment Kaizen	Six Sigma (Cpk) Lean (SMED)	Lean (5S, SOPS) Six Sigma (SPC, DOE, DMAIC)	Lean supply Six Sigma (SPC, DOE)	Lean (policy deployment) Six Sigma (DPMO, Gage R&R)	Six Sigma DOE
Mistakes	Lean pokayoke	Lean pokayoke	Lean pokayoke	Lean pokayoke	Six Sigma Lean	Six Sigma (DOE?)
Complexity	Lean (cross training, waste removal)	Lean (TPM, 5S)	Lean (waste removal)	DFSS Lean (GT, design)	Lean (policy deployment)	Six Sigma (DOE?)

Improvement

The essence of Lean is improvement. Without improvement, any organization will fail. To be pervasive, improvement needs to reach all levels and involve all value streams or processes, internally and along the supply chain.

PDCA, DMAIC and Improvement Cycles

It is appropriate to begin the section on improvement with the major tool – the Plan, Do, Check, Act cycle.

Deming originally called the PDCA cycle "the Shewart Cycle" after his mentor and father of statistical quality control, but the cycle has come to be named after Deming himself. PDCA sounds simple and is easily glossed over, but if well done is a powerhouse for improvement. PDCA is considered a foundation of the Toyota Production System. In the West many organisations are apt to just "do" and neglect the P-C-A.

PDCA is used with several frequencies on several levels. In the Hoshin process it is used annually and monthly – perhaps even over a longer cycle to review the process itself. In Kaizen it is used to guide any length of project. It should form part of the measurement cycle. And, on implementation, the "unfreezing, changing, refreezing" cycle is a variation. The role of PDCA in sustainability is discussed in the People section.

Plan. Plan is not just about planning what to do, but about communication, "scoping", discussion, consensus gaining and deployment. Begin with the customer - seek to understand their needs. It is about setting the time plan. It is claimed that leading Japanese companies take much longer to plan, but then implement far faster and more smoothly. Deming taught that one should think about change and improvement like a scientific experi-

ment – predicting, setting up a hypothesis, observing, and explaining deviations. You need to be clear what the goals are, and how to get there. Attempt to identify constraints beforehand, so force field analysis is a good idea. Try to identify root causes - at least ask the 5 whys. You may have to do some training before proceeding.

Do. An easy stage if you have planned well. It is about carrying out the improvement, often in a test phase.

Check. The learning stage, but too frequently an opportunity lost. Is it working as you predicted? Did it work out as planned? If not, why not, and what can we learn for next time? The US Marines call this "after action review" or AAR. Time needs to be set aside to Check. Like at the end of a meeting, or after completion of a set number of cycles. Keki Bhote refers to B vs. C (Better vs. Current) analysis. This is to see if the improvement is sustained or is the result of the "Hawthorne effect' which ceases when observation ceases. Six Sigma black belts would check the statistical significance – assessing the alpha and beta risks (accepting what should have

PDCA

Plan	Determine customer needs Identify the concern or problem Set objectives Set out the working plan Collect data and study Seek root causes Train as necessary
Do	Implement the improvement

Check	Were the objectives met?
	Review root causes
	Confirm the results "B vs C" analysis
	    (consider alpha and beta risks)
	After Action Review
	    what was learned?
	    what can be done better next time?
	Is the problem completely solved?

Act	Identify further improvements Write and adopt new standards Communicate the requirements Recurrence prevention Celebrate and congratulate

been rejected, and rejecting what should have been accepted). Once again ask about root causes. Also check if there are any outstanding issues.

Act (or Standardise). As Juran says, "Hold the gains". A standard reflects the current best and safest known way, but is not fixed in stone forever. Without this step all previous steps are wasted. So, a vital, but frequently neglected, step. Think about improvement as moving from standard to improved standard. A deviation from standard procedures indicates that something is amiss. (See the section on standardisation.) Consider if the new way can be incorporated elsewhere. Communicate the requirements to everyone concerned - this includes people on the boundary of the problem. Give some thought to recurrence prevention - can both the people and the processes be made more capable? Finally prepare for the next round of the cycle by identifying any necessary further improvements. And don't forget to celebrate and congratulate if gains have been achieved.

The SDCA or standardise, do, check, act emphasises stability. If variability is excessive it is difficult to distinguish between real improvement and chance variation. In this case, stabilise first before planning.

A last word: Don't let the Deming PDCA cycle stand for "Please Don't Change Anything".

DMAIC

The Six Sigma methodology uses a variation of PDCA known as DMAIC (or Define Measure Analyse Improve Control). This has added several useful points. (See also the section on Six Sigma). You will notice that there is not a one-to-one relationship between PDCA and DMAIC. DMAIC has expanded upon the critical "Plan" stage.

Define. Define the problem.
Sub stages are identify what is important to the customer and scope the project.
Choosing the right project also means not doing an alternative project. An organisation or improvement team has limited time so should select carefully. Use Pareto. Use Cost of Quality analysis. Begin with customer priorities. Be specific on project aims; go

SMART (simple, measurable, agreed-to, realistic, and time-based). Six Sigma is strong on financial returns, so a savings estimate should be made. Scoping the project is critical - where are the problem boundaries, and what will be considered outside and inside? Of course, the "project" will be found within a process, not necessarily a department. So, "systems thinking" is required. (See Mess Management below.)
Typical tools: SIPOC analysis, Pareto analysis, Cost of Quality analysis, Kano model.

Measure. How are we doing?
The sub stages are: determine what to measure and validate the measurement system, quantify current performance, and estimate the improvement target.
Six Sigma places strong emphasis on measurement. Find a suitable measure – preferably related to the process customer or output. Six Sigma prefers to use quantitative rather than qualitative data. Think defects per million opportunities. Are current measures appropriate? Define the measure clearly, the sources of the data, the sampling plan. Think validity (is what I am measuring a good indicator - preferably a lead indicator?) and reliability (would another observer get the same result?). Think about appropriate defect classification – for instance record the total number of complaints in a hotel, or by type, by location, by customer? Check the consistency in the way defects are recorded. Also, be clear on the boundary of the process.
Typical tools: 7 tools of Quality.

Analyse. What's wrong?
The sub stages are identifying the causes of variation and defects, and providing statistical evidence that causes are real.
Try to get to the root cause. Use the "7 tools" or process mapping. (See separate sections). The majority of tools in this book are useful here. Creative thinking, Benchmarking, QFD, Value Analysis, Design of Experiments, are but a few of the possibilities. Six Sigma places emphasis on statistical validation of results using tests.
Typical tools: 7 tools of Quality, FMEA, Design of experiments (DOE).

Improve. Fix what is wrong.
Sub stages are determine the solutions including

operating levels and tolerances, then install solutions and provide statistical evidence that the solutions work. Now you have to implement. "Go to Gemba" and do it. You may use Kaizen or Kaizen Blitz. You may also have to plan by using project management tools.
Typical tools: DOE, Pokayoke, Hypothesis testing.

Force Field Analysis done with the team should precede implementation.

Control. Hold the gains, and sustain.
Sub stages are putting controls in place to sustain the improvements over time, and provide statistical evidence of sustainment.
Verify. Measure again. And celebrate with the team. Set up SPC charts. Set new standard operating procedures. Test to see whether gains are real by going back to the old process and forward to the new.
Typical tools: SPC, visual management, TPM, Standard Work.

The Ford 8D Cycle is another improvement cycle possibility. The "8 D"'s are eight disciplines: (1) Use a team (2) Describe the problem (3) Contain the symptom (4) Find the root cause (5) Choose and verify the corrective action (6) Implement permanent corrective action (7) Prevent recurrence (8) Congratulate and celebrate.

Further reading:
Peter R Scholtes, *The Leader's Handbook: Making Things Happen Getting Things Done*. McGraw Hill, New York, 1999. Although not a book specifically on Six Sigma this is a great reference for many sections relating to the tools used with PDCA.
Forrest W Breyfogle III, *Implementing Six Sigma*, Wiley, New York, 1999 (for the techniques).
Forrest W Breyfogle, James Cupello, Becki Meadows, *Managing Six Sigma*, Wiley, New York, 2001. For a management overview.

Organizing for Improvement

There are two aspects of improvement organization. The first is the improvement organization itself centred on the Lean Promotion Office, champions and steering groups. The second aspect is the improvement structure comprising five levels from individual to supply chain project.

The Lean Promotion Office

When an organization grows beyond perhaps 100 people, certainly 200, it becomes necessary to institutionalise improvement and sustainability. The Lean Promotion Office is a good name, but alternatives are a Kaizen office, or a continuous improvement (CI) office. A rule of thumb is that the Lean Promotion Office (LPO) should comprise 1 to 2% of the workforce full time during a major implementation, and 0.5 to 1% thereafter. These are the internal Lean consultants. If Six Sigma is in place, a parallel but closely linked office of a similar size is appropriate.

Many organizations, including Toyota, have found that implementing and sustaining Lean requires full time expert facilitators. They are the repository of expertise and should have general responsibility for Lean momentum. Note that the LPO cannot have authority for Lean implementation – that will always lie with line managers. So the ideal head of the LPO is a respected, Lean believer, and an influential individual who works through line managers, helping them to achieve their Lean goals. But the LPO is strictly a facilitating function – in no way should it be seen as 'the guys who do Lean around here'. Apart from the head, Lean enthusiasts or Lean disciples irrespective of age or position should of course, staff the LPO.

Remember the wise words of Lao Tzu, in *The Art of War*, "Go to the people. Live amongst them. Start with what they have. Build on what they know. And when the deed is done, the mission accomplished, of the best leaders the people will say 'We have done it ourselves'".

The LPO has specific responsibility for facilitating the general roadmap or Master Schedule for Lean implementation. Specific tasks that the LPO undertakes include assistance with mapping and the development of future state maps, advice on specific aspects such as number of kanbans, tailoring 5S and lean audit assessment tools for specific value streams, preparing waste questionnaires, running short courses on specific topics such as Lean accounting, coaching on facilitation and presentation skills, and preparing newsletters and videos. Several larger organizations, for instance Ford, have established libraries and on-line information. Dell has packaged on-line training into two hour modules that can be taken in slack periods.

In addition to the LPO, some organizations have appointed various line managers as expert internal consultants on relevant aspects such as lean accounting, changeover, pokayoke, pull systems, and demand management. These people have the responsibility of keeping up with developments on their topic.

The question of the relationship of a Six Sigma function to the LPO is controversial. What seems to be emerging is a strong case for these two functions as separate but closely coordinated. The reason is that the Lean Promotion Office is a support role, not doing projects themselves. The Six Sigma office, with Master Black Belts and Black Belts is actually engaged in the more difficult improvement projects that are inappropriate for kaizen teams. The Six Sigma office, however, is also involved with training – for Green Belts and the next generation of Black Belts.

The very existence of a LPO is an indication of the organization's commitment to Lean.

The Hierarchy of Improvement

Kaizen, or Lean improvement needs to be organised on five levels in most, if not all, organizations aspiring towards Lean.

Level 1: The Individual

The individual needs to be the recognised expert of her own process. This does not happen by chance and should not be built on trial-and-error. She needs to understand not only the process itself in great detail but also why the process is necessary and how it fits into the wider value stream. So, not only inserting a cars trunk seal in the best possible way, but knowing the necessity for keeping out damp and dust. Shingo suggested that the "know why" or underlying philosophy is the most important stage of learning. So both improvement and sustainability begin with the individual at the workplace.

At the individual workstation level there are always opportunities for waste reduction – work piece orientation, inventory and tool location, work sequence, ergonomics, pokayoke, and on and on. Some initiatives would arise as a result of workstation-level record keeping. Toyota South Africa calls their individual program 'Eyako' – the Zulu word for 'my own'. The team leader has an important role to play here – encouraging, facilitating and recognising achievement – and bring individual improvements to the attention of others. Individual 'thank you' notes carry much weight.

Level 2: The Work Team or Mini Point Kaizen

Groups or Teams of perhaps 6, that work in a cell or on a line segment undertake improvement workshop affecting their collective work area. Examples include work flows, cell layout, line re-balance, 5S, footprinting, and cell-level quality. Some activities may result from 'point kaizens' identified during wider current state mapping. These initiatives may be done 'on the fly' as a result of team meetings, or 1 or 2 day workshop activities. They may facilitated or assisted by the section leader or LPO. Many of the initiatives would arise as a result of record keeping and analysis undertaken at the cell and shown on display boards held in the team's own break area. Recognition is crucial, so the team needs to present to a wider audience. Do not make the mistake of using a level 3 blitz event when the team can comfortably do it themselves.

Scholtes recognises that there is a difference between 'teams' and 'teamwork'. He says that "Teams refers to small groups of people working together towards some common purpose. Teamwork refers to an environment in the larger organisation that creates and sustains

relationships of trust, support, respect, interdependence, and collaboration". This understanding recognises that it is relatively easy to establish a team, but to establish an environment for teamworking is a lot more difficult. He quotes Petronius Arbiter in what would be well recognised within many organizations:
"We trained hard, but it seemed that every time we were beginning to form up into teams, we would be reorganised. I was to learn later in life that we tend to meet any new situation by reorganising; and a wonderful method it can be for creating the illusion of progress while producing confusion, inefficiency and demoralisation."

Level 3: Kaizen Blitz Group or Point Kaizen

The Blitz event is carried out in a local area, but involves both more time (typically 3 to 5 days full time) and outsiders. These events address more complex issues than the work group can handle comfortably. Examples include more substantial layout changes, the implementation of a single pacemaker-based scheduling system together with runner route, and integrating manufacturing and information flows. For many companies, blitz groups and level 2 workshops, are the prime engine for improvement – to ignore is folly. Unlike the level 2 improvement teams, this type of group forms for the specific purpose of the event, and disbands thereafter. Blitz events are discussed in greater detail later in this chapter.

Level 4: Value Steam Improvements: Flow Kaizen Groups.

Flow kaizen groups work across a full internal value stream, taking weeks to 3 months for a project. They are the prime engines for creating future states. Their targets would be those set out in a future state and action plan exercise. (Refer to the mapping section). Value Stream groups are normally not full time (unlike level 3 groups), although some members may work uninterrupted for a number of days. They would be led by a project manager, often assisted by the LPO, and sometimes mentored by consultants. The group would be a multi-disciplinary, working along a complete process or value stream and across several areas and functions. Flow kaizen projects would usually have to address process issues, system issues, and organizational issues.

Level 5: Supply Chain Kaizen Groups.

Similar to Flow Kaizen Groups, but these groups work in the supply chain. They will invariably comprise part-time representatives from each participating organization. A respected project manager, typically from the OEM company would be appointed, and there is a greater role for consultants. A 'Seeing the Whole' value stream map would typically be the centrepiece.

Toyota's Learning and Improvement Organization for the Supply Chain.

Jeffrey Dyer reports six types of improvement and development organization at Toyota. He usefully associates acquiring a type of knowledge, explicit (or 'hard know-how), and tacit (or 'soft', 'sticky', intangible), with each.

- The Supplier Association (explicit) is a club of suppliers described in the supply chain section of this book.
- On site consulting (tacit) is carried by Toyota Supplier Support Centre, described by Womack and Jones in *Lean Thinking*.
- Jishuken groups (tacit) are voluntary groups much like quality circles but concentrating on supply chain and purchasing issues with member companies. The group selects a member company and then all participate in making improvements on the particular process. The knowledge gained is diffused to participants.
- A problem solving team is similar but concentrates on emerging issues between Toyota and its suppliers.
- Employee transfers (tacit) operate by moving staff between the parent and suppliers on a permanent or secondment basis.
- Finally, performance is monitored by audits (explicit).

Further reading:
Jeffrey Dyer, *Collaborative Advantage*, Oxford University Press, 2000
Peter Hines, *Creating World Class Suppliers*, Pitman, 1994

Continuous Improvement Approaches

It has become clear that there are two elements to improvement, namely continuous improvement and breakthrough improvement. Thus Juran refers to "breakthrough" activities, using "project by project" improvement, to attack "chronic" underlying quality problems as being different from "sporadic" problems. Davenport, in the context of business process reengineering, has referred to "the sequence of continuous alteration" between continuous improvement and more radical breakthroughs by reengineering. And Womack and Jones discuss "kaikaku" resulting in large, infrequent gains as being different from kaizen or continuous improvement resulting in frequent but small gains.

A traditional industrial engineering idea is that breakthrough or major event improvement activities are not continuous at all, but take place infrequently in response to a major change such as a new product introduction or in response to a "crisis". But during the past few years, through blitz events, we have learned that effective breakthrough should be both proactive and frequent.

More senior management working across a value stream generally drives breakthrough or Flow kaizen. Incremental or Point Kaizen is led by team leaders, and sometimes by Six Sigma Black Belts working on local issues that have arisen either through value stream analysis (proactive) or from workplace suggestions (reactive).

There are therefore five types of improvement, as shown in the figure. There is, or should be, a place for all five types in every organisation. Adopting lean manufacturing does not mean ignoring other forms of improvement to concentrate on kaizen and blitz. Passive approaches are a useful supplement and should con-

tinue. However, if all improvement is of the passive, reactive type the company may well slip behind.

A CLASSIFICATION OF IMPROVEMENT TYPES

Unfortunately, several British factories think they are doing kaizen, but their brand of kaizen is "passive" or left to chance. Improvements are left to the initiative of operators or industrial engineers or managers. If they make improvements - good. If they don't - "oh well, sometime". Passive incremental may also be termed "reactive". A reaction takes place in response to a crisis. By contrast, enforced improvement is proactive. "Crises" are actually engineered and the pressure kept on. For example, Intel brings out a new chip at regular, paced intervals and does not wait passively for technological breakthrough. 3M dictate that 30% of revenues will come from new products every year. This forces the pace.

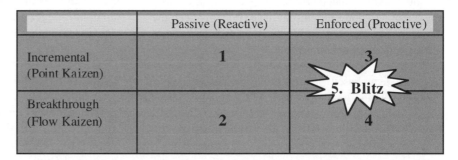

	Passive (Reactive)	Enforced (Proactive)
Incremental (Point Kaizen)	1	3
Breakthrough (Flow Kaizen)	2	4

5. Blitz

Passive improvement has been around for many years, and it too is found in two categories - incremental and breakthrough. Classic "passive incremental" improvement approaches are the suggestion scheme and the quality circle. Passive breakthrough is classic industrial engineering or work-study, especially where such methodologies are used for factory layout, and new technology introduction.

1. Passive Incremental

The classic type of passive incremental improvement is the suggestion scheme, with or without rewards, and with or without team emphasis. The classic team based passive incremental improvement method is the Quality Circle. Contrary to popular conception, the reward-based suggestion scheme is alive and well at many Japanese companies. At Toyota's US plant, for instance, awards are based on points and range from $10 to $10,000. Toyota has the attitude that all suggestions are valuable, so the company is prepared to make a loss on more mundane suggestions to develop the culture of improvement. At the top end of the Pareto the company reckons that the top 2.5% of suggestions pay for the entire reward programme, even though a good number of suggestions at the bottom end are loss-making, taking into account the implementation time. (One is reminded of the classic statement about advertising, "I waste half of the money I spend, but the problem is I don't know which half".)

Thomas Edison is reported to have said that the way to have great inventions to have many inventions. Toyota also insists that all suggestions are acknowledged within 24 hours and evaluated within a week. Non-acknowledgement and non-recognition have probably been the major reason for suggestions schemes producing poor results and being abandoned.

Likewise, team based Quality Circles are an integral part of the Toyota Production System. At Toyota, QC presentations to senior management occur almost every day. At Japanese companies QCs often meet in their own time. Management involvement and support are crucial elements. Edward Lawler has described a "cycle of failure" for many Western QCs. The following sequence is typical. In early days the first circles make a big impact as pent-up ideas are released and management listens. Then the scheme is extended, usually too rapidly, to other areas. Management cannot cope with attending all these events, and is in any case often less interested. In the initial phases, the concerns of first line supervisors, who often see QCs as a threat to their authority, are not sufficiently taken care of in the rush to expand. Some supervisors may actively sabotage the scheme; others simply do not support it. Then, as time goes on, with less support from management and supervision, ideas begin to run out. The scheme fades. And it is said, "QCs are a Japanese idea which do not work in the Western culture". (By the way, it was Deming who introduced circles to Japan, albeit that Ishikawa refined the methods.)

Yuso Yasuda has described the Toyota suggestion scheme or "Kaizen system". The scheme is co-ordinated by a "creative idea suggestion committee" whose chairmanship has included Toyota chairmen (Toyoda and Saito) as well as Taiichi Ohno. Rewards for suggestions are given at Toyota based on a points system. Points are scored for tangible and intangible benefits, and for adaptability, creativity, originality, and effort. The rewards are invariably small amounts, and are not based on a percentage of savings. However operators value the token reward and the presentation ceremony itself. Note the contrast with typical Western Suggestion Schemes.

From the above we learn a few important lessons; (1) not all improvements will pay, but creating the culture of improvement is more important. (2) Give it time, and expand slowly. (3) Recognition is important - management cannot always be expected to give personal support, so establish a facilitator or LPO that can. (4) Do not underestimate potential opposition. (5) React rapidly to suggestions. (6) Give groups the tools and techniques, and probably the time.

2. Passive Breakthrough

Many traditional industrial engineering and work-study projects are of the passive breakthrough type, particularly when left to the initiative of the IE or work-study department. Of course, IEs also work on enforced breakthrough activities initiated by management or by crisis, but passive breakthrough activities, led by IEs, have probably been the greatest source of productivity improvement over the past 100 years. Many of Taiichi Ohno's activities could be classified as passive breakthrough. (Apparently Ohno was a great experimenter on his own in the dead of night.) But today we recognise that many IE (or for that matter Six Sigma) projects done in an elitist way are unlikely to be sustained.

3. Enforced Incremental

Kaizen, as practised at Toyota, is the classic here. Waste elimination should not only be a matter of chance that relies upon operator initiative, but is driven. There are a number of ways in which this is done:

- *Response Analysis*. At Toyota operators can signal, by switch or chord, when they encounter a problem. At some workstations, there are a range of switches covering quality, maintenance, and materials shortage. When an operator activates the switch, the overhead Andon Board lights up highlighting the workstation and type of problem. People literally come running in response. But the sting is in the tail: a clock also starts running which is only stopped when the problem is resolved. These recorded times accumulate in a computer system. They are not used to apportion blame, but for analysis. Thus at the end of an appropriate period, say a fortnight, a Pareto analysis is done which reveals the most pressing problems and workstations.

- *Line Stop*. A Toyota classic, related to the above, allows operators on the line to pull a chord if a problem is encountered. Again, the Andon Board lights up. Again, the stoppage is time recorded. But the motivation to solve the problem is intense because stopping the line stops a whole section. This means application of the 5 Whys root cause technique. (See later section.) Toyota in fact splits the assembly line into sections that are separated by small (one car?) buffers, so line stop only stops that section not the whole line.

- *Inventory withdrawal*. Many will be familiar with the classic JIT "water and rocks" analogy, whereby dropping the water level (inventory) exposes the rocks (problems). This is done systematically at Toyota. Whenever there is stability, deliberate experimentation takes place by withdrawing inventory to see what will happen. Less well known is that this is a "win win" strategy: either nothing happens in which case the system runs tighter, or a "rock" is encountered which according to Toyota philosophy is a good thing. It is not any rock, but the most urgent rock. Deliberate destabilisation creates what Robert Hall has referred to as a "production laboratory". However, Toyota is not averse to adding

inventory where necessary. (Refer to the inventory section on Ford's SMART process.)

- *Waste Checklists*. Toyota makes extensive use of waste checklists in production and non-production areas alike. A waste checklist is a set of questions, distributed to all employees in a particular area, and drawn up by the LPO, asking them simple questions: "Do you bend to pick up a tool", "Do you walk more than 2 yards to fetch material", and so on. Where there is a positive response, there is waste. The result is that individuals and teams never run out of ideas for areas requiring improvement.

- *The "Stage 1, Stage 2" cycle*. At Toyota there is a culture that drives improvement. This culture or belief stems from the widely held attitude that each completed improvement project necessarily opens up opportunity for yet another improvement activity. For want of a better phrase, Bicheno has termed this "stage 1, stage 2" (See *Cause and Effect Lean*) after a list of Lean "stage 1" activities that lead to "stage 2" opportunities which in turn lead to stage 1 opportunities, and so on. The list of possible chains is very large, but an example will suffice. Thus setup reduction (stage 1) may lead to reduced buffers (stage 2), which may lead to improved layout (stage 1), leading to Improved visibility (stage 2), leading to improved quality (stage 1), leading to improved scheduling (stage 2), and so on and on.

4. Enforced Breakthrough Improvement

Active value stream current and future state mapping drive this category of improvement. They generally target a complete value stream. This type must be subject to regular action review cycles and an action plan or master schedule. (Refer to the Mapping section.) If a value stream map simply hangs on the wall without an accompanying master schedule it would be classified as passive breakthrough, if at all. Supply chain ('Seeing the Whole') projects would also be classified as enforced breakthrough.

5. Blitz

Blitz or Kaizen events are the subject of a separate section in this book. It is breakthrough because typical blitz events achieve between 25% and 70% improvements within either a week or within a month at most. On the other hand blitz events are typically related to a small area, so are frequently more 'point kaizen' than 'flow kaizen'. It is enforced because the expectations and opportunities are all in place. "No" and "it can't be done" are simply not acceptable. Concentrated resources are applied.

It may be argued that blitz events are not "continuous" improvement. Strictly, this is correct. But blitz events can and should be repeated in the same area at regular intervals. Products change, priorities change, people change, and technology improves.

Further reading:
John Bicheno, *Cause and Effect Lean*, PICSIE Books, 2002
Yuasa Yasuda, *40 Years, 20 Million Ideas*, Productivity Press, Cambridge MA, 1991

Kaizen

Kaizen is the Japanese name for continuous improvement. As such it is central to Lean operations. It brings together several of the tools and techniques described in this book plus a few besides. The word originates from Maasaki Imai who wrote a book of the same name and made Kaizen popular in the West. Although a registered name of the Kaizen Institute, the word is now widely used and understood and has appeared in the English dictionary.

According to Imai, Kaizen comprises several elements. Kaizen is both a philosophy and a set of tools.

The Philosophy of Kaizen: Quality begins with the customer. But customers' views are continuously changing and standards are rising, so continuous improvement is required. Kaizen is dedicated to continuous improvement, in small increments, at all levels, forever. Everyone has a role, from top management to shop floor employees.

Imai believes that without active attention, the gains made will simply deteriorate (like the engineers' concept of entropy). But Imai goes further. Unlike Juran who emphasises "holding the gains", Kaizen involves building on the gains by continuing experimentation and innovation.

According to Imai there are several guiding principles. These include:

- Questioning the rules (standards are necessary but work rules are there to be broken and must be broken with time)
- Developing resourcefulness (it is a management priority to develop the resourcefulness and participation of everyone)
- Try to get to the Root Cause (try not to solve problems superficially)
- Eliminate the whole task (question whether the task is necessary at all; in this respect Kaizen is similar to BPR),

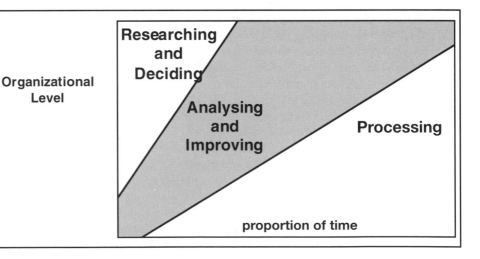

- Reduce or change activities (be aware of opportunities to combine tasks).

The Kaizen Flag

The Kaizen Flag is a famous diagram developed by Imai and widely copied and adapted. The flag portrays the three types of activity that everyone in a Kaizen organization should be involved with. These three are 'Innovation, 'Kaizen', and "Standardization' against level in the organization. (An adapted version is discussed below). In the original, senior management spends more time on 'innovation' (to do with tomorrow's products and processes), a definite proportion on 'kaizen' (to do with improving today's products and processes), but also a small proportion of time on 'standardisation' (that is, following the established best way of doing tasks such as, in top management's case, policy deployment and budgeting). A standard method is the current best and safest known way to do a task, until a better way is found through kaizen.

Middle managers spend less time than top managers on innovation, about the same time on kaizen and more time on standardisation. Operators spend a small, but definite, proportion of time on innovation, more time on kaizen, and the majority of time on standardisation.

Kate Mackle, former head of the British Kaizen Institute and now Principal in the consultancy Thinkflow, explains that innovation is concerned with preventing waste from entering tomorrow's processes, kaizen is concerned with getting waste out of today's processes, and standardisation is concerned with keeping waste out.
The version of the flag presented opposite has been developed based on Imai's original, but taking into account both experience and the ideas of the decision process developed by Ilbury and Sunter.
Here 'processing' is following the current standard best and safest known way.

Further reading:
Maasaki Imai, *Kaizen: The Key to Japan's Competitive Success*, McGraw Hill, New York, 1986
Maasaki Imai, *Gemba Kaizen*, McGraw Hill, New York, 1997

Improvement or 'Blitz' Events

Blitz or Kaizen Events (referred to as 'Kaikaku' by Womack and Jones) deliver results in a very short space of time. Literally within one week a company could be benefiting from a leap in productivity in one area of your plant or office. Blitz is about "going for it", about a preference for doing it now and reasonably rather than later (but perhaps never) even though it may be done better, about learning by doing, by trial and error. It is also about involvement on the shop floor by shop floor people. It is about real empowerment to just do it without asking for permission to make every little change.

Today, "Kaizen Blitz" (the name used by the US Association for Manufacturing Excellence) has been proven in both service and manufacturing companies. In the UK, Industry Forum (IF) has adopted blitz events as a standard approach originally for automotive suppliers – referred to as the Master Class process. The IF methodology has spread to, amongst others, aerospace, metals industry, and ceramics. Some consulting groups such as TBM and Simpler have developed their own versions.

Many of the better Lean organizations do regular and frequent blitz workshops of between 2 and 5 days, using a standard methodology, based on Plan Do Check Act, and shown on a display board.

An appropriate quote to introduce Blitz is:

> "Whether you believe you can,
> or whether you believe you can't,
> you're absolutely right."
>
> (Henry Ford)

Today we recognise that successful Blitz events require a great deal of both preparation and follow up to be successful. The IF methodology, for instance, comprises:

- A 1 day pre-diagnostic to select the area, discuss expectations, and to review measures and the measurement system that is in place.

- An initial preparation period during which time measures and basic data is collected – typically OEE, takt time, quality and demand information

- After about two weeks, a 3 day Diagnostic event takes place. The aim here is to establish and clarify what is to be the aim of the event itself. The team is chosen. Mapping is typical here, as is basic education on 7 wastes and 7 tools of quality. The 7 DTI measures are set up (See the section on measures). The chosen team makes a presentation to management and all concerned on what they aim to do during the event. Objectives are agreed, and all necessary authorisations made. (During the event, you do not want to have to seek permission to make changes.) Assurances must be established on possible reduction in manning levels. Sometimes a Lean game is played by the team and perhaps by the operators from the area.

- A further period of preparation takes place over the next few weeks. The measures are firmed up. Final preparation takes place – this may include, for instance building ahead of schedule to ensure continuity of service during the event, and warning support staff such as maintenance and electricians to be on hand for the event. Any foreseen resources such as tools, tables, boards, racks, and post-its must be acquired.

- A check day takes place during this period for any final arrangements

- The event itself is a five-day workshop. The idea is go around the PDCA cycle a few times, ending with some tested, standardised changes. The workshop is facilitated by an IF engineer. Measures are taken each day. On the last day a presentation is made. Follow up actions are given to specific people.

- After the 5 day workshop, three one-day follow up sessions are held at monthly intervals. These are to ensure that changes that were not able to have been put in place during the workshop are implemented. Examples are moving a machine embedded in concrete or targeting a quality issue that was not 'cracked' during the workshop.

- Finally, the IF engineer will stay in contact with the organisation for an extended period to check sustainability.

A blitz event can target different aspects. Often layout and 5S comes first. Safety may be chosen in an environment with difficult union issues. Later, follow up events can address lead time and manning.

A Brief Overview of a typical Blitz Event
(Based on an actual event, and assuming prior preparation).

Days 1 and 2

After an initial briefing the team split into three sub-teams, each tasked to complete their study by the end of the first morning. The three cell operators were each involved in a different initial analysis team. The layout team made a cut-out model of the cell and adjacent areas during the first morning, and measured total distances moved. The inventory and material handling team quickly got into questioning the amount of parts stored in the cell (several weeks supply in some cases), and the material movement quantities and methods. The process team addressed the ergonomics of the workstations and assembly methods that were the apparent cause of some quality problems.

Immediately after lunch the sub-teams each made a brief presentation to fellow team members. Brainstorming and prioritising took place during the first afternoon. The team spent a good part of the first afternoon at the cell, discussing alternatives in situ. Some immediate changes were decided upon and a number of airlines and electrical connection points were moved overnight. During the second day, the changes that were actually implemented included: relocation of a small press, the swapping around of a bicycle shed and a storage area, the relocation of a material store in the cell enabling a smoother flow to take place, changes to the assembly process itself, the repair of a door which was causing a draft, a drastic reduction of batch quantities (changeover was already very short), and, as a result, new material handling procedures. Interestingly, some of the women cell operators were initially opposed to any change on the basis of safety, but became enthusiastic supporters when changes proposed by their fellow operators were put in place. The afternoon of the second day was spent prioritising actions, and assigning responsibilities. The list ran to several pages.

Days 3, 4 and 5

Overnight, alterations to some work desks were made by maintenance, racks were acquired (from another part of the plant), preparations to move a machine were made, and a variety of materials (e.g. paint), signs, and tools were acquired. The operators who had participated in the initial days were encouraged to discuss what had happened and what was planned with their work mates.

On days 3, 4 the agreed upon changes were made. The major change was to layout, including the relocation of a semi-automated assembly machine. New material handling arrangements were begun. Then the line was run and observed. Some further changes were necessary. A number of new ideas emerged; some of which were immediately attempted. During late day 4 and overnight, after final adjustments, the team attempted to write new standards. These could not be completed. All the operators were to be involved, not just the three operators on the team. At midday on day 5 a final presentation was made to plant management, discussing and displaying progress. Follow up actions were identified. A small party to celebrate the gains was held.

On day 5, one of the women operators commented, "I have been in this company for 15 years, and I have seen more change during the last two weeks than I saw during all those years put together." Another commented, "Now I have seen the new system, I really don't know how we managed previously."

Some lessons learned about Blitz events over the past five years

- The workshop itself is the easy part. The harder and longer part is preparation and follow-up. An approximate time split is 40% preparation, 30% workshop itself, and 30% follow-up.
- The participation of managers in events is essential. Without this they will be lukewarm or even critical. Participation also helps overcome the problem of seeing authorization.

- The participation of the supervisor or team leader from the area is essential.
- Moreover, the supervisor should attend one or two events in other areas before it is the turn of his or her area. Think how you would feel if a team descended on your area for a week and produced a 40% productivity improvement. (Not too good – you may be motivated to show that what has been done was not all that good in retrospect.) Ideally, when it is the turn of the supervisor to have a blitz event in his area, he will already be the most enthusiastic participant – having experienced it elsewhere.
- Blitz events should be co-ordinated through the LPO in relation to a wider Lean implementation programme, via value stream mapping.
- All participants should have a clear understanding how the particular event contributes to the overall Lean vision or objectives.
- A good facilitator is invaluable. The ability to spot waste and opportunity builds slowly. Take the opportunity to transfer some of these skills.
- Blitz events work better in supportive companies. See the Ford quotation above. Do not set expectations too high. Under promise and over deliver.
- Sustainability remains the big issue. See the separate section on this.

Further reading:
Nicola Bateman, *Sustainability.... A Guide to Process Improvement*, Lean Enterprise Research Centre, Cardiff University and Industry Forum, 2001.
Sid Joynson and Andrew Forrester, *Sid's Heroes: 30% Improvement in Productivity in 2 Days*, BBC, London, 1996
Edward E Lawler III, *From the Ground Up: Six Principles for Building the New Logic Organisation*, Jossey-Bass, San Francisco, 1996, Chapter 6
Anthony C Laraia, Patricia Moody, and Robert Hall, *The Kaizen Blitz: Accelerating Breakthroughs in Productivity and Performance,* John Wiley and Sons, New York, 1999

The best magazine / journal on "kaizen blitz" is *Target: The Periodical of the Association for Manufacturing Excellence.*

Mess Management

Russell Ackoff, Emeritus Professor of Systems at Wharton School, University of Pennsylvania has a useful classification for problem solving, of high relevance to continuous improvement. He says there are three levels

1. 'Resolving' problems. This approach relies on past experience. Call a meeting and discuss the issues based on qualitative opinion. Ackoff says this is by far the most common approach, and although appropriate for truly messy problems is often ineffective. Better is:
2. 'Solving problems'. This approach is based on the scientific approach. It uses quantitative methods. Gemba. PDCA. Six Sigma. It is far preferable where it can be used. Often, split a problem into those parts that are amenable to a scientific approach, leaving the remainder to the 'resolving' approach. A good way is to use the Ilbury and Sunter procedure: (a) establish the 'rules of the game' over which you have no control and where there is little uncertainty, (b) collect and analyse the facts and develop scenarios for the variables over which you have control but where there is uncertainty, (c) develop the options, (d) make appropriate decisions. This cycle can take a few seconds (as when driving) or months (as when making a major strategic decision). But, says Ackoff, better still is:
3. 'Dissolving' problems. Change the nature of the problem. Take a 'Systems' view. Instead of developing complex scheduling to cope with changing and uncertain demand, influence demand variation in the first place.

So, pause to think. Are you resolving, solving, or dissolving?

Root Causes

The 5 whys is a technique to ensure that the root causes of problems are sought out. It simply requires that the user asks "why?" several times over. The technique is called the "5 whys" because it is the experience of its inventor, the Toyota company, that "why" needs to be asked successively five times before the root cause is established.

This simple but very effective technique really amounts to a questioning attitude. Never accept the first reason given; always probe behind the answer. It goes along with the philosophy that a defect or problem is something precious; not to be wasted by merely solving it, but taking full benefit by exposing the underlying causes that have led to it in the first place. Many believe that it is this unrelenting seeking out of root causes that have given the Japanese motor industry the edge on quality, reliability and productivity.

An example follows: A door does not appear to close as well as it should. Why? Because the alignment is not perfect. Why? Because the hinges are not always located in exactly the right place. Why? Because, although the robot that locates the hinge has high consistency, the frame onto which it is fixed is not always resting in exactly the same place. Why? Because the overall unit containing the frame is not stiff enough. Why? Because stiffness of the unit during manufacture does not appear to have been fully accounted for. So the real solution is to look at the redesign of the support unit.

Perhaps there are even more whys. Why did this happen in the first place? (Insufficient cooperation between design and manufacturing.) Why? (It was a rushed priority.) Why? (Marketing had not given sufficient notice.) Why? And so on.

A variation of the 5 Why technique is the "5 How" technique. This is often used in tracing the cause of a failure in a product or in service delivery. ("How did that happen?"....) The thinking and procedure is exactly the same.

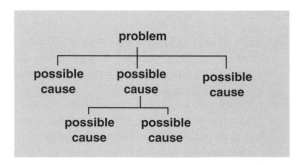

A Well-Defined Problem

Before discussing root causes, it is useful to have the criteria for a well-defined problem. Ammerman suggests the following:

- It focuses on the gap between what is and what should be
- It states the effect
- It is measurable
- It describes the pain
- It avoids 'lack of' and 'no' statements (that imply the solution)
- It highlights the significance of the effects.

An example. Over the past 3 weeks, 83 work orders were returned to Maintenance Department for required signatures, resulting in a 30% increase in processing time.

Root Cause Problem Solving

The emphasis on "root cause" problem solving is fundamental to the Lean philosophy. It means solving problems at the root rather than at the superficial or immediately obvious levels. But how do you get to the root cause? In the following sections two techniques are examined. But first, we should look at the whole concept of root cause analysis.

In a thoughtful article Finlow-Bates concludes that there are no ultimate root causes. Rather, root causes are dependent upon the problem owner; there can be more than one potential root cause and that the final choice of root cause cannot be made until the economics of possible solutions have been considered. He illustrates the point by the example of a delivery failure. The root cause for the customer is that the parcel is late. The root cause for the delivery company is that the problem delivery failure was due to the van not starting which can be traced to the root cause of a leaking fuel tank. For the tank supplier the root cause was a failure in the solder. For the solder supplier the root cause was …. Each person along the chain is not interested in the problems of lower echelons. Each of these causes represents a failure in control or in communication. The real issue is therefore not what is

the root cause, but how can the problem be (temporarily?) solved most economically and effectively to prevent recurrence.

Finlow-Bates suggests following six steps:
1. What is the unwanted effect? (Finlow-Bates suggests two words; subject and deviation, for example parcels late)
2. What is the direct physical cause?
3. Follow the direct physical line of the cause. For example, parcels late, van won't start, etc. This establishes the "staircase"
4. Ask who owns the problem at each stage.
5. Identify where should one intervene in the staircase to effect a long-term solutions.
6. Identify the most cost-effective of the solutions.

Barrier Analysis

Barrier Analysis (Wilson et al) may be used where implementation problems are being experienced. It amounts to a straightforward set of questions that are addressed to an unwanted problem or event:

- What are the threats, hazards or potential problems that can influence the situation? Threats may be physical or psychological, or influence status, security, or self esteem.
- Who or what are the "Targets" for change? In any change there will be victims and beneficiaries, some perhaps unintended. It is useful to list these. The target may be human, animal, organisation, environment, group, team, family, or other.
- What are the barriers? These may be physical, geographic, communication, language, culture, administrative, organisational.
- What are the safeguards that are supposed to be in place to make the change easier or more acceptable, and if they are not in place, why are they not? Should the threat be isolated, or should the target be isolated, or both?
- What is the "Trace"? That is, what is the sequence of events or history that has lead up to this situation? Real or imaginary. The history is often the root of the problem. Ask the Irish, or Palestinians.

Six Honest Working Men

Rudyard Kipling's "Six Honest Serving Men" remains, some 100 years after it was first written, one of the most useful problem analysis tools. The original verse is,

"I knew six honest serving men,
they taught me all I knew;
their names are what and why and when,
and where and how and who".

Such a simple little verse; so much wisdom – so often ignored!

The six men are a very useful way of defining customers, their requirements and what is really valued.

Further reading:
T Finlow-Bates, "The Root Cause Myth", *The TQM Magazine*, Volume 10 Number 1, 1998, pp10-15
Max Ammermann, *The Root Cause Analysis Handbook*, Productivity, 1998
Paul Wilson, Larry Dell, Gaylord Anderson, *Root Cause Analysis: A Tool for Total Quality Management*, ASQ Quality Press, Milwaukee, WI, 1993

theory. By not pursuing instances where (the thoery) does not work, or is not needed, we may be denying ourselves the opportunity of discovering or evolving a better theory"
Karl Popper

A Warning on Lean Improvement

We must never be complacenent about Lean or Lean improvement.

Consider:
Because researchers learn the basis of their field from concrete models and case studies there is seldom disagreement over fundamentals. 'Individuals who break through by inventing a new paradigm are almost always... either very young or very new to the field whose paradigm they change. These are the men who, being little committed by prior practise to the traditional rules... are particularly likely to see that those rules no longer define a playable game and conceive another set that can replace them'.
Thomas Kuhn, *The Structure of Scientic Revolutions*

and
"It is easy to obtain evidence in favour of virtually any

People and Sustainability

Basics

'Lean' people, from CEO to junior, share two related characteristics, both related to Learning.

Humility. The more one knows about Lean, the more one realises how little one really knows. Dan Jones speaks about 'peeling the onion' to uncover waste – the same is true learning about Lean. A sure sign of impending failure is a manager who claims to 'know it all' or 'we tried that in 1990'. Visitors to Dell in Ireland, that has very impressive inventory turns, are invariably struck by the humility of their managers ('we have lots to learn') and their willingness to learn from others, no matter whom. Stephen Covey says that genuine listening is the most important of his 7 habits of highly effective people.

Respect. The expert is the person nearest the actual job. But respect goes far beyond this. It is about regarding the workforce as a family. A good family downplays hierarchy, listens genuinely, is genuinely interested. But it also expects contribution. Parents know that kids have new skills that they may never possess. In organisations, non genuine respect is quickly detected. Peter Wickens, former HR director of Nissan UK explained in *The Road to Nissan* about the necessity of reducing organisational levels, working towards single status, eliminating benefits based on position, and opened information flow.

How to achieve Humility and Respect? It begins at senior levels and percolates down. Consistent demonstration over a long period of time is required. So is Gemba style management – you cannot genuinely listen if you aren't there. Both take a long time to build up, and unfortunately both are quickly destroyed.

Culture?

Perhaps Humility and Respect is ultimately about Culture. (That great and misused word.) Scholtes describes organisational culture as the day to day experience of the ordinary worker. The experience is affected by two aspects of the organisation, the apparent organisation and the 'below the surface' organisation. The apparent organisation is that which is visible: products, services, customer segments, and markets; the hierarchical structure and chain of command; the official roles, functions, job descriptions and accountabilities; the facilities, equipment, machinery, materials, supplies; official systems, processes and work methods; policies, goals, plans objectives and procedures. The below the surface organisation is one which is much less tangible but far more wide reaching in terms of affecting behaviour. It will have its unofficial leaders and unwritten rules, its own communication channels of rumour and grapevine. It will be shaped by past victories and setbacks, old feuds and rivalries. The informal organisation will often determine how well included and respected an employee feels, and will have a marked effect of the efficacy of teamworking and productivity.

Further reading
Peter Scholtes, *The Leaders Handbook,* McGraw Hill, 1998

Change

In *Learning to See*, Rother and Shook discuss Current State, Future State and Action Plans as the trilogy in mapping and transformation. These three are also the basics of a change management programme.

Current State. The need for change must be recognised. The Why. This involves benchmarking current

performance and identifying gaps. Future developments (such as 'disruptive technologies' – see separate section) are even more important. Womack and Jones say that if necessary you should 'create a crisis' – the writer's experience is that if you look around sufficiently well you will identify real threats. Then the need to change must be communicated. Not just communicated, but explained and discussed in detail.

Future State. Where we are going must be explained. The vision. What must be changed. 'Without a vision the people perish' says the Bible. Great visions get everyone on board 'Getting a man to the moon and returning him safely to Earth before the end of the decade'. On the other hand, said Alice, 'Would you tell me, please, which way I ought to go from here?' 'That depends a good deal on where you want to get to', said the Cat. 'I don't much care where' said Alice. 'Then it doesn't matter which way you go', said the Cat.

Action Plan. The plan to get there must be agreed. The how and when. Another of Stephen Covey's habits is essential here: seek 'Win Win'. You must and can find a way that all win – reject TINA (there is no alternative), and embrace TEMBA (there exist many better alternatives). There may be no alternative to the need to change, but win win must be sought for the how.

So the change process has many similarities with the Hoshin process. Ted Hutchin usefully talks about five distinct stages (that he refers to as the Constraint Management Wheel of Change) – gaining consensus (on the need), gaining consensus on the direction (of change), gaining consensus on the benefits of the solution, overcoming all reservations, making it happen.

Kurt Lewin's Force Field Analysis is a simple but powerful tool throughout. Draw a vertical line on a board. List and explain the forces for change. Open a discussion on the forces working against change. Do this level by level. Listen genuinely. Another useful tool is the Route Learning Map (see Mapping section.)

Weltanschauung or Paradigms

Peter Checkland reminds us of the power of weltanschauung (or world view) on the change process.

Joel Barker speaks of Paradigms. These are the views of people as to what works and what does not. They are built up over a lifetime time as a result of background and experience. They form the lens through which we interpret the world. We all have different world views. So there is no such thing as an agreed view of 'Lean' (or any other concept). They evolve, but slowly. Only very rarely do they change rapidly. The implication is that change occurs as a result of experience, not vice versa. You have to demonstrate a new way consistently over an extended period.

Learning and Lean

The conventional learning curve is certainly applicable to simple tasks and to the addition of knowledge to our knowledge base. But Scholtes has observed a "false learning curve". The normal S-shaped learning curve of slow start but then steady progress levelling off, is assumed. But Scholtes says that true learning really begins in a second phase following the realisation that (Lean) is much more complex than first thought. This may go some way to explaining why so many change programmes fail since to get to the point of realising "we don't know much" can be between one and five years. This longer-than-expected timescale has been also observed by Koenigsaeker. The white flag of surrender is hung out by managers too early, when in fact good but unobserved progress is being made. This is made worse by manager mobility and short-term results orientation. In this sense a major reason for lack of sustainability lies with managers, simply giving up.

Several authors have suggested that learning needs to progress through four stages
- Unconscious incompetence
- Conscious incompetence
- Conscious competence
- Unconscious competence.

Each stage has its problems. In the first you don't know what you don't know. Ignorance is bliss. In the second, with realisation, may come despair and abandonment. In the third arrogance could be a problem. In the last, either one may assume, incorrectly, that most have been through the same long journey and now share the insights or that looking back you forget the difficulties and that it is all so easy to pick up quickly.

11 People Pitfalls of Implementation

Mike Rother, co-author of the *Learning to See* mapping book gives five pitfalls of implementing Lean.

1. Confusing techniques with objectives. This book has also made the point that Lean is not tools.
2. Expecting training to make Lean happen. Mike says this is 'pure bunk'. You need to change the system. (Recall here Deming's 85/15 rule whereby 85% of problems stem from the system – that only management can fix, and only 15% from operators). Change cannot come purely from the bottom.
3. Leading from the office, via plans, maps and charts. Mike makes the point that Lean can only be achieved through Gemba (he does not use the word but means it).
4. Relying solely on Blitz workshops. Issues here are the lack of the big picture, sub-optimisation and sustainability. (Refer to the Blitz section)
5. Quitting after failures. See the last section.

To this list can be added.

6. Management commitment. An old cliché perhaps, but it is difficult to think of a successful Lean transformation that has not had real commitment and involvement from the top. Sending out a clear signal helps – like asking the top team to apply for their own jobs.
7. Cherrypicking. Pursuing a fairly random selection of tools in a fairly random selection of locations. Changeover reduction here, kanban there, mapping everywhere but with little follow through. Often these follow from the latest conference, book or meeting.
8. "We are different" – so we need to re-invent our own system.
9. "We can do it ourselves". Toyota did it themselves, but it took them two decades with some exceptional people. Can you wait? Are you confident that you have the people, and that they will be around in a decade. Ultimately you can only do it yourself, but you will need guidance. A problem is that a fair proportion of Lean consultants have limited exposure outside of a small area. Even ex-Toyota people have crashed in other environments.

10. Not thinking that "80% is greater than 100%" meaning that a set of decisions 80% correct but bought into by all will be better than an optimal 100% correct solution imposed by the 'experts'.
11. Lack of ull time facilitation. Most companies will need a Lean promotion office to keep the momentum going.

Further reading:
Peter Scholtes, *The Leaders Handbook,* McGraw Hill, 1998
Peter Checkland, *Systems Thinking, Systems Practice,* Wiley, 1973
Mike Rother, Crossroads: Which Way Will You Turn on the Road to Lean?, Chapter 14, of Jeff Liker (ed), *Becoming Lean*, Productivity, 1998

The Adoption Curve

Getting the right people is a perennial theme in Lean. Jim Collins in *Good to Great*, studied various successful transformations and believes that their leaders did not do so by setting a new vision and a new strategy but 'first got the right people on the bus, the wrong people off the bus, and the right people in the right seats – and then figured out where to drive it'.

Various writers have discussed an adoption curve from early adopters to 'anchor draggers' This has merit in thinking about people aspects of Lean implementation. Here an adaptation based on the author's experience (and background) is given.

The figure shows a notional distribution of a workforce. Areas represent approximate proportions.

The Lean Champion is a farmer not a hunter. Farmers take the long view, and win in the long term. Hunters take the short view, get early gains but ultimately die out. Farmers are shepherds. Early adopters are found on the right hand side of the figure. These people are 'gung ho' for change. They require very little convincing. But experience shows that there are two sub-groups here. Dogs are faithful, but are also intelligent. This valuable group will be the core of the change initiative. By

contrast, Lemmings are easily up for change, any change, and, in a sense, are not the people you want. ('If he thinks it is a good thing, then it must be a bad idea.) They leap in just too quickly, without thought.

Horses are the key group. They need guidance from a Lean champion. They require to be trained, to be broken in. Horses are also intelligent. Most horses work well in teams. The strategy to be adopted with horses depends on the situation. In normal circumstances the rider is in

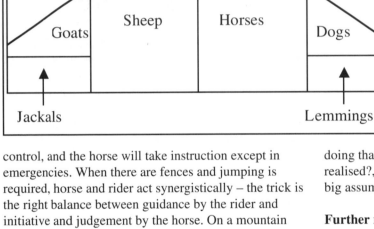

control, and the horse will take instruction except in emergencies. When there are fences and jumping is required, horse and rider act synergistically – the trick is the right balance between guidance by the rider and initiative and judgement by the horse. On a mountain hike, however, the best strategy for the rider is to let the horse take most of the control, relying on it to pick out the safest path.

Sheep can be led by riders with horses and dogs. Generally they cannot be relied upon to get there without considerable guidance. Shepherding is required. Sheep are multi-function providing wool and mutton. They are adaptive to a wide range of climates. Sheep can also be led to an extent by goats, either into the abbatoir or into a lush field. (Note: Sheep is not a derogatory term – they are the backbone of much farming.)

Goats are much more cautious. They have good reason to doubt, and some of those doubts are valuable

insights. But they can be made into valuable assistants. When they are convinced they are more useful than sheep. Goats lead sheep.

Finally Jackals cannot be trained. They eat goats and sheep, and may scare horses. They are the true anchor draggers.

Note that in this analogy, groups traditionally regarded as anchor draggers and early adopters both have sub groups. These sub groups need to be distinguished.

Beware of lemmings. Listen to the goats – they may have good, thoughtful reasons for reluctance.

As an aside on what are here called Goats, Kegan and Lahey contend that a major reason why some people (and groups) are reluctant to change is 'competing commitments'. For example a manager is offered promotion but is committed to spending time with an aging relative. The person then makes a 'big assumption' that the commitments are mutually exclusive. To uncover this, Kegan and Lahey suggest that managers ask a series of questions. For instance, What would you like to see changed?. Then, what commitments does your complaint imply? And, what are you doing that is keeping your commitment from being realised?, leading to working out a way to reconcile this big assumption with the change. Download the reprint!

Further reading

Robert Kegan and Lisa Lahey, 'The Real Reson People Won't change', *Harvard Business Review*, November 2001, pp 84-92. Reprint R0110E

Ubuntu and Kyosei

This section is a bit of fun, not necessarily connected directly with lean operations. It is included because

- the author of this publication is South African, and
- the phrases reflect the spirit of Lean enterprise.

Ubuntu is a word used in South African management circles to mean the fusion of modern management with tribal thinking. In an African tribe there is a hierarchy, but anyone may speak and will be listened to sympathetically in the knowledge that anyone can have good ideas. The literal translation from the Zulu is to do with dignity and humanity, or "a person becomes a person through other persons" or "I am because we are". In tribal societies there is the concept of the extended family with mutual help being given between age groups and between immediate family groupings. In South Africa, Ubuntu has come to mean a more people-oriented approach. It is a team-based approach to management; we are all in this together. So, "that's not Ubuntu" means it does not suit the aspirations of all; it does not fit in with the common good, it may suit the management and may even be the optimal economic thing to do, but some will be harmed. This is in line with, or should be in line with, Lean Thinking. It's a good sentiment, and about time some Lean thinking came out of Africa.

In a similar vein, Kyosei, means to work together in a spirit of co-operation for the common good, of employees, of customers, of all people, of the environment. It is a word that has become associated with the Canon Company and the Canon Production System. According to Ryuzaburo Kaku, ex president of Canon, it is like a pyramid. At the base is economic survival. Then comes co-operation with labour, and then co-operation outside the company, with customers and suppliers. Following these comes "global activism" when the company starts international operations and cooperates internationally and responsibly with foreign employees, people, and environmentally friendly technology, and lastly the company works with and uses its influence with governments around the world to act responsibly.

Too philosophical? Perhaps. But good Lean thinking.

References:
Ryuzaburo Kaku, "The Path of Kyosei", *Harvard Business Review*, July-August 1997, pp55-63

Meetings and Memos

This section covers two simple but vital issues, which are sometimes uncontrolled even in otherwise lean organisations.

Meetings

The first principle of meetings is that, if at all possible, they should be held at "Gemba". Gemba management means going to the location and using the facts, rather than sitting in a meeting room and discussing opinions. Use the "four actuals": go to the actual workplace, look at the actual objects in question, collect the actual data, and observe what is actually happening.

The second principle, adopted at Toyota in product design and development, is to have focused, short meetings on one topic only and to demand that all participants arrive fully prepared to discuss that one topic. Typically such meetings take 15 minutes. Meetings with long agendas and with participants unprepared but nevertheless keen to give their opinion on all topics, are definitely not Lean.

Memos

Minutes of meetings and memos should be standardised. (Standards apply in the office as well!). At Toyota, most minutes and memos use a standardised A3 sheet of paper. One side of one sheet. By the way, this is an old idea possibly stemming from Joseph Juran's insistence on such brief notes during his trips to Japan in the 1950's.

Going for It!

Delay can be a self fulfilling prophesy. As Johann Goethe so elegantly wrote:

"Until one is committed there is always hesitancy, the chance to draw back, always ineffectiveness. Concerning all acts of initiative (and creation) there is one elementary truth, the ignorance of which kills countles ideas and splendid plans: that the moment one

definitely commits oneself, then providence moves too. All sorts of things occur to help one that would not otherwise have occurred. A whole stream of events issue from the decision, raising in one's favour all manner of unforseen incidents and meetings and material assistance which no man could have dreamt would come his way."
(Thanks to Lee Flinders for bringing this excellent quote to my attention.)

Sustainability

Sustainability is one of the great issues in management, never mind Lean. Ask GEC/Marconi or ICI. In their book *Creative Destruction*, Richard Foster and Sarah Kaplan report that of the 500 top US companies in 1957, 37% survived to 1997, and of those only 6% outperformed the stockmarket.

One view of sustainability is simply 'Doing a Cortes' – that is burning his boats so that his men had no choice but to make their old-world ways succeed in the new world. The equivalent may be an option in a time of real crisis, but is not really available to most.

Sustainability and Tools

Several organisations have failed to produce the desired results from the direct and prescriptive application of Lean tools whilst other have been more successful. The tools themselves have been proven to work in many situations. The difference must then be in how the tools were applied and not what tools were applied.

Spear and Bowen state that observers of Lean often confuse the tools and techniques with the system itself. They point to the paradox of the Toyota Production System (TPS) that relates to a very rigid framework of activities and production flows coupled with extremely flexible and adaptable operations. This paradox is partially explained by the authors' revelation that Toyota actually practices the *scientific* method in its operational activities. Plan Do Check Act is the principle mechanism for this scientific approach. Tools and techniques are thus treated as hypotheses to be tested in

the particular situation at hand. If the results are unfavourable the tools must be modified. Companies without this understanding often fail to allow for local factors influencing the successful application and sustainability of tools and techniques

Nakane and Hall also studied TPS and came to a similar conclusion to Spear and Bowen with regard to the tools and techniques based approach. They found companies that merely implement the techniques without developing the people and hence the culture of an organisation fail to fully realise the expected gains. TPS firstly relies the idea of developing, "direct action people to function autonomously, both running processes and improving them". These people then develop the appropriate tools.

Sustainability and the Systems View

Systems thinking is way of viewing and interpreting the universe as a series of interconnected hierarchies and interrelated wholes. Within organizational systems there are both complex technical and social interactions and interrelationships that govern the output of the system. The famous Tavistock research amongst miners, illustrated that both technical and social aspects need to be considered if a new system (in their case long wall mining) was to be successful and sustained. The 'socio' side involves understanding the system of mutually supporting roles and relationships, both formal and informal, within the organization.

A further Systems aspect on sustainability is discussed by Senge who describes the phenomena of links and reinforcing loops in systems. Systems bite back! Latent forces emerge from unexpected quarters. Loops can become reinforcing and can lead to highly amplified growth or decline. Feedback loops are beginning to be understood in natural and eco systems but exist in human organizations also. Just as with Goldratt's theory of constraints, systems theory describes the ubiquitous presence of balancing forces that limit the growth of the system. These self correcting loops must be understood if organisations wish to positively influence the sustainability of their systems. Change generates antibodies that automatically grow to fight the change. This is like Newton's Third Law – for every action there is an equal and opposite reaction. The antibodies need to be managed or the fever will take hold. Those in favour of change may be neutralised. So identify the antibodies as early as possible. Inject them. Antibodies that continue to react need to be moved out decisively and quickly.

This is the state of "quasi stationary equilibrium" described by Kurt Lewin that led to his diagnostic technique known as force-field analysis. For both Senge and Lewin the most important lesson from this realisation is that it is preferable to reduce the restraining forces before increasing the driving forces. If we think purely in terms of systems and inputs it is clearly better to reduce the overall energy input than to negate the effects of a force with an equal or greater counter-force.

Sustainability and Motivation

The sustainability of tools is related to the degree to which people are motivated to use them. Recall some classic theories of motivation. Herzberg's motivator hygiene theory says that hygiene factors such as pay and conditions can de-motivate but not motivate. Only motivators, such as recognition and personal satisfaction actually motivate. And Maslow talked about the Hierarchy of Needs. This suggests that a foundation of trust and support is necessary, but sustainability requires interest and involvement.

Deming spoke about the necessity to 'drive out fear' as one of his famous 14 points. Surely it is a pre-requisite for sustainability. Research by the author shows that fear about the short term remains one of the prime concerns in Western companies. 'So, if I do all this Lean stuff, will I really retain my job?' Forget the issue of long term (company) survival so often voiced by management – it is short term personal survival that is of far more concern.

Stephen Covey, as one his 7 Habits of Highly Effective People, discusses the 'Win-win or walk away' habit. Both sides must win. A way must and can be found, or else both parties should walk away. Covey believes that without this fundamental principle there can no sustainability – in business, in personal life, or in

society. Ask Black South Africans. Reject TINA (there is no alternative); embrace TEMBA (there exist many better alternatives).

Finally, on motivation, the excellent diagnostic booklet *Analysing Performance Problems* by Mager and Pipe, suggests that several questions need to cleared before getting down to motivational issues. These issues include: has training been adequate?, is what is expected clear?, has sufficient time been allowed?, and have adequate resources been provided?. Only then should you ask about the motivational issues: Is performance punishing? (in terms, for instance of extra work), is non-performance rewarding? (for instance, letting others do the work and being rewarded by more free time), and does it make a difference? (for instance, will anyone notice or will there be any recognition?).

Sustainability and Discipline

For Hirano the concept of sustainability is dependent upon discipline and in the context of 5S this means "making a habit of properly maintaining the correct procedures". Without good discipline the 5S system will not be maintained and the workplace will revert to chaos. The need for discipline is not restricted to the 5S's but is also essential in all aspects of business according to Hirano. In the classic Japanese definition of 5S the fifth S or pillar is *Shitsuke* or Discipline. (Refer to the 5S section).

Hirano firmly believes that management and supervision must teach discipline and that problems with discipline arise when management fails to correct lapses as they occur. The workplace "faithfully reflects the attitudes and intentions of managers, from the top brass to the shop floor supervision". The art of correcting another person is also emphasised and the need for compassion and not passion is said to be key. The person correcting another must also acknowledge his or her own failings. This particular aspect of discipline has a cultural slant that is highlighted by the description of the worker being criticised thanking the critic for their correction followed by a bow of acknowledgement. This is a scenario seldom seen in the West and may go some way to explaining why discipline is easier for Japanese companies to cultivate.

With regard to the application of 5S in a manufacturing environment Kobayashi's experience is that it cannot be sustained unless it is as part of a complete system of workplace organisation. (Refer to the section on Audit Tools.) Does this suggest that sustainability can only happen as part of a total Lean package?

Sustainability and Managers

In the Change section above, the tendency for managers to give up too early was identified. Sustainability begins at the top. Lower down, researchers into self-directed work teams have found that these simply do not work when staff turnover is greater than about 30% per year. They are always in the 'forming' and 'storming' stages, never progressing to 'norming' or 'performing'.

Schedule Stability and Sustainability

It is well known in British automotive that the Japanese car companies have far more stable schedules than others. No doubt this has an impact on sustainability of operations. For example, a heijunka system, cell re-balancing, and regular 5S and TPM activities will all fall down with instability of demands. The customer therefore has a vital role to play in sustaining improvements in his supply base.

Dynamic Sustainability

Slack and Lewis usefully view sustainability as the achievement of fit (of policy, strategy) over time. Recall the product process matrix discussed under Manufacturing Strategy. This suggests that as volumes change layout must change. The same is true for competition and technology. Slack and Lewis point out the need for both single loop and double loop learning or evolution. Slack and Lewis give an example of single loop learning from a tennis player who can rely on a power serve during a period when wooden rackets are the norm. Opponents seek other ways of attack, mainly in vain. But when a new technology, carbon-fibre rackets develops, suddenly the alternatives become much more effective, and the strong server has to adapt or die. So a core strength becomes a liability. Double loop adaptation is more fundamental requiring

questioning of basic operating procedures. Examples are Amazon completely re-defining the way books are sold, or Dell's build to order policy decimating many computer manufacturers. (There are similarities here to Disruptive Technology – see the strategy section.) Slack and Lewis say that companies need both single and double loop learning for dynamic sustainability.

Sustainability of Blitz Events

Nicola Bateman has carried out probably the most thorough study on the sustainability of blitz events or Kaizen workshops. She identified 'enablers' for both class A (situations where improvements continue to build after an event), and class B (situations where improvement builds after an event but tails off to a plateau above the level attained during the event). Briefly, the top enablers were found to be:

For Class B
- There should be a formal way of documenting ideas from the shop floor. This should not be too onerous and could be a flip chart or post-it board.
- Ensure that operators can make decisions in a team about the way they work. Emphasise teamwork and consensus decision-making.
- Make sure there is time dedicated to maintaining the 5S standard every day. Include audits and daily 5S condition checks. Sign off daily audit sheet by Manager at end of week.
- Ensure there are measures to monitor the improvements made – at an appropriate level. Continue monitoring the measure the event was intended to improve.
- Manager (cell leader and his or her manager) should stay focused on PI activity. This supports the previous enablers.

For Class A
- Changes to operating methods of the cell should be formally introduced to all cell members. Introduce changes to all those who were unable to take part in the event.
- There is time dedicated to housekeeping every day.

- The cell should have a strategy. After initial activities the cell needs direction on which issues to tackle next.
- There should be a person co-ordinating improvement activities across the factory. The person does not execute the improvements but facilitates and aids cell leaders.
- Senior Managers should be involved in improvement activities. Take part in at least one event and numerous reviews.
- Senior management should stay focused on improvement activities – by reviewing progress as a whole and not imposing unnecessary initiatives

Other Aspects of Sustainability

Choi lists the pitfalls of improvement initiatives, based on his research, as
- Alienation of line leaders (involvement and improvement being seen as interfering with their performances objective).
- Seeing improvement as the same as regular problem-solving activity – which confuses those outside and inside
- Identifying improvement teams as special – thereby building resentment
- Seeing improvement as a management programme – bypassing workers
- Seeing improvement as solely a worker thing – lacking communication, interest, and involvement from above
- Intermittent – stop go initiatives – here we go again.

Standard and Davis suggest that sustaining a transformation requires
- A formalised organisational structure – like a kaizen office
- A higher degree of job specialisation – begin with deeper skills, and only later on cross training
- An organisation structure with few levels – to aid cross-functional communication and to keep 'close to the action'.

Military intelligence officers know that a situation is only dangerous when there is capability and intention. Both are necessary; otherwise there is no danger. The same goes for sustainability – there must be both the capability (time, resources) and the intention (determination, drive, and insistence).

Two theories from change management seem relevant. "Cognitive Dissonance" says that people try to be consistent in attitude and behaviour. Thus if a change is out of kilter with prevailing attitudes it will fail. The "psychological contract" says that there is an unwritten implicit set of expectations (covering, for instance, a sense of dignity and worth) which if breached will lead to disruption and implementation failure.

Further reading:
Fraser Wilkinson, *Sustainability of 5S*, MSc Dissertation, Lean Enterprise Research Centre, Cardiff Business School. The author is grateful to Fraser for pointing out several of the concepts discussed here.
Nicola Bateman, *Sustainability*, Lean Enterprise Research Centre, Cardiff Business School, April 2001
Peter Senge, *The Dance of Change*, Nicholas Brealey, London, 1999.
Schaffer, R.,H., & Thompson, H., A., *Successful Change Programmes Begin with Results*, Harvard Business Review, Jan-Feb 1992.
Nakane, J. & Hall, R. W., *Ohno's Method – Creating a Survival Work Culture*, Target Vol 18, No 1.
Thomas Choi, "The Successes and Failures of Implementing Continuous Improvement Programs', in Jeff Liker (ed), *Becoming Lean*, Productivity Press, Portland, 1998
Charles Standard and Dale Davis, *Running Today's Factory*, Hanser Gardner, Cincinnati, 1999, Chapter 13
Nigel Slack and Michael Lewis, *Operations Strategy*, Chapter 14, FT Prentice Hall, 2002
Michael Lewis, 'Lean Production and Sustainable Competitive Advantage', *IJOPM*, Vol 20, No 8, 2000
Bernard Burns, *Managing Change*, Third edition, FT/ Pitman, Harlow, 2000, Chapter 12
Spenser Johnson, *Who Moved My Cheese?*, Vermillion, London, 1998
David Hutchens, *Shadows of the Neanderthal: Illuminating the Beliefs that Limit our Organizations*, Pegasus, 1999

New Product Development and Introduction

Good new product management is essential in Lean operations because perhaps 80% or 90% of costs may be locked in after the design and process planning stage, yet incur perhaps 10% of cost. The time taken to bring a new design or product to market is where much of the competitive edge is gained or lost. And, the earlier a problem is detected the less expensive it is to solve. The NPD / NPI area is where leading Lean companies are increasingly competing. In this section a range of concepts and organisational issues are looked at. Many of them can be, and are being, used together. Here an attempt is made to give a Lean-oriented overview covering Ulrich and Eppinger's five phase process for new products

- Concept development
- System level design
- Detail design
- Testing and refinement
- Production ramp up.

(Karl Ulrich and Steven Eppinger, *Product Design and Development*, McGraw Hill, New York, 1995)

Design for Six Sigma

Design for Six Sigma (DFSS) is a methodology that parallels Six Sigma improvement, with the former focusing on new designs and products and the latter on improving existing processes. The experience of many is that conventional Six Sigma can achieve around 4 or 5 sigma performance, but to get to six sigma requires attacking the design side. An analogy is the public

health engineer (DFSS) and the doctor (six sigma) who ultimately relies on good sanitary conditions. It is useful to see DFSS as working together with Design for Manufacture, described later.

Six Sigma uses the DMAIC steps (refer to the Quality chapter). DFSS uses the IDDOV steps (identify, define, develop, optimise, verify). Both have a strict sequence of steps. Both aim at robust, low variation processes. Both share the same organizational hierarchy of Master black Belts, Black Belts and Green Belts and both require senior management commitment. Probably a DFSS project takes longer, but potentially has larger and longer-lasting payoff, and likely has greater sustainability.

Identify. The first step concerns clarifying the scope of the project. It involves doing a preliminary cost benefit / business case and scoping exercise. It will often include a project charter statement.

Define. This is concerned with clarifying the requirements for the product (or service). Customer requirements are the starting point. Two principle tools are the Kano model and Quality Function Deployment (QFD). (The Kano model is discussed in the Lean Philosophy section, QFD is discussed later in this section.) In fact, QFD is a 'meta technique' that runs all the way through a DFSS exercise.

Develop. With desired customer requirements and ideas on design and processes clarified, the next step is to identify and evaluate various product design options.

Three techniques are common – brainstorming, TRIZ and concept screening. The latter two are discussed later in this section. Also, Failure mode and effect analysis (FMEA) will usually be included – compulsorily so in some industries such as aerospace and automotive.

Optimise. This step is analogous to the Six Sigma steps of analyse and improve. In DFSS the Taguchi Loss Function is used – this postulates that customers suffer a loss proportional to the square of the distance from the optimal point. In DFSS 'parameter design' involves maximizing the function (energy use or efficiency, for instance), rather than reducing variation. Six Sigma uses design of experiments to identify the most sensitive variables, and to reduce the spread of the variation. DFSS uses parameter design to find the best combination of variable factors to maximise the function and to test the robustness against various operating conditions. The next stage is Tolerance Design that looks at which are the most critical tolerances – which have to be tight and which less tight – in other words, which tolerances have the greatest impact on overall variability.

Verify. The final step involves testing the design. Substeps involve looking at the capability of the manufacturing process, testing prototypes, and establishing process control plans. The latter may involve looking at statistical process control and failsafing (pokayoke) aspects – refer to the Quality section.

The last two steps can be viewed against the Hinckley framework of variation, mistakes and complexity against people (men), machines, method, measures, materials, mother nature. DFSS is an elegant way of addressing most of these cells at the design stage. For the Hinckley framework refer to the Quality section.

Further reading:
Geoff Tennant, *Design for Six Sigma*, Gower Press, 2002
Subir Chowdhury, *Design for Six Sigma*, Dearborn Press, Chicago, 2002

Four Objectives and Six Trade-offs

In their ground breaking work on accelerated new product development, Smith and Reinertsen identified four objectives (Development Speed, Product Cost, Product Performance, and Development Programme Expense) as being central to the management of new product development. These four areas interact in six ways. Smith and Reinertsen believe that it is necessary to quantify the trade-offs since every new product introduction is a compromise that needs to be understood and managed.

Development Speed and Product Cost. Rationalising and improving a design through part count, weight analysis, part commonality, DFM, and value engineering can save future costs. But they take time, thereby delaying the introduction of the product and possibly losing market share.

Development Speed and Product Performance: Improving a design can make it more attractive to customers thereby improving future sales through a larger market, a higher price, and a longer product life. These improvements take time and may sacrifice initial sales and initial market share.

Development Speed and Development Programme Expense: This is the traditional "project crashing" trade-off from classic project management. Most projects have "fixed" costs such as management and overhead that accumulate with time. On the other hand, within limits, adding extra resources decreases project duration but costs more. Is it worthwhile spending more to finish earlier? There are non-linear effects – digging a trench with six men does not take one sixth of the time it takes with one man.

Product Performance and Product Cost: Adding or redesigning a feature may improve performance but at what product cost? What marginal performance are customers prepared to pay for?

Product Cost and Development Programme Expense: By spending more on development, say through value engineering, we may be able to reduce cost. Is it worth it?

Development Programme Expense and Product Performance: Improving a design and improving performance may result in improved sales. But improving performance may involve additional cost.

In a less complex way, Mascitelli suggests a 'least discernable difference test' which is to ask whether customers will pay a penny more for a feature that is being considered. There is a conceptual maximum number of satisfied customers that reduces on the one hand due to reduced benefits and on the other hand due to price increases.

Smith and Reinertsen suggest that a simple spreadsheet model be developed to quantify these six relationships. Remember to use the time value of money, trading off immediate project costs against discounted future sales. Quantifying the six relationships forces marketing, design and engineering to think carefully about additions and rationalisations. Play around with the sensitivity. Clearly, as Michael Cusumano and Kentaro Nobeoka, show in their comparisons of Japanese approaches to car development between 1980 and 1990, the answers to these tradeoffs change with time and environment.

Further reading:
Michael Cusumano and Kentaro Nobeoka, *Thinking Beyond Lean*, The Free Press, New York, 1998
Preston Smith and Donald Reinertsen, *Developing Products in Half The Time*, Van Nostrand Reinhold, New York, 1991
Ronald Mascitelli, *Building a Project-Driven Enterprise: How to Slash Waste and Boost Profits through Lean Project Management*, Technology Perspectives, 2002

Critical Chain and Lean Project Management

Goldratt's ideas on project management, as explained in his book *The Critical Chain*, are most relevant for reducing the time and variation in new product introduction. His ideas represent a big advance on traditional project management critical path analysis. Mascitelli has added usefully to ideas on Lean project management. Mascitelli and Goldratt make a powerful combination for projects and new product development.

Goldratt explains that, in many projects, safety times are added to estimates of activity durations to allow for variation and other contingencies. In traditional project planning the critical path is the longest path by time through the network, but along this path there is 'float' as a result of a propensity to over-estimate time durations. Of course there is natural variation of time in activities – some taking longer than estimated, some taking shorter. But in traditional project management activities that take a shorter time than planned result in the next activity often having to wait for non-critical resources before proceeding. Activities that take longer than planned of course extend the entire project duration. Putting these two situations together means that most projects end up late. Using conventional project management software such as Microsoft Project does not address these issues of variation.

The Critical Chain solution is to recognize and manage constraints. The TOC rules of recognise, exploit, subordinate, elevate, and repeat (see the Theory of Constraints (TOC) section) is exactly what is done. As with TOC theory, completion of the entire project on time depends on the management of the critical resources. The project activity network logic is built up and validated by participants as in conventional project management. But from that point there are differences. First, activity times need to be estimated as realistically as possible but without allowing for any 'float' or contingencies. Second, the critical chain is the longest path through the network by resource usage. In other words if there is one of a particular resource it cannot be used in two places at once, so the critical chain may be longer than the conventional critical path. (A complex project may require special software to determine the critical chain, but for many projects this can be determined by inspection.) Third, time and resource buffers must be located in order to protect the critical chain.

Appropriate resource buffers must be located in front of critical chain activities, for two reasons. One reason is to prevent delay by having to wait for critical resources. These must be warned in good time to be available if needed. Another is to make sure that if the activity finishes early, the <u>next</u> activity is able to be started without delay. Resource buffers are necessary whenever there is a change in the resource used along the critical chain. (This is 'exploiting' the constraint and 'subordinating' non-critical activities.)

Finally, buffers are grouped together at the end of the project network to allow for variation in time estimates. A project time buffer protects the whole project, and a feeding buffer protects non-critical activities. The size of each buffer is discussed as a totality by the project team depending on the risks to the project as a whole, and not to individual activities. Try to arrange high risk activities as early as possible, so there is more time to catch up.

Having now determined the project duration, the duration is compared with the allowable or target completion time. If the project duration is longer, the constraints must be 'elevated' or broken by providing additional resources.

When project execution begins, concentrate on the critical chain and 'exploit' the critical resources. Monitor the buffers. Keep a focus on the time remaining in the project as against the allowable time remaining. If necessary 'elevate'. Ignore activities that have been completed. Monitor the buffers ahead, most of which are likely to have changed as against the original plan.

Time buffers can be monitored in a statistical process control (SPC) fashion – in other words some natural variation is to be expected and is ignored, but large variations signal special remedial actions. In fact, it is a good idea to ignore time deviations within a certain pre-

determined range of natural variation. This is management by exception, saving huge time and bother.

Mascitelli adds 12 points for Lean project management. These cover, amongst others, 'testing for customer value' (is the customer prepared to pay for extras? – refer to the Four Objectives section above), being clear on the deliverables and hand-offs of each activity, decreasing and eliminating design reviews to retain only those that are essential, 'staged-freezed specifications' (similar to the 'Set Based' concurrent engineering described in a section below), using visual management and standard work (two Lean basics), risk buffering (a variation on the critical chain idea), 'dedicated time staffing' whereby resources working on critical chain activities are allowed uninterrupted blocks of time, and the Goldratt concept of resource managers and project managers (the latter taking over control of resources where activities become critical).

Further reading:
Eli Goldratt, *The Critical Chain*, North River, 1997
Ted Hutchin, *Constraint Management in Manufacturing*, Taylor and Francis, 2002
Ronald Mascitelli, *Building a Project-Driven Enterprise: How to Slash Waste and Boost Profits through Lean Project Management*, Technology Perspectives, 2002
Lawrence Leach, *Critical Chain Project Management*, Artech, 2000

Simultaneous and Concurrent Engineering

Simultaneous or Concurrent Engineering (the words are interchangeable, sometimes depending on American or British usage) is an established Lean Technique. The idea is for all relevant parties in a product introduction to work concurrently on the project. This is in contrast to the traditional practice of sequential design, where the design for a new product is "thrown over the wall" to the next department, thereby resulting in what Womack and Jones refer to as batch and queue processing. Traditional practice is organised around strong functional departments (marketing, R&D, design, engineering, production, manufacturing, materials management, quality, logistics and distribution). Typically these functions do not share the same priorities, and interpret the requirements differently. Each may try to "optimise" the design from their own perspective, but as a result suboptimising the general product in relation to the customer and the product life cycle. A now-classic cartoon shows the development of a swing as it moves through the various functions, moving further and further away from the customer's requirement. Not only that, it is also slow, usually with numerous rework loops. Failure mode analysis and legal considerations may result in yet further delay.

Simultaneous Engineering uses a strong product champion or project leader and a matrix form of structure. The real power is vested in the project leader rather than the functional department heads. The project manager often holds budget responsibility, and staff report to her or him in the first instance. A critical arrangement is co-location of the team. Close proximity allows instant resolution of problems and a single clear view of requirements. There may still be gateways or sign-offs through which the design must pass, but such approvals are best done in a committee of functional heads, rather than one at a time. Although staff is seconded from functional departments to the project team, they return to the functional department at the end of the project and may call on functional expertise during the project. The functional head typically retains the responsibility for maintaining the up-to-date skills of his staff and databases. Generally, in traditional practice there is little involvement with suppliers in the design process, although there is also the concept of "open specifications" whereby a supplier is given the broad spec and asked to come up with the detail. The project manager controls the budget and can contract in staff from functional departments and outside firms, as is deemed necessary.

The simultaneous engineering approach described here is referred to by Ward et al as a so-called "point based process". Although a team based approach and excellent common software may be used, the design moves in approved stages from styling, to system design, to component design, to manufacturing engineering, to

maintenance planning, and at each point or stage the design is frozen before moving ahead.

By contrast, Toyota uses an approach referred to by Ward et al as a "set based approach". Ward gives the analogy of setting up a meeting. One alternative is for an overall organiser to select date and time, then negotiate with a second participant and if necessary revise, then with a third, revising yet again if necessary, and so on. This represents the traditional form of design. Concurrent engineering can be used to shorten the process by either having a short meeting to decide when the longer one is to be held, or have the more powerful participants pre-decide the time, and then force the others to attend at that time. This is equivalent to the strong project manager form of concurrent engineering.

The set based approach (or Toyota) system is based around a strong technical manager who manages by experience and influence rather than by authority and control. Toyota uses broad constraints or checklists of infeasible designs but allows suppliers and internal designers to suggest their own alternatives. The most important supplier partners can not only influence component design but also the whole car concept. Second level (not necessarily tier) suppliers wait for Toyota to define the needs but then work with Toyota to define component designs. Third level suppliers' design to specification or use Toyota's own design. Throughout the process there is a constant two-way negotiation process. The amount of communication, however, appears to be less than with traditional concurrent engineering. Because of the high degree of trust between partners, manual milestones rather than computer-based project management software is used. Within the milestones there is considerable individual flexibility.

The Toyota process follows a set-narrowing procedure. Concepts are gradually narrowed using "Concept Screening" techniques (see later). Possible "solution sets" are explored in parallel, but once a particular solution is decided upon it is frozen unless a change is absolutely necessary. This is similar to the Lean concept of postponement - delaying freezing specifications until the last possible moment.

While car design is proceeding, engineering and die production also proceeds. During the early concept stages, engineering makes from 5 to 20 one-fifth scale clay models. The engineering team begins full-scale clay modelling at intermediate stages as well as at final stage, unlike other car manufacturers who only make half size models during early stages. This enables tool and die designers to begin work. They too use engineering check sheets, built up from experience, about what can and cannot be done. Difficulties are fed back immediately to the design team.

Further Reading:

Alan Ward and Michael Kennedy, *Product Development for the Lean Enterprise,* Oaklea Press, 2003.
James Womack, Daniel Jones, Daniel Roos, *The Machine that Changed the World*, Rawson Associates, New York, 1990, Chapter 5.
John Wesner, Jeffrey Haitt, David Trimble, *Winning with Quality: Applying Quality Principles in Product Development*, Addison Wesley, Reading MA, 1995
Preston Smith and Donald Reinertsen, *Developing Products in Half The Time,* Van Nostrand Reinhold, New York, 1991
Durward Sobek, Jeffrey Liker, Allen Ward, "Another Look at How Toyota Integrates Product Development", *Harvard Business Review*, July-August 1998, pp36-49

Mass Customisation, Modularity and Platforms

These three related concepts aim at the apparently contradictory objectives of low cost with high, or even infinite, variety. As the trend towards Build to Order gathers pace all three are likely to be increasingly relevant.

Mass customisation

Pine discusses five methods:

Customise services around standard products or services. Although standard products are used, customisation takes place at the delivery stage. For example, airline passengers may be offered different meals or in-flight entertainment, and pizza customers are offered substantial choice. On the Internet it is possible to receive a customised news service. Standard hotel rooms may nevertheless be offered in non-smoking, secretarial support, quiet-during-day, or close-to-entertainment or pool varieties. Customisation through service may be the way, for instance through individual support of a standard computer or through knowledge of the specific requirements of individual customers using a dry cleaner. The key to this method is good information on customer, especially repeat customer, needs.

Create customisable products and services. Here, customisation is designed into standard products which customers tailor for themselves. Examples are adjustable office chairs, automatically adjustable seats, steering wheels or even gearing on some cars, or the flexible razor which automatically adjusts to the user's face. The key here is often technology, but technology that follows customer need. The automatic teller machine offering a variety of services is a prime example.

Point of Delivery Customisation. Here variety is built in just prior to delivery, even later than the first type of customisation. For instance, software specific to a customer's requirements may be added. In-store point of delivery customisation - spectacles, photo developing, quick-fit tyres - are now commonplace. This type of customisation often requires "raw material" or semi-processes inventory to be held at the point of delivery, but the advantage is zero finished goods inventory and improved speed of response.

Quick Response. Quick response usually involves integration along much of the supply chain. A classic example is Benetton's "jerseys in grey" which are kept undyed until actual demand is communicated, often via electronic data interchange (EDI), and supplied on a quick delivery service. Inventory is only kept in a partly processed state at a central factory, none in the distribution chain, and minimal is kept in shops. (By the way, Quick Response is also known as Efficient Consumer Response (or ECR), the former associated with apparel, and the latter with groceries.) ECR has grown into a major field in itself with its own journal.

Modularity

This long-established form of customisation simply involves assembly to order from standard modules. Examples are legion: calculators or cars having different appearance but sharing the same "platform", aeroplanes, and many restaurant meals. Pine lists six types: "Component sharing", where variety of components is kept to a minimum by using Group Technology (see separate section), Design for Manufacture (see separate section), "Component swapping" (cars with different engines), "Cut-to-fit modularity" (a classic example being made to order bicycles), "Mix modularity", combining several of the above, and "bus modularity", where components, such as on a hi-fi are linked together. Baldwin and Clark take this further, believing modularity to be a fundamental organising principle for the future. Thus today Johnson Controls makes the complete driver's cockpit for Mercedes, and VW runs a truck factory using not only the modules of suppliers but their operators also.

Gilmore and Pine (1997) have gone on to state that there are four approaches to module customisation. "Collaborative customizers" work with customers in understanding or articulating their needs (a wedding catering service), "adaptive customizers" offer standard but self-adjusting or adapting products or services (offering hi-fi, or car seats which the customer adjusts), "cosmetic customizers" offer standard products but present them differently (the same product is offered but in customer specified sizes, own-labels), and "transparent customizers" take on the customisation task themselves often without the customer knowing (providing the right blend of lubricant to match the seasons or the wear rate).

Johnson and Bröms give a description of Scandia trucks approach to modularity. Four basic modules – generate power, transmit power, carry load, house and protect driver – have been developed as modules to meet various environmental conditions encountered around the world. A matrix has been developed for parts and modules. These remain standardised until an improvement takes place, but are used 'Lego brick' style to act as the foundation for any new model. Scandia builds to order using the matrix.

Platforms

A product platform is a design from which many derivative designs or products can be launched, often over an extended period. So, instead of designing each new product one at a time, a product platform concept is worked out which leads to a family of products sharing common design characteristics, components, modules, and manufacturing methods and technology. This in turn leads to dramatic reductions in new product introduction time, design and manufacturing staff, evaluation methods such as FMEA, as well as inventory, training, and manufacturing productivity; in short, Lean design. There are similarities to the Modularity concept and GT (group technology), but product platforms goes far wider. Product platforms are found from calculators (e.g. Casio) to Cars (VW / Audi). The Apple Macintosh uses the platform of a common operating system (MacOSX) and common microprocessors (the G5 processor) for a variety of computers.

A classic case, cited by Meyer and Lehnerd, is Black and Decker. In the 1970s, Black and Decker's product portfolio comprised scores of different motors, armatures, materials, and tooling, most of it simply evolving piecemeal one at a time. The company began their product platform strategy by bringing together design and manufacturing engineers to work in teams. They started, Pareto fashion, with the motor, and created a common core design with a single diameter but varying length, able to be adapted to power output from 60 to 650 watts. The range of motors now shared common manufacturing facilities, reduced changeover, and dramatically better quality. After motors, armatures and then drill bits were tackled. This led to reductions of 85% in operators, and 39% in cost. The cycle time for new product introduction was slashed, eventually enabling B&D to introduce new products at the rate of one per week. The extra investment needed for process technology was repaid within months. Lower costs were passed on to customers, and new markets created, resulting in a surge of demand and the decimation of competitors. Notice the similarities with 'The Essential Paretos'. (See separate section).

Meyer and Lehnerd, identify five principles. These are
• Families should be identified, which share

technology and are related to a market. (Note again similarity with GT which shares manufacturing process steps, but says nothing about markets). From this basic family feature-rich derivations are developed over time.

- Product design takes place alongside production design. Product platforms are a strong argument in favour of the Lean "small machine" principle; too often, because of the existence of an expensive big machine, product designs are undertaken which seek to make use of the machine rather than giving first consideration to the customer. Simultaneous design or concurrent design (a good Lean principle) should be used.
- Try to design for global standards, logistics, and component supply. An example is the internationally adaptable power requirement used on HP printers.
- Try to capitalise on latent demands that a product platform can create. VHS VCRs, and CDs are outstanding examples.
- Seek design elegance, not mere extension. (Java seems to be the reaction against bloated software packages with more and more features seldom used.)

The building blocks of product platforms, according to Meyer and Lehnerd are

- Market orientation, designers close to the customer (Lexus' design team living in California, Olympus designers working periodically in camera shops.) And derivative products should be aimed at different market segments using the same basic platform; this should be part of the initial concept (example VW and Audi using the same platform but aimed at different segments, and through derivatives in engine size, and features, at different groups).
- Using design building blocks - both internal and external, capitalising on the best product modules, rather than starting afresh.
- Using the most appropriate manufacturing technologies, and
- Using the whole organisation - "total" innovation. Like Quality, product platforms require a cross-functional total approach along the whole chain.

Product platform thinking is also totally compatible with the ideas of target costing, where derivatives are rolled out over time whilst capitalising on platform economies. All the derivatives form a stream of target costed products. And, as Robin Cooper has pointed out this is done through Value Engineering.

Further reading:
B. Joseph Pine, *Mass Customisation*, Harvard Business School Press, Boston, MA, 1993
James H. Gilmore and B. Joseph Pine, "The Four Faces of Mass Customisation", *Harvard Business Review*, Jan/Feb 1997, pp 91-101
Carliss Baldwin and Kim Clark, Managing in an Age of Modularity", *Harvard Business Review*, Sept-Oct, 1997, pp 84-93
Marc Meyer and Alvin Lehnerd, *The Power of Product Platforms*, Free Press, New York, 1997
Behnan Tabrizi and Rick Walleigh, "Defining Next Generation Products: An Inside Look", *Harvard Business Review*, Nov-Dec 1997, pp116-124
David Robertson and Karl Ulrich, "Planning for Product Platforms", *Sloan Management Review*, Summer 1998, pp 19-31
H Thomas Johnson and Anders Bröms, *Profit Beyond Measure*, Nicholas Brealey, 2000.
Anon, 'Why Detroit is Going to Pieces', *Business Week*, Sept 3, 2001, p 60
See the *ECR Journal*. www.ecr.org

Design for Manufacture

Design for manufacture (DFM) is a key "enabling" concept for lean manufacture. Easy and fast assembly has an impact right through the manufacturing life of the product, so time spent up front is well spent. A wider view of DFM should be considering the cost of components, the cost and ease of assembly, and the support costs.

Cost of Components should be the starting point. Much will depend upon the envisaged production volume: for instance, machined components may be most cost effective for low volumes, pressings (requiring tooling investment) best for middle volumes, and mouldings (requiring even higher initial investment but low unit costs) best for higher volumes.

Other considerations include
- Variety as late as possible
- Design for no changeover or minimal changeovers
- Design for minimum fixturing
- Design for maximum commonality (Group Technology)
- Design to minimise the number of parts

Complexity of Assembly

Boothroyd and Dewhurst have suggested a DFA index aimed at assessing the complexity of assembly. This is the ratio of (the theoretical minimum number of parts x 3 seconds) to the estimated total assembly time. The theoretically minimum number of parts can be calculated by having each candidate part meet at least one of the following:

- Does the part need to move relative to the rest of the assembly?
- Must the part be made of a different material?
- Does the part have to be physically separated for access, replacement, or repair?

If not theoretically necessary, then the designer should consider the physical integration with one or more other parts. And why 3 seconds? Merely because that is a good average unit assembly time. Once this is done, then Boothroyd and Dewhurst suggest further rules for maximum ease of assembly. These are:

- Insert part from the top of the assembly
- Make part self-aligning
- Avoid having to orient the part
- Arrange for one-handed assembly
- No tools are required for assembly
- Assembly takes place in a single, linear motion
- The part is secured immediately upon insertion

Boothroyd and Dewhurst now market a software package to assist with DFM. They suggest that for both DFA and Design Complexity (see below), not only should there be measurement and monitoring of one's

own products, but that the measures should be determined for competitor's products as well. This is a form of benchmarking. Targets should be set. Such measures should also be used for value engineering. Continuous improvement is therefore driven by specific targets, measures, and benchmarks, and not left to chance.

It should be possible to create design and assembly indices for each subassembly, to rank them by complexity, and Pareto fashion to tackle complexity systematically. Further, it should be possible to determine, from benchmarking competitor products, the best of each type of assembly and then to construct a theoretical overall best product even though one may not yet exist in practice. This is a form of Stuart Pugh's "Concept Screening" method (see later section).

Assembly Support Costs should be considered at the design stage. This includes consideration of:

- Inventory management and sourcing
- The necessity for new vendors
- A requirement for new tools to be used
- A requirement for new operator skills to be acquired
- The possibility of failsafing

More recently C Martin Hinckley has estimated that assembly defects are directly proportional to assembly time. To this end he has developed so-called Quality Control of Complexity that is a straightforward way of estimating assembly time. Details are given in his book. Assembly alternatives can now be considered relatively easily for their impact on assembly defects due to mistakes.

Complexity of Design

Boothroyd and Dewhurst have also suggested a measure for the assessment of design complexity. They use three factors: the number of parts (Np), the number of types of parts (Nt), and the number of interfaces between parts (Ni). First, the numeric value of each of these factors is determined by addition. Then, the factors are multiplied and the cube root taken. This yields the design complexity factor. Note that reducing the number of parts usually also reduces the number of interfaces, which are points at which defects and difficulties are most common. Also, reducing the number of types of part has a direct impact upon inventory management and quality.

Other Types

"Design for" is not limited to "assembly" (DFA) or "manufacture" (DFM). There are other types too: Design for Performance (DFP), Design for Testability (DFT), Design for Serviceability (DFS), and Design for Compliance (DFC). And, of course, Design for Six Sigma (DFSS).

Further Reading:

G. Boothroyd and P. Dewhurst, *Product Design for Assembly Handbook*, Boothroyd Dewhurst Inc., Wakefield, RI, 1987

Karl Ulrich and Steven Eppinger, *Product Design and Development*, McGraw Hill, New York, 1995, Chapter 3

Subir Chowdhury, *Design for Six Sigma*, Dearborn Press, Chicago, 2002

C Martin Hinckley, *Make No Mistake!*, Productivity Press, Portland, 2001

Quality Function Deployment (QFD)

Quality Function Deployment is a "meta" technique that has grown hugely in importance over the last decade and is now used in both product and service design. It is a meta technique because many other techniques described in this book can or should be used in undertaking QFD design or analysis. These other techniques include several of the "new tools", benchmarking, market surveys, the Kano model, the performance - importance matrix, and FMEA.

Customer needs are identified and systematically compared with the technical or operating characteristics of the product or service. The process brings out the relative importance of customer needs which, when set against the characteristics of the product leads to the identification of the most important or sensitive characteristics. These are the characteristics that need development or attention. Although the word "product" is used in the descriptions that follow, QFD is equally applicable in services. Technical characteristics then become the service characteristics.

Perhaps a chief advantage of QFD is that a multi-disciplinary team all concerned with the particular product carries it out. QFD acts as a forum for marketing, design, engineering, manufacturing, distribution and others to work together using a concurrent or simultaneous engineering approach. QFD is then the vehicle for these specialists to attack a problem together rather than by "throwing the design over the wall" to the next stage. QFD is therefore not only concerned with quality but with the simultaneous objectives of reducing overall development time, meeting customer requirements, reducing cost, and producing a product or service which fits together and works well the first time. The mechanics of QFD are not cast in stone, and can easily be adapted to local innovation.

The first QFD matrix is also referred to as the "house of quality". This is because of the way the matrices in QFD fit together to form a house-shaped diagram. A full QFD exercise may deploy several matrix diagrams, forming a sequence that gradually translates customer requirements into specific manufacturing steps and detailed manufacturing process requirements. For instance, a complete new car could be considered at the top level but subsequent exercises may be concerned with the engine, body shell, doors, instrumentation, brakes, and so on. Thereafter the detail would be deployed into manufacturing and production. But the most basic QFD exercise would use only one matrix diagram that seeks to take customer requirements and to translate them into specific technical requirements.

The "House of Quality" Diagram

In the sections below the essential composition of the basic house of quality diagram is explained. Refer to the figure.

Customer requirements

The usual starting point for QFD is the identification of customer needs and benefits. This is also referred to as "the voice of the customer" or "the whats". Customers

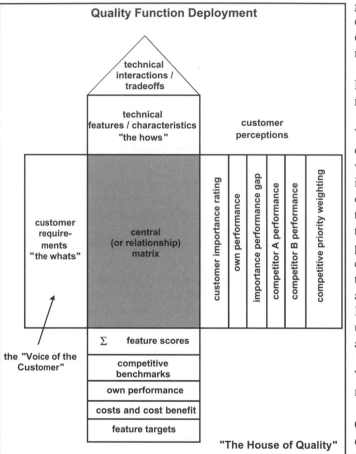

Quality Function Deployment

technical
interactions /
tradeoffs

technical
features / characteristics
"the hows"

customer
perceptions

customer
require-
ments
"the whats"

central
(or relationship)
matrix

customer importance rating

own performance

importance performance gap

competitor A performance

competitor B performance

competitive priority weighting

the "Voice of the
Customer"

Σ   feature scores

competitive
benchmarks

own performance

costs and cost benefit

feature targets

"The House of Quality"

may be present or future, internal or external, primary or secondary. All the conventional tools of marketing research are relevant, as well as techniques such as complaint analysis and focus groups. Customers may include owners, users, and maintainers, all of whom have separate requirements. After collection comes the problem of how to assemble the information before entering it into the rows. In this the "new tools" of affinity and tree diagrams have been found to be especially useful. This results in a hierarchy; on the primary level are the broad customer requirements, with the secondary requirements adding the detail.

Marketing would have responsibility for assembling much of the customer information, but the team puts it together. Marketing may begin by circulating the results of surveys and by a briefing. It is important to preserve the "voice of the customer", but the team may group like requirements using the affinity diagram. The team must not try to "second guess" or to assume that they know best what customers need.

Rankings or relative importance of customer requirements

When the customer requirements are assembled onto the matrix on the left of the house diagram, weightings are added on the right to indicate the importance of each requirement. Market research or focus groups establish weightings or, failing these, the team may determine rankings by a technique such as "pairwise comparison". (In pairwise comparison, each requirement is compared with each other. The more important of the two requirements gains a point, and all scores are added up to determine final rankings.) The Kano model (see separate section) is very often used with QFD as an aid in determining appropriate weightings.

Technical characteristics and associated rankings

Customer requirements and weightings are displayed in rows. The technical characteristics (or "hows" or "technical responses") form the columns. These characteristics are the features that the organisation provides in the design to respond to the customer requirements (For a kettle this may include power used, strength of the materials, insulation, sealing, materials used, and noise.) Once again these could be assembled into groups to form a hierarchy, using the Tree Diagram. Here the team will rely on its own internal expertise. There are at least two ways to develop technical characteristics. One way is go via measures that respond to customer needs. For instance a customer need for a kettle may be "quick boil". The measure is "minutes to boil" and the technical response is the power of the heating element. Another is to go directly to functions, based on the team's experience or on current technology.

The Planning Matrix

To the right of the central matrix is found the planning matrix. This is a series of columns that evaluate the importance, satisfaction, and goal for each customer need. (See the QFD figure). The first column shows importance to the customer of each need. Here a group of customers may be asked to evaluate the importance of each need on a 1 to 5 scale (1=not important, 5=vital, of highest importance). In the next column the current performance of each product or service need, is rated by the group of customers. The difference between the columns is the gap - a negative number indicates possible overprovision, a positive number indicates a shortfall. The next few columns give the competitor's current performance on each customer need. The aim of this part of the exercise is to clearly identify the "SWOT" (strengths, weaknesses, opportunities, threats) of competitor products as against your own. For example, the kettle manufacturer may be well known for product sturdiness, but be weak on economy. If economy is highly ranked, this will point out an opportunity and, through the central matrix, show what technical characteristics can be used to make up this deficiency. The gap (if any) between own and competitors performance can then be determined. Since the QFD team now has detail on the gap for each need and of the importance of each need, they can then decide the desired goal for each customer need - normally expressed in the same units as the performance column. Deciding the goal for each need is an important task for the QFD team. These goals are the weights to be used in the relationship matrix. (Note: in some versions of QFD there are additional columns.)

The Central (or Relationship) Matrix

The central matrix lies at the heart of the house of quality diagram. This is where customer needs are matched against each technical characteristic. The nature of the relationship is noted in the matrix by an

appropriate symbol. The team can devise their own symbols; for instance, numbers may indicate the relative strength of the relationship or simply ticks may suffice. The strength of the relationship or impact is recorded in the matrix. These relationships may be nil, possibly linked, moderately linked or strongly linked. Corresponding weights (typically 0, 1, 3, 9) are assigned. Thereafter the scores for each technical characteristic are determined. The team, based on their experience and judgement, carries out this matching exercise. The idea is to clearly identify all means by which the "whats" can be achieved by the "hows". It will also check if all "whats" can in fact be achieved (insufficient technical

Matrix Analysis for QFD

Example : Design of a Hamburger to Customer preferences

Begin with a Focus Group to determine Customer Requirements and relative weightings. Then :

Customer Requirements	Customer preference weighting	Features			
		Beef	Bun	Lettuce	Ketchup
Seasoning	1	0 0	0 0	1 1	9 9
Flavour	3	27 9	0 0	0 0	9 3
Nutrition	3	27 9	9 3	0 0	0 0
Visual Appeal	5	45 9	5 1	5 1	5 1
Value for Money	5	45 9	5 1	0 0	5 1

	Beef	Bun	Lettuce	Ketchup
Weighted scores	144	19	6	28
Benchmarks				
Relative Cost	6	2	1	1
Score / Cost	24	9.5	6	28

Conclusion : Concentrate attention on Beef and Ketchup

characteristics?), and if some technical characteristics are not apparently doing anything (redundancy?). A blank row indicates a customer requirement not met. A blank column indicates a redundant technical feature. In practice, matrix evaluation can be a very large task (a moderate size QFD matrix of 30 x 30 has 900 cells to be evaluated). The team may split the task between them.

Technical Matrix

Immediately below the relationship matrix appears one or more rows for rankings such as cost or technical difficulty or development time. The choice of these is dependent on the product. These will enable the team to judge the efficacy of various technical solutions. The prime row uses the customer weightings and central matrix to derive the relative technical characteristic rankings. A full example is shown on the previous page.

Next, below the relationship matrix in the QFD figure, comes one or more rows for competitive evaluation. Here, where possible, "hard" data is used to compare the actual physical or engineering characteristics of your product against those of competitors. In the kettle example these would include watts of electricity, mass, and thermal conductivity of the kettle walls. This is where benchmarking is done. By now the QFD team will know the critical technical characteristics, and these should be benchmarked against competitors (See the section on Benchmarking - especially competitive benchmarking). So to the right of the relationship matrix one can judge relative customer perceptions and below the relative technical performance.

The bottom row of the house, which is also the "bottom line" of the QFD process, is the target technical characteristics. These are expressed in physical terms and are decided upon after team discussion of the complete house contents, as described below. The target characteristics are, for some, the final output of the exercise, but many would agree that it is the whole process of information assembly, ranking, and team discussion that goes into QFD which is the real benefit, so that the real output is improved inter-functional understanding.

The Roof of the House

The roof of the house is the technical interaction matrix. The diagonal format allows each technical characteristic to be viewed against each other one. This simply reflects any technical tradeoffs that may exist. For example with the kettle two technical characteristics may be insulation ability and water capacity. These have a negative relationship; increasing the insulation decreases the capacity. These interactions are made explicit, using the technical knowledge and experience of the team. Some cells may highlight challenging technical issues - for instance thin insulation in a kettle, which may be the subject of R&D work leading to competitive advantage. The roof is therefore useful to highlight areas in which R&D work could best be focused.

Using the house as a decision tool

The central matrix shows what the required technical characteristics are that will need design attention. The costs of these can be seen with reference to the base rows. This may have the effect of shifting priorities if costs are important. Then the technical tradeoffs are examined. Often there will be more than one technical way to impact a particular customer requirement, and this is clear from rows in the matrix. It may also be that one technical alternative has a negative influence on another customer requirement. This is found out by using the roof matrix. Eventually, through a process of team discussion, a team consensus will emerge. This may take some time, but experience shows that time and cost is repaid many times over as the actual design, engineering and manufacturing steps proceed.

The bottom line is now the target values of technical characteristics. This set can now go into the next house diagram. This time the target technical characteristics become the "customer requirements" or "whats", and the new vertical columns (or "hows") are, perhaps, the technologies, the assemblies, the materials, or the layouts. And so the process "deploys" until the team feels that sufficient detail has been considered to cover all co-ordination considerations in the process of bringing the product to market.

Note: QFD may be used in several stages in order to "deploy" customer requirements all the way to the final manufacturing or procedural stages. Here the outcome of one QFD matrix (e.g. the technical specifications) becomes the input into the next matrix that may aim to look at process specifications to make the product.

Assembling the team

A QFD team should have up to a dozen members with representation from all sections concerned with the development and launch of the product. Team composition may vary depending on whether new products or the improvement of existing products is under consideration. The important thing is that there is representation from all relevant sections and disciplines. There may well be a case for bringing in outsiders to stimulate the creative process and to ask the "silly" questions. Team members must have the support of their section heads. These section heads may feel it necessary to form a steering group. QFD teams are not usually full time, but must be given sufficient time priority to avoid time clashes. The team leader may be full time for an important QFD. The essential characteristics are team leadership skills rather than a particular branch of knowledge.

Relationship with other techniques

As mentioned, QFD is a "meta" technique in that several other techniques can be fitted in with it. For example, value management may be used to explore some of the technical alternatives, costs and tradeoffs in greater detail. Taguchi analysis is commonly used with QFD because it is ideally suited to examining the most sensitive engineering characteristics so as to produce a robust design. Failure mode and effect analysis (FMEA) can be used to examine consequences of failure, and so to throw more light on the technical interactions matrix. In the way the QFD team carries out its work, weights alternatives, generates alternatives, groups characteristics, and so on, there are many possibilities. QFD only provides the broad concept. There is much opportunity for adaptation and innovation.

Further reading:
Ronald G. Day, *Quality Function Deployment*, ASQC Quality Press, Milwaukee, WI, 1994
Lou Cohen, *Quality Function Deployment: How to make QFD work for you*, Addison Wesley, Reading MA, 1995

Value Engineering and Value Analysis

Value engineering and analysis (VE/VA) has traditionally been used for cost reduction in engineering design. But the power of its methodology means that it is an effective weapon for quality and productivity improvement in manufacturing and in services. Today the term value management (VM) recognises this fact.

The first step in any VA/VE/VM project is Orientation. This involves selecting the appropriate team, and training them in basic value concepts. The best VE/VA/VM is done in multidisciplinary teams. "Half of VE is done by providing the relevant information," says Jaganathan. By this he means that clarity of communication about customer (internal or external) is half the battle, particularly if customer needs have changed without anyone taking notice.

VM proper begins by systematically identifying the most important functions of a product or service. Then alternatives for the way the function can be undertaken are examined using creative thinking. A search procedure homes in on the most promising alternatives, and eventually the best alternative is implemented. One can recognise in these steps much similarity with various other quality techniques such as quality function deployment, the systematic use of the 7 tools of quality, and the Deming cycle. In fact these are all mutually reinforcing. VM brings added insight, and a powerful analytical and creative force to bear.

Value engineering was pioneered in the USA by General Electric, but has gained from value specialists such as Mudge and from the writers on creative thinking such as Edward de Bono. Today the concepts of TRIZ are most relevant. The Society of American Value Engineers (SAVE) has fostered the development.

VM usually works at the fairly detailed level of a particular component or sub-system, but has also been used in a hierarchical fashion working down level by

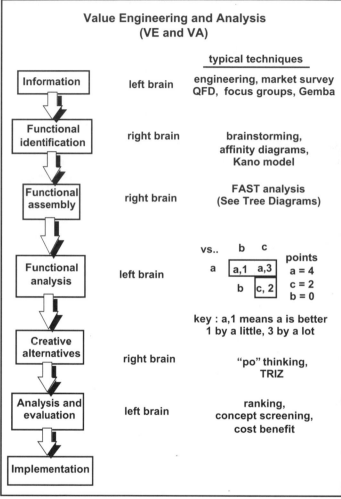

level from an overall product or service concept to the detail. At each level the procedure described would be repeated. Like many other quality and productivity techniques, VM is a group activity. It requires a knowledgeable group of people, sharing their insights and stimulating one another's ideas, to make progress. But there is no limitation on who can participate. VM can and has been used at every level from chief executive to shop floor.

What appears to give value management particular power is the deliberate movement from "left brain" (linear) analysis to "right brain" (creative) thinking. (Stringer has explained this.) Effective problem solving requires both the logical step forward and the "illogical" creative leap. Edward de Bono, of lateral thinking fame, talks about "provolution" - faster than evolution but more controlled than revolution.

Functional analysis

Functional analysis is the first step. The basic functions or customer requirements of the product or service are listed, or brainstormed out. (Right brain thinking.) A function is best described by a verb and a noun, such as "make sound", "transfer pressure", "record personal details" or "greet customer". The question to be answered is "what functions does this product/service undertake?" Typically there will be a list of half a dozen or more functions. There is a temptation to take the basic function for granted. Do not do this; working through often gives very valuable insights. For instance, for a domestic heating time controller, some possible functions are "activate at required times", "encourage economy", and "supply heat when needed". The example shows a hamburger design.

Pairwise comparison or points distribution may be used to weight the functions or requirements. In pairwise comparison, each function is compared with each other function, and 1 point is given to the most important of the two, or zero points if the functions are considered equally important. Adding up the scores gives the relative weightings These relative weightings need to be converted to percentages such that the sum adds up to 100%. Now the components of the product are listed as columns in the matrix. See the figure. Then the importance of each component to each function is estimated and converted to a percentage of total cost. In the example, the function "taste good" is estimated to be influenced 50% by the beef and 25% each by bun and ketchup. The influence is written in the bottom left hand corner of each cell. The weighted influence (i.e. the weight x the influence) is written in the top right of each cell. The overall influence of each component is the sum of the top right hand cell entries, and is written in a row below the matrix. Then the cost of each component is estimated, and written in a row. The last step is to calculate a value index, which is the influence % divided by the cost %. Ratios less than one are prime candidates for cost reduction. Ratios substantially greater than one indicate the possibility of enhancing the feature. Back to the right brain.

Creativity
Now the creative phase begins. This is concerned with developing alternative, more cost effective, ways of achieving the basic functions and reducing costs of the most important components. Here the rules of brainstorming must be allowed - no criticism, listing

customer requirements	importance	percentage importance	components			
			beef	bun	lettuce	ketchup
taste good	6	46	23 .5	11.5 .25		11.5 .25
provide nutrition	2	15	10.5 .7	4.5 .3		
appeal visually	1	8	2.4 .3	1.6 .2	2.4 .3	1.6 .2
value for money	4	31	15.5 .5	15.5 .5		
		100%				
overall influence		%	51.4	33.1	2.4	13.1
cost (%)		%	62	30	20	8
value index		influence/ cost	0.83	1.1	0.12	1.6
			reduce cost ?	OK	reduce cost !	enhance

down all ideas, writing down as many ideas as possible however apparently ridiculous. Various "tricks" can be used; deliberate short periods of silence, writing ideas on cards anonymously, sequencing suggestions in a "round robin" fashion, making a sketch, role-playing out a typical event, viewing the scene from an imaginary helicopter or explaining the product to an "extra terrestrial". Humour can be an important part of creativity. See also TRIZ, later.

A particularly powerful tool is the use of the de Bono "po" word. This is simply a random noun selected from a dictionary to conjure up mental images that are then used to develop new ideas. For instance "cloud" could

be used in conjunction with the design of packaging where the basic function was "give protection". The word cloud conjures images of fluffiness (padding?), air (air pockets?), rain (waterproof?), silver lining (metal reinforcement?), shadow (can't see the light, leads to giving the user information), cloud is "hard to pick up" (how is the packaging lifted?), wind (whistling leading to a warning of overload?), moisture (water/humidity resistant? water can take the shape of its container - can the packaging?), obscuring the view (a look inside panel?), and so on. Do not jump to other "po" words; select one and let the group exhaust its possibilities.

Analysis and evaluation

Now back to the left brain. Sometimes a really outstanding idea will emerge. Otherwise there may be several candidates. Some of these candidates may need further investigation before they can be recommended. (In the above example, is it feasible or possible to introduce some sort of metal reinforcement?). Beware of throwing out ideas too early - the best ideas are often a development from an apparently poor idea. So take time to discuss them. In some cases it may be necessary for the team to take a break while more technical feasibility is evaluated or costs determined, by specialists.

There are several ways to evaluate. Pairwise comparison with multi-discipline group discussion is good possibility. Another possibility is to write all ideas on cards, then give a set of cards to pairs of group members, and ask each pair to come up with the best two ideas. Then get the full group to discuss all the leading ideas. Yet another is to draw up a cost-benefit chart (cost along one axis, benefits along another). Ask the group members to plot the locations of ideas on the chart. There is no reason why several of these methods cannot be used together. Do what makes the group happy - it is their project and their ideas.

Implementation
Implementation of the most favourable change is the last step. One of the benefits of the VM process is that group members tend to identify with the final solution, and to understand the reasons behind it. This should make implementation easier and faster.

Further reading:
Kaneo Akiyama, *Function Analysis*, Productivity Press, Cambridge MA, 1991
G. Jaganathan, *Getting More at Less Cost*, Tata McGraw Hill, New Delhi, 1996

Acknowledgement
Many of the original ideas on value engineering are due to Art Mudge. These and other ideas have been further developed by Dick Stringer and Graham Bodman of the South African Value Management Foundation.

TRIZ

TRIZ is a family of techniques, developed originally in Russia, for product invention and creativity. It is superb for innovative product design, and for production process problem solving. TRIZ is a Russian acronym for the theory of inventive problem solving. In 1948, the originator of TRIZ, Genrich Altshuller, suggested his ideas on improving inventive work to Stalin (a big mistake!), and was imprisoned in Siberia until 1954. His ideas once again fell into disfavour and only emerged with perestroyka. The first TRIZ ideas reached the U.S. in the mid 1980s.

TRIZ is already linking up with Lean in Policy Deployment and QFD, and with Six Sigma in Design for Six Sigma. Lean TRIZ Six Sigma seems destined for a big future.

The fundamental belief of TRIZ is that invention can be taught. All (?) inventions can be reduced to a set of rules or principles and that the generic problem has almost certainly already been solved. The principles, relying on physics, engineering, and knowledge of materials can be learned. A TRIZ team uses the basic principles to generate specific solutions. Here, only a brief overview or flavour of some of the 40 principles can be attempted. TRIZ is bound to, and deserves to, become better known. We hope this will be a stimulant to you to acquire some TRIZ publications.

Darrell Mann has summarized TRIZ into five main elements.

Contradictions TRIZ believes that the world's best innovations have emerged from situations where the inventor has sought to avoid conventional trade-offs. For example, composite materials that are strong and light. TRIZ uses a matrix to identify which of the 40 principles are most likely to apply in any contradiction.

Idealists TRIZ encourages problem solvers to begin with the Ideal Final Result and work backwards, rather than moving forward from the current state.

Functionality This is an extension of value engineering principles. (See last section.)

Use of Resource TRIZ encourages making best use of any resource that is not being used to its maximum potential. 'Turning lemons into lemonade'.

Thinking in Space and Time Don't just think about the current state in the present, but also about the past and future, and about wider states (supply chains?) and narrower states (sub processes?).

All hugely relevant to Lean!

A partial list of some of the 40 inventive problems includes: partial or overdone action (if you can't solve the whole problem, solve just a part to simplify it), moving to a new dimension (use multi layers, turn it on its side, move it along a plane, etc.) self-service (make the product service itself, make use of wasted energy), changing the colour (or make it transparent, use a coloured additive), mechanical vibration (make use of the energy of vibrations or oscillations), hydraulic or pneumatic assembly (replace solids with gas or liquid, join parts hydraulically), porous material (make the part porous, or fill the pores in advance), thermal expansion (use these properties, change to more than one material with different coefficients of expansion), copying (instead of using the object use a copy or a projection of it), thin membranes (use flexible membranes, insulate or isolate using membranes), regenerating parts (recycle), use a composite material. This is a powerful list - just reading them can stimulate ideas.

Altschuller emphasises thinking in terms of the "ideal machine" or ideal solution as a first step to problem solving. You have a hot conservatory? It should open by itself when the temperature rises! So now think of devices that will achieve this: bimetallic expansion strips, expanding gas balloons, a solar powered fan.

A general methodology comprises three steps: First, determine why the problem exists. Second, "state the contradiction". Third, "imagine the ideal solution", or imagine yourself as a magician who can create anything. For example, consider the problem of moving a steel beam. Why is it a problem? Because it cannot roll. The contradiction is that the shape prevents it from rolling. So, ideally, it should roll. How? By placing semi-circular inserts on each side along the beam.

Finally, invention requires practice and method. Like golfer Gary Player who said the more he practised the better his luck seemed to get, Altschuller suggests starting young and keeping one's mind in shape with practice problems. Also keeping a database of ideas gleaned from a variety of publications.

Many TRIZ ideas require some technical knowledge, or at least technical aptitude. Therefore it will not work well with every group. However, it is most useful for designers, technical problem solvers, persons involved with QFD, and for implementation of lean manufacturing (particularly the technical issues).

Further reading:
 G. Altschuller, *And Suddenly the Inventor Appeared*, Technical Innovation Centre, Inc., Worcester MA, 1996
Darrell Mann, *Hands on Systemic Innovation*, CREAX, 2002
Semyan Sarransky and Ellen Domb, *Simplified TRIZ*, St Lucie, 2002.

Concept Screening

Concept screening is a simple but powerful tool used not only to home in on the best concept or alternative, but also to improve it. The late Stuart Pugh's method is widely used for QFD, but also with lean implementation and layout, product design and development, and project selection.

Concept screening uses a matrix approach. See the figure. A team, preferably multidisciplinary or from a "diagonal slice" should do the work. Competing concepts are listed in the columns. It is often useful to include a sketch in each column. Concept screening works best when there are less than about 10 competing concepts, so if the number is greater than this use multi voting to select the top 10. Multi voting simply gives 5 votes to each participant who may allocate them between the concepts as he or she pleases.

The selection criteria are listed in the rows, and are chosen based on customer needs and organisation needs. The latter may include cash flow, manufacturability, and marketing compatibility. Generally there would be a maximum of around 20 selection criteria. One important consideration, however, is that the selection criteria (at this stage) should exclude relatively unimportant factors.

Then, following team discussion, one of the concepts is selected as the benchmark or baseline. This may be a competitors product or an industry standard.

Thereafter, each concept is evaluated against the baseline concept, for each criteria, simply using a + sign where better than, - (negative sign) where worse than, and 0 where approximately the same. The team should seek consensus on these evaluations. Many will be clear, but where there is direct quantitative information available this should be used directly. For instance, in evaluating competing factory layouts one of the criteria may be flow length. The lengths in each concept should be measured. Other examples are the number of parts where inventory or assembly time is one of the criteria.

Following the rating exercise, the scores for each concept are added up. A + counts +1, a - (negative) counts -1, and a zero counts zero. This establishes the rank order.

Before discarding any concept, ways should first be sought of improving it. Look at the negatives and ask if features affecting these criteria can be incorporated. The TRIZ concept may be useful here - see above. Another option may be to create a hybrid design, combining the best features from two or more options. Such re-evaluations may require the concept screening session to be delayed to allow greater investigation or redesign.

Pugh's Concept Screening Technique

	Concept			
Selection Criteria	Layout 1	Layout 2	Layout 3	Layout 4
Speed	0	- 1	0	+1
Cost	0	+1	- 1	+1
Reliability	0	+1	+1	0
Flow Length	0	- 1	0	+1
Flexibility	0	- 1	+1	- 1
Quality	0	- 1	0	+1
Score	0	- 2	+1	+3

Conclusion : Layout 4 looks most promising, but can the Reliability features from Layout 2 or 3 be incorporated ? Flexibility features from Layout 3 be incorporated ?

Finally the team reassembles and makes the final selection, often involving a repeat of the scoring process and now incorporating less important criteria. Again, consensus should be sought, and the outcome should make sense to all. If anyone is uncomfortable with the outcome it may be that one or more selection criteria is redundant or missing. This may involve yet another round of evaluation. The outcome is not the best answer, but a short list of the most promising options - for further investigation.

Further Reading:
Stuart Pugh, *Total Design*, Addison Wesley, Reading MA, 1990
Stuart Pugh, *Creating Innovative Products Using Total Design*, Addison Wesley, 1996

New Product Ramp Up

There appear to be distinct differences between traditional and Lean ways doing new product introduction and ramp up. The following are a few:

- The Lean way is to separate out the variables. The famous catapult exercise in Six Sigma training

dramatically illustrates the necessity for removing as much variation as possible before attempting to maximise the length of throw. Otherwise you don't know if changes are the result of changing the variables or inherent variation in the process. The same applies in ramp up. First, concentrate on the machines and methods. When these are proven capable, move to the next stage. Second, concentrate on the people and the materials. Third, concentrate on meeting the takt time, and reducing it as real production begins. Do not try to sort it all out at once.

- Extending this idea, a complete new product – say a car with new body and new engine is risky. Master one major introduction at a time.

- And yet further, do not overlap major new product introductions. Finish one off, and learn the lessons before introducing the next major new product.

- In early days, before manufacture of customer-destined products begins, hold short sharp blitz-type runs as several separate exercises using non-saleable product. Learn the maximum from each. This is PDCA – with deliberate stops in between.

- Ramp up the capacity by adjusting the takt time. Don't try to prove the maximum rate is possible and then settle down to a much slower rate. In other words, control the learning curve.

- In slowly decreasing the takt time, try to get quality right for each level – rather than talking about 'unit losses' – meaning the number of imperfect units for a particular takt time.

- Accumulate the lessons learned systematically – and use as a check list next time around.

- Have specific individual responsibility and accountability for each aspect. This must be completely sorted out before transferring to the next stage gate. Do not allow carry over.

- Separate out new product development from ramp up. To attempt to combine them risks many cycles of adjustment and missing the target launch time.

- Well before the start of saleable product production, set targets concerning design freeze, except for safety, which is the responsibility of design, and for options freeze which is the responsibility of marketing.

Acknowledgement
Emma Wilson highlighted many of these points during her MSc dissertation at Cardiff Business School.

Lean Supply

Supply Chain Thinking

Today we understand that supply chains compete rather than companies competing. This section, developed from Kopczak and Johnson, reviews some of the shifts in thinking that have occurred.

- *From Segment cost reduction to a Systems Approach*. A supply chain is a system of customers, distributors, suppliers, manufacturers, and transporters, held together by physical and information flows. It is total cost and total performance that needs focus, rather than local objectives such as minimizing transportation or inventory costs. Moreover, a supply chain is a dynamic, evolving system.

- *From Single Stage to End-to-End*. Unfortunately some software vendors (and even some consultants) talk about 'supply chain software' meaning establishing links with the first tier of supply and the first tier of distribution. A fair start, but a great limitation on potential. The true chain is end-to-end, raw material to final customer, and beyond.

- *From Supply Chain to Demand Chain*. The very phrase 'supply chain' is misleading from a Lean perspective, because it implies push rather than pull. A Lean supply chain needs to be pulled, preferably by one pacemaker. Demand management implies managing demand information proactively along the end-to-end chain. Despite this name problem, we will stick with the supply chain phrase.

- *From Linear Chain to Network*. Most supply chains are complex networks rather than simple linear chains. There will often be convergences and conflicts of resources requiring complex scheduling. Unfortunately some supply chain mapping tools do not give sufficient emphasis to this point. The Lean Building Blocks and the location of supply chain supermarkets are useful.

- *From Order Fulfillment to Life Cycle*. A supply chain may be thought of as linear flow from raw material to end customer. But today we should think of a matrix. One axis shows the stages from raw material to final customer. The other axis shows the process of product design, process design, marketing, order fulfillment, field service and support, and disposal and recycling. The cells of the matrix are linked by information flows, physical flows, and money flows.

- *From Purchasing links to Multi-Function links to Enterprise links*. Once co-ordination was primarily through purchasing thinking primarily about cost. Then design, engineering, quality, accounting and materials management links became the norm. Supplier evaluation became multi factored. The next shift is towards gaining competitive advantage for the entire chain – for example segmenting by demand and response type. It also implies supply chain mediation – working through the costs of inventory, capacity, discounts and yield management, postponement and variety decisions for the end-to-end chain.

- *From 'Single Company Product Design to Collaborative, Concurrent Product, Process and Supply-Chain Design'* (Kopczak and Johnson). Manufacturing has recognized that perhaps 80% of product costs are locked in at the design stage. So also with supply chains. Design for supply can involve decisions on build to order strategies such as postponement.

- *From Mass-Market Chains to Mass-Customization Chains*. A summary point. Lean supply chain thinking means a shift from batch push to one-piece customized build to order. It's a long process involving all the activities in this section of the book.

The American Production and Inventory Control Society (APICS) has five principles for supply chain. They make an excellent set. They are:

1. "Velocity" (or 365 / annual inventory turns) – to focus on flow.
2. "Variability" – the stability of the chain (see sections Demand Management and Variation).
3. "Vocalize" – ensuring good communication right along the chain.
4. "Visualize" – being able to see the full chain, like Seeing the Whole mapping.
5. "Value" – establishing the connections of daily decisions and execution with the creation of value for customers.

Further reading:
David Simchi-Levi, Philip Kamonsky, Edith Simchi-Levi, *Designing and Managing the Supply Chain*, Irwin McGraw Hill, Boston, 2000
Laura Rock Kopczak and M Eric Johnson, 'The Supply Chain Management Effect', *MIT Sloan Management Review*, Spring 2003, pp27-34
APICS web site:

Lean Supply Chain Basics

Trust and Partnership

Jeffrey Dyer produced a seminal book in 2000 in which he identified three key characteristics that make the Toyota US supply chain so effective. Although much has changed since Dyer's analysis - for instance Ford has hived off Visteon, GM has hived of Delphi, and Mercedes has acquired Chrysler, the points made remain valid and important in many industries. The three interrelated chararcteristics are:
The critical role of Trust. Trust is where the trustworthy partner builds confidence in its promises and commitments and does not exploit the vulnerabilities of its partners. Building trust takes time (for example in selecting and favouring suppliers) but then allows fast, flexible flow in new product introduction and in the supply chain. Bureaucracy and waste in the form of transactions can be dramatically cut. Dyer gives

impressive evidence of the extent of transaction costs, and the cost of mistrust. He points out that trust also encourages investment, innovation, and stable employment. Dyer shows Toyota in the USA well ahead in trustworthiness.
Investment in dedicated assets. Building on trust allows investment in dedicated assets. Dyer shows that Ford and GM during the 1990s internally manufactured about twice as much as Toyota, had approximately the same proportion of arms-length suppliers, but had approximately one fifth the proportion of supplier partners as Toyota. (Things have changed, since.) Dedicated assets are possible with partners, and in turn allow better productivity, quality, design, and speed. Incidentally, Dyer points out that the advantages of dedicated assets and partnership are much more important in complex industries - (it is here where Japanese industries are much more efficient), but are far less efficient in simple product industries where arms-length relationships may be beneficial.
The development and transfer of knowledge throughout the network. Again, made possible with trust and dedicated asssets, knowledge transfer (of both explicit and tacit knowledge) is a key factor in improvement in productivity and quality.

In the writer's experience Toyota cells in the UK are often far more productive than cells run for other manufacturers within the same supplier site. This is because they enjoy more assistance, get more stable schedules, have more confidence in the future, have more simple procedures, often get better terms, enjoy better coaching, and are less fearful about visits from Toyota improvement experts and engineers than most other customers.

Further reading:
Jeffrey Dyer, *Collaborative Advantage*, Oxford Univ Press, 2000

In the following sections other basics for Lean Supply are discussed.

Understanding and Managing Demand

The nature of demand needs to be understood. This relates to

- Kipling's 'Six Honest Serving Mean', What, Why, When, Where, How, Who. This amounts to detail on market segmentation. Take a hotel example: who are the customers (businessmen and tourists), what do they need (support and leisure), when (daytime and evening), why (working away from home, having a break), where (customized by location), how (focused hotels? separate blocks? secretarial support for business, video for tourists, etc).
- The Runners, Repeaters and Strangers concept (see the Essential Paretos).
- The Expected response time of different customer groups.
- The Possibility of influencing demand patterns by discounts and promotions.
- Trend, Seasonality and Variation – the last four taken together have an important influence on location of supply chain nodes, and on supply chain scheduling. It may be possible to fill-in troughs in demand with customer groups having longer response time and price expectations. For example, scheduling car assembly for hire cars in non-peak months, or pricing according to lead time like airlines.

Rationalizing Parts and Materials

As with companies, so with supply chains. Supplier rationalization, supplier partnership, supplier development, and supply chain scheduling are all waste if they are carried out on parts and components that should not be there in the first place. Rationalizing parts and materials is an essential early step in moving towards build to order, quick response, and low inventory supply chains. Part rationalization may even involve cutting a whole tier in the supply chain where parts and materials are taken in-house. For example a furniture manufacturer was able to do just that when he rationalized materials and purchased an NC laser cutter (with minimal changeover!) capable of cutting out hundreds of shapes previously supplied by half a dozen suppliers.

Refer to the section: The Essential Paretos: Part and Material Rationalization.

Supply Chain Structure

Supply Chain Structure is a first stage mapping exercise, involving drawing up the supply chain *network*. This is a cross between a value stream map and a 'brown paper' map. Locate this diagram on a large piece of paper in a central War Room, and encourage participants to add notes. Try to make it end-to-end if possible. Include on the network the demand information and response times segmented as appropriate. Use colored pens for different transport channels and write in the volumes. Certainly write in current inventory holdings at distribution warehouses and plants. Draw the various customer segments on the right, each with their own annual demands and a note on trend, seasonality, and variation. A series from / to matrix charts in one corner is often useful. It is simply a tool for understanding.

Costs are a useful addition. Where possible write these in. It may be possible to produce a set of Cost-Time Profiles (see separate section).

Finally, draw in the broad information flows. Use icons to indicate telephone, e-mail, EPOS or whatever, links.

Supply Chain Channel Selection

A basic principle of Lean, Business Process Reengineering, and modern Supply Chains is that not all products of the same category need to, or should, go along the same channel. A classic is Coca Cola that used to distribute drinks along one channel irrespective of customer. Now the channels are tailored to the requirements of supermarkets, pubs, vending machines, sporting events, and so on.

Refer to the section 'The Right Supply Chain' in the Strategy section.

With the demand information above, channels and locations can be tentatively selected. For instance, it may make sense to locate stable production in a low-cost but long response-time area, but to locate volatile demand products nearer to the markets even though manufacturing costs are higher. Consider also the location of design centres – for high tech products consider the penalties of design separated from manufacture.

Four Objectives and Six Trade-Offs

The four objectives and six trade-offs discussed in the Design section are also relevant to Supply Chains. In the case of supply chains they are – for each location and channel (and supplier):

- Cost: the costs of manufacture and distribution
- Time: customer expectations on delivery, and nominal response times
- Performance: Current performance on cost, quality, delivery
- Resources: skills and constraints
- Cost and Time: which is critical?
- Cost and Performance: what is the risk of performance shortfall?
- Cost and Resources: how much to develop?
- Time and Performance: what is the risk of performance shortfall?
- Time and Resources: how long to develop?
- Performance and Resources: are they capable?

Refer also to the section on Location Decisions.

Supplier Selection and Rationalization

For Lean supply to work there must of necessity be few or single suppliers per part. The idea is to work with a few good, trusted suppliers who supply a wide range of parts. During the last decade drastic reductions in many a company's supplier base have taken place. An objective is to remove the long tail of the supplier Pareto curve whereby perhaps 10% of parts are supplied by 80% of the suppliers.

Generally, supplier partnership makes sense for "A" and possibly "B" parts; less so for commodity items, where commodity purchasing via internet auctions may be developing. Part criticality and risk also influence the rationalization decision; you would not risk partnership with a company having poor industrial relations, or weak finances, or poor quality assurance. This means that a team approach is necessary in supplier selection. The Purchasing Officer may co-ordinate, but throughout the partnership Design would talk to their opposite number in Design, Quality to Quality, Production control to Production control, and so on.

There should be little risk of "being taken for a ride" because the supplier has too much to lose. But there are ways around this too: having one supplier exclusively supplying a part to one plant, but another supplier exclusively supplying the same part to another plant. This spreads the risk whilst still achieving single supplier advantages. Alternatively there is the Japanese practice of cultivating several suppliers simultaneously but then awarding an exclusive contract to one supplier for a part for the life of the product, and selecting another supplier for a similar part going into another end product.

Four Models for Supplier Strategy

There are at least four models for thinking about supplier selection and sourcing that should be considered by Lean supply chain managers. Several logistics managers make use of more than one of the following to help structure their selection and rationalization process.

The Runner Repeater Stranger / ABC inventory model, discussed under inventory considerations in the Future State section of the book. Clearly a difference in sourcing policy between A category runner parts (close partnership?) and A category stranger parts (loose partnership?), should be considered. Also a difference between A category runners and C category runner parts (arms-length?). And so on.

Part complexity and logistics supply chain complexity. Consider a two by two matrix with part or process complexity along one axis and logistics supply chain complexity along the other axis. Logistics complexity may also refer to the needs for flexibility and responsive lead times. Long lead time in itself does not indicate logistics complexity. High High (both process complexity and logistics complexity): here close partnerships are a possibility. The 'low-low' segment may suggest global low cost purchasing via perhaps E Bay. Complex parts and processes but with low logistics difficulties may suggest partnership sourcing on a worldwide basis. Finally, high logistics difficulties but with low part or process complexity may suggest local sourcing but from arms length suppliers.

Jeffrey Dyer suggests three categories - internally manufactured, partner suppliers, and arms-length independent suppliers. His analysis shows the huge advantages gained by Toyota in sourcing approximately half its component costs from partner suppliers. But the other two categories each make up approximately one quarter of total component costs. Dyer refers to this mix as the governance profile. But the ideal profile differs by industry favoring a higher proportion of partners in high-tech adaptive industry. Note however that Toyota does not seem to have joined the E Bay electronic purchasing revolution, preferring to deal with a limited number of suppliers even in arms-length relationships.

Clayton Christensen has a concept based on his 'disruptive technologies' thesis (see the Strategy section). This is not a supplier selection concept, but more to do with sourcing strategy. The performance of a product type (such as a PC) or major subassembly type (such as hard disk) improves with time. The needs of customers also grows, but generally at a slower rate. In early days in the life cycle, when the needs of customers are above the product performance curve, Christensen calls this 'not good enough'. But as performance grows, the product or subassembly outstrips the needs of customers, even demanding ones. PCs are now in this category for most customers. Christensen calls this 'good enough'. When a product is strongly good enough it is vulnerable to disruptive technologies (see the Strategy section). Christensen believes that a sea change occurs as products or assemblies move from the not good enough to the good enough category. In the former case, integration is critical to success, (say the early days of Ford), because R&D, design, and manufacture have to be tightly integrated. The integrators make the money. But in the good enough category, a company must compete on new dimensions of speed and flexibility. Modules and interfaces are more clearly specifiable. In this case disintegration is required - being able to source the current best components from the appropriate suppliers. Here, power shifts to those that are able to supply the needed modules with the required flexibility. But the OEMs have power also - forcing suppliers to develop more innovative components; in fact saying to them that they are 'not good enough'. Has Ford/Visteon and GM/Delphi done the right thing? They had no choice but to divest, but could they have retained a partnership interest in a profitable sector and will they be able to adapt themselves to fast, flexible, flow?

Further reading:
Jeffrey Dyer, *Collaborative Advantage*, Oxford Univ Press, 2000
Clayton Christensen et al, 'Skate to Where the Money Will Be', *Harvard Business Review*, November 2001, pp72-81

The Bullwhip Effect and Amplification

The Bullwhip effect is a supply chain phenomenon in which fluctuations in orders amplify as they move along a supply chain. There is a vertical dimension to do with instability and growth in magnitude and a horizontal dimension to do with fluctuations over time. The Bullwhip effect can seriously damage the performance of a supply chain, however Lean an individual player in the chain. The effects are having to keep overcapacity, fluctuations between low and high demand even when there is little fluctuation at the customer end, and poor customer service.

Lee et al and Simchi-Levi et al identify five inter-related factors as causes:

1. *Demand forecasting and signal processing*. Thesis one element of the so-called the Forrester or amplification effect. Forecasters at each stage of the supply chain try to hold and adjust safety stocks that are a buffer against variation. A chain reaction takes place often as a result of a minor disturbance leading to greater variation and hence more safety stock all along the chain. Signal processing amplification also results from the way orders are interpreted, so is linked to batching below. Improving the forecasts and reducing uncertainty by sharing information is an effective counter.

2. *Lead times*. The other element of the so-called Forrester effect, results directly from the fact that safety stocks and order quantities are calculated from lead times and variability. Reducing the lead-time improves performance.

3. *Batching*. Also known as the Burbidge effect this results orders being placed in batches – a large batch followed by no orders, in a repeating cycle. Batches may be ordered for transportation or order cost reasons. The EPE and milkround concept can help here.

4. *Price fluctuations and promotions*. Supply chain players may try to anticipate price increases or take advantage of quantity discounts. Information sharing and coordination of response to increases can help. Elimination of inappropriate quantity discounts in favor of 'every day low pricing' is effective.

5. *Rationing and Inflated orders*. Also known as the Houlihan effect, this results from supply chain partners trying to anticipate shortages or distributors rationing supplies in the interests or fairness. Over ordering can lead to a vicious cycle where the increase is interpreted as an increase in ultimate customer demand rather than a safety stock policy change. Orders lead to shortages leading to higher orders and so on until extra capacity is installed, leading a collapse in orders. Again, sharing of information is a way to go.

Note that these bullwhip factors are usually thought of in a supply chain context but may also occur internally within a plant.

A centralized information system, with actual demand forecasts provided by the first stage to all players in the chain is an effective method of significantly reducing the bullwhip effect. Not quite as good is where each player determines target inventory levels determined from moving averages from the next stage downstream, and uses this target as the basis for orders to the next stage upstream.

Disney and Towill suggest that the appropriate use of VMI (vendor manager inventory) may be a solution. Here the customer passes inventory information to the supplier instead of orders. The actual inventory at the customer is compared with a pre-agreed reorder point (ROP), set to cover adequate availability. Both parties also agree an order-up-to point (OUP). When actual inventory is at or below the ROP the supplier delivers the difference up to the OUP. This system can work well between each tier in a supply chain, and is made more effective using milkrounds.

Further reading:
David Simchi-Levi, Philip Kaminsky, Edith Simchi-Levi, *Designing and Managing the Supply Chain*, (Second edition), McGraw Hill, 2003
Steve Disney and Denis Towill, 'Vendor-managed inventory and bullwhip reduction in a two-level supply chain', *IJOPM*, v 23, nos 5 and 6, 2003

Milkrounds

The long-established Milkround concept has recently begun to 'take-off'. The idea is that a vehicle travels frequently around a set route starting and ending at the plant, and visiting several suppliers en route. At each supplier a small (daily?) batch of (several?) parts is colleted in a particular window slot – typically a half hour. A milkround may also be found in distribution.

The milkround concept is similar to the waterspider or runner concept within a plant. Runners have proved a hugely effective concept within plant. Likewise milkrounds are proving a hugely affective way to reduce amplification and to encourage steady flow between supply chain members. The runner is the internal drumbeat; the milkround is the external drumbeat. The greater the degree of mixed model, or the lower the EPE, the better it will all work. Milkrounds are also an aid to problem surfacing and improvement. See the separate section on runners and waterspider.

Milkrounds can reduce the waste of transport, improve fast, flexible flow and reduce leadtimes. It encourages confidence, and as a result reduces buffer inventories and encourages synchronized scheduling. Perhaps a small batch of several parts is collected every day rather than a large batch of one part number every week. Moreover, an efficient routing calling at several suppliers can reduce total distance. If the company is really clever it can deliver finished products, return totes or even move parts from one supplier to another. Some milkrounds include cross docking, whereby parts are picked up on a milkround from more distant suppliers, perhaps using smaller vehicles that consolidate into a larger vehicle. Synchronization is needed to minimize the length of time inventory spends on the cross dock.

The marginal cost of joining a milkround circuit may be small. This idea should be sold to supplier meetings. The more suppliers or distributors that join, the less the cost to everyone. Today, milkrounds are 'owned' by either OEMs or first tier suppliers, although the vehicles may be owned by a third party contactor.

Supplier Partnerships

This section expands on the Partnership concept. There is some overlap with sections throughout the book.

The Partnership philosophy is that, through co-operation rather than confrontation, both parties benefit. It is a longer-term view, emphasizing total cost rather than product price. Cost includes not only today's price of the part or product, but also its quality (defect / ppm rate), delivery reliability, the simplicity with which the transaction is processed, and the future potential for price reductions.

But partnership goes further: Long term, stable relationships are sought rather than short term, adversarial,

quick advantage. The analogy of a marriage is often used. It may have its ups and downs, but commitment remains. In a partnership, contracts will be longer term to give the supplier confidence and the motivation to invest and improve. Both parties recognize that the game whereby low prices are bid and then argued up on contingencies once the contract is awarded is wasteful and counter-productive. Instead, it may be possible for both parties to co-operate on price reduction, sharing the benefits between them. Such co-operation may be achieved through the temporary secondment of staff. See the next section on Supplier Associations.

For partnership to work there must of necessity be few or single suppliers per part. There is not necessarily a risk of "being taken for a ride" because there is too much to lose. But there are ways around this too: having one supplier exclusively supplying a part to one plant, but another supplier exclusively supplying the same part to another plant. This spreads the risk whilst still achieving single supplier advantages. Alternatively there is the Japanese practice of cultivating several suppliers simultaneously but then awarding an exclusive contract to one supplier for a part for the life of the product, and selecting another supplier for a similar part going into another end product. The idea is to work with a few good, trusted suppliers who supply a wide range of parts. Partnership has therefore resulted in drastic reductions in many a company's supplier base. An objective is to remove the long tail of the supplier Pareto curve whereby perhaps 10% of parts are supplied by 80% of the suppliers.

On Partnership on the Distribution side, Caterpillar is a famous example, treating its dealers as integral with the parent company. Dealers in turn build close relationships with customers. Relationships are built over the long term by some simple rules: 'share gain as well as pain', 'strive for continuity in relationships and consistency in policies', and 'communicate constantly'. (See Fites reference). Caterpillar dealers together are worth more than the parent company, and invest with the company in new product line introduction, so 'us' and 'them' becomes meaningless.

In common with Lean Thinking, partnership aims at waste reduction. Purchasing and Supply muda include multiple quotes, order acknowledgement, remittance advices, invoices, counting, repackaging, checking, returns, expediting, double handling, and of course storage.

Usually, partnership begins with a Pareto-type analysis of suppliers by cost and number of parts. Then, exploration as to how to reduce or combine sourcing begins. Supplier days are held, often annually, when company plans and objectives are explained, measures given, prizes for best performance given out, and factory tours held. For true partnership, director level meetings are held periodically, with much more frequent manager and engineer contact.

On quality, the partnership aims at zero receiving inspection and at delivery directly to the point of use. By the way, partnership quality should talk in terms of ppm levels, not percentages. Packaging and part orientation may be specifically designed to reduce waste. Delivery would often be subject to kanban call-off: the partner would be warned of gross requirements far out, more detailed requirements close in, but the actual sequence and timing of delivery is controlled by kanban. Many attempt this, far fewer achieve it. Both sides need to work towards schedule stability: the customer not to change his mind at the last moment, and the supplier to provide reliable delivery. Unstable schedules ultimately cost the customer in terms of money and risk, and reduce the possibility of productivity gain at the supplier. Sometimes, the supplier is responsible for maintaining inventory levels at a customer, called VMI (vendor managed inventory) that is increasingly found for consumables. Other times, a manufacturer may write the production schedule of the supplier. As trust builds, self-billing or reconciliation becomes possible "we built 100 cars, so here is our cheque for the 500 tyres we must have used".

Improved communication links via EDI or EPOS further enhance partnership advantages. Delivery co-operation becomes possible either through "milkrounds" (whereby small quantities are collected from several firms in an area every day, rather than from one firm once per week), or, where more work is given to one supplier, mixed loads are sent every day rather than one-product loads once per week. This improves flow and reduces inventories.

Co-operation on design is part of partnership. The manufacturer recognizes the supplier's ability to design the parts that it makes, rather than simply specifying. This policy of "open specs" or "black box" specs can lead to faster, lower cost, and more up to date part supply. The partnership idea encourages the concept of a company sticking to its core business, whilst putting out non-core business.

Generally, supplier partnership makes sense for "A" and possibly "B" parts; less so for commodity items. Part criticality and risk also influence the partnership decision; you would not risk partnership with a company having poor industrial relations, or weak finances, or poor quality assurance. This means that a team approach is necessary in supplier selection. The Purchasing Officer may co-ordinate, but throughout the partnership Design would talk to their opposite number in Design, Quality to Quality, Production control to Production control, and so on.

Disadvantages? Time, commitment, costs of establishment, risk of inappropriate choices of partner, and short term cost reduction opportunities foregone against medium term gains.

Value engineering (see Design chapter) is a technique that both parties may adopt for mutual advantage. VE/VA is a powerful technique for cost, quality and delivery. In advanced partnerships a "satellite plant" dedicated to a particular customer and located nearby, or "suppliers in residence" where the supplier's operation and or some of its staff are permanently located on the customer's site, may be worth consideration. Volkswagen's Brazilian plants are reported to use supplier's employees on the VW assembly line - is this the future of partnership, or a quest for flexibility?

In Japan, and increasingly in the rest of the world, supplier partnership is now expanding down from relationships with first tier suppliers, to second and even third tier. Larger firms in the car industry have been leaders, but other industries and smaller firms are following. The thought, in common with TQM, is that quality is only as good as the weakest link.

Supplier Associations

The supplier association concept is an extension of the supplier partnership concept. Supplier associations are "clubs" of suppliers who form together for mutual help and learning. Members may all supply one company, or are all from one region serving different customers. The associations seek to learn best practices from other members or to gain competitive advantage and/or productivity through co-operation. In Japan, Supplier Associations are known as kyoryoku kai.

There are three types of association: for operations (to gain cost, quality, delivery improvements), for purchasing (to gain from economies of scale), and for marketing (to gain from synergistic practices or by pooling expertise).

Peter Hines defines the former type as "a mutually benefiting group of a company's most important subcontractors brought together on a regular basis for the purpose of co-ordination and co-operation as well as (to) assist all the members (by benefiting) from the type of development associated with large Japanese assemblers: such as kaizen, just in time, kanban, U-cell production, and the achievement of zero defects."

The aims (following Hines) are:

- to improve skills in JIT, TQM, SPC, VE/VA, CAD/CAM, Flexibility, Cost
- to produce a uniform supply system
- to facilitate the flow of information
- to increase trust
- to keep suppliers in touch with market developments
- to enhance the reputation of the customer as a good business partner
- to help smaller suppliers lacking specialist trainers and facilities
- to increase the length of relations
- to share developmental benefits
- to provide an example to subcontractors as to how they should develop their own suppliers.

The company-sponsored variety may benefit from the parent company's expertise and resources, often given free. The regional variety simply shares resources such as training seminar costs and training materials, but also will share expertise by lending key staff experts to other member companies for short periods. The regional type may be partially funded from government, and may have a full-time facilitator. In Japan it is considered an honor to be asked to join a prestigious supplier association, as run by a major corporation.

Joint projects, assistance in areas of expertise, development of common standards, training, courses, an interchange or secondment of staff for short periods, benchmarking, hiring of consultants or trainers, factory visits within the association, joint visits to outside companies or other associations, are all common.

The type of supplier who may join an association is not necessarily dependent on size - in fact, larger suppliers with their own corporate resources may benefit less. Also, suppliers of common or catalogue parts may not be invited. Suppliers that are usually targeted are those dependent upon a parent for a significant (perhaps 25% or more) proportion of their business. The purchasing department of the parent company often plays a key role, but some supplier associations have been set up on the initiative of lower tier suppliers or academic groups such as the Cardiff's Lean Enterprise Unit.

Often, a supplier association will hold an annual or biannual assembly to look at performance figures. Ranking of suppliers by different measures is presented. This is often sufficient motivation for lower ranking members to ask for help or to take action on their own.

A supplier association usually will have its own set of rules and regulations and be run by (perhaps) a retired senior engineer from the parent company or increasingly by a full- or part-time co-coordinator from one of the companies. Support staff is seconded for short periods, depending on projects and needs. Often member companies pay a subscription fee. At the top level, the association will have a steering group at MD level, which meets perhaps annually. Some functional directors may meet quarterly. Engineers and front line staff may meet more frequently or may form temporary full-time task groups to address particular problems. Some associations consider social events to be important icebreakers. Within the association there may be a functional split by product category, or by area of concern cost, quality, delivery, production planning, etc.

Purchasing Associations

A variation is an association that bands together for mutual purchasing advantage, gaining from improved quantity discounts and greater "clout" than a single company can bring to bear. A database of required materials and goods is usually maintained, sometimes by a third party. These have been successful in Australia, often on the initiative of a purchasing consultant. A purchasing association does not necessarily go in for all the activities of an operations association, and may be confined to purchasing staff.

A type that has become fairly common in JIT plants is where a contractor takes on the responsibility for the inventory management and supply of numerous small items. This is a form of "vendor managed inventory". Because such contractors operate in different regions they may be able to gain quantity discounts some of which are passed on. Typically such a contractor supplies one large plant, but there are variations where a contractor supplies numerous small firms in a region. This is almost like having a co-operative shop, except that the contractor is a professional inventory manager and re-stocker.

A **Marketing Association** may have characteristics similar to "Agile Manufacturers". That is, they pool resources for synergistic gain or to win large contracts. Such groupings, often known as consortia, have been common in defence, computing, and construction.

Further reading:
James Womack, Daniel Jones, Daniel Roos, *The Machine that Changed the World*, Rawson Associates, 1990
Jeffrey Dyer, *Collaborative Advantage*, Oxford Univ Press, 2000
Richard Schonberger and Edward Knod, *Operations Management* (Sixth Edition), Irwin, Illinois, 1997, Chapter 9.

Peter Hines, *Creating World Class Suppliers: Unlocking mutual competitive advantage*, Pitman, 1994
Richard Lamming, *Beyond Partnership*, Prentice Hall, 1993
Donald Fites, 'Make your Dealers your Partners', *Harvard Business Review*, March/April 1996

For a case study on the establishment of a supplier association in Wales see
Dan Dimancescu, Peter Hines, Nick Rich, *The Lean Enterprise*, AmaCom, New York, 1997

Accounting and Measurement

Lean Accounting

Lean accounting is a developing field. After several centuries of little change the basic assumptions of accounting are at last being questioned in the light of Lean and Theory of Constraints. We need to distinguish between Financial Accounting that is required for tax and shareholder purposes and is subject to GAAP, and Management Accounting that is used for decision-making. Lean Accounting falls into the second category.

What should Lean Accounting give us?
- More relevant information for decision-making. More relevant means the ability to identify factors that are becoming uncompetitive, and where there are potential opportunities for improvement.
- Positive support and evidence for doing the right things – fast, flexible, flow. For reducing inventories and lead times, for improving quality, and for improving delivery performance
- Financial numbers that are able to be understood by non-accountants without having to go through several days of education
- A simplified system that cuts waste and unnecessary transactions. A Lean accounting system needs to be a minimalist system – tracking only the absolute minimum transactions with the lowest frequency possible.
- A system that highlights when to take action, but more importantly when not to.
- Guidance on medium term product costing and target costing.
- Though accountants, planners and managers probably may not like it, recall that Ohno said that an aim of Lean / TPS should be to make the system so simple and visible that there would be little need for complex controls. A reason for doing Lean is to cut overhead!

- Ohno also said, 'excess information must be suppressed!'

What should Lean Accounting NOT give us?
- Evidence that implementing Lean is exactly the wrong thing to do. Cutting inventory can show up on a Profit and Loss statement as a nasty shock to top management.
- Product costing on a month-by-month basis. There is a Western obsession with detailed product costing brought about by the belief that costs can be controlled by the financials. They cannot. Only productivity improvement can make a difference. Product costing, traditional style, relies on detailed assumptions with regard to the allocation of overhead often by labour and machine hours. Some problems with this are given in the section on Activity Based Costing. Costing and profit calculations often include valuation of inventory being built up as an asset as it moves through a plant, encouraging overproduction and manipulation. Many cost categories, including labour and machines are fixed in the short term. Plant and machines are sunk costs. These costs cannot be changed in the short term, only manipulated. In fact, there is no such thing as the true product cost, at least in the short-term. A radical idea – forget product cost, think contribution!
- Detailed variance analysis. Variances are tracked in detail against standards, resulting in for example labour efficiency variances, volume variances, material usage variances, and purchase price variances. Variance analysis is almost pure waste. Worse, it can generate non-Lean behaviour. Many non-accountants do not understand where the numbers come from. But

they learn that overhead is absorbed as labour and machine hours accumulate, and they do not want to be caught with unfavourable variances. This encourages overproduction. Since standards are often fixed on the basis of a forecast at the beginning of an accounting period, actual demand may become irrelevant. The point is, what can a manager do about an unfavourable variance in the short term? Answer: almost nothing favourable for Lean. Senior managers need to ponder that one.

- Being 'precise' but late (and worse, expensive) is far worse from a Lean perspective from being approximate but fast.

- Maskell makes the point that Lean should not be regarded as a short-term cost cutting strategy, but rather as a long term competitive strategy. Cutting waste creates opportunity for growth, and accountants have an important role to help identify what is to be done with freed capacity. Use marginal costing? Certainly, standard costing is inappropriate.

To summarise, a quote:
"Perhaps the most surprising feature of both Toyota's and Scandia's management is the approach to measurement and goal setting. It has become almost an unquestioned tenet of contemporary management that bosses set quantitative targets and then create control systems to assure that management goals are met. …. Toyota's management uses neither overall cost nor productivity targets to influence day-to-day operations. Even if such targets were set, they would have little meaning - for the simple reason that there is no practical way in the short run to speed up the pace of work simply to achieve such cost or productivity targets. Similarly, Scandia employs a unique set of metrics, such as total part counts and part commonality indices, in managing its product design process, rather than relying on aggregate measures of cost and productivity. Both firms believe that the key to superior performance lies in the 'minute particulars' of how local work is done, not in sacrificing those particulars to the pursuit of management-imposed metrics."

Peter Senge, in Johnson and Bröms, *Profit Beyond Measure*

A Lean accounting System

Some pointers for a Lean accounting system follow:

- Work towards direct costs. Rather than trying to 'solve' the overhead allocation problem by some 'elegant' procedure such as Activity Based Costing (ABC), set an objective to decentralise overhead functions such that they can be directly associated with cells or product lines. So for example have schedulers, quality, maintenance, purchasing, and training associated with particular products.

- Allocate the remaining overhead in a way that supports Lean – a good way is allocation based on lead-time. Report the unallocated overhead percentage, and measure the accountants on this.

- Eliminate variance reporting. Just do it.

- Eliminate detailed product cost reporting. Instead do a periodic estimation exercise together with line managers. Look ahead rather than back. Direct cost association helps considerably. ABC (cost driver) methodology can be used to identify cost drivers. Do not do regular or continuous ABC. Report product contributions rather than product costs. Accountants have a useful role in costing alternative materials and features working with designers and market researchers.

- Reduce the number transactions. Lean should increase the regularity of operations – so take advantage of this. Backflush transactions. Use blanket transactions for purchasing.

- Reduce reporting time. As with changeover reduction, do as much prior work as possible prior to period end. Then make adjustments only. Do a Pareto analysis on transaction size – do not delay reporting on many small items that can be carried over to the next period with minimal consequence. Be fast and approximate rather than slow and 'precise'.

- Get accountants to think about variation of costs rather than cost variances. Cost variation means looking into the distribution of product costs by estimation. For example, what are the cost components in making and distributing a product, and from this what is the spread from worst case to best case. Then, why are the worst cases occurring? This is much like the six sigma methodology.

Tackle the worst cases. This concept is developed by Johnson and Bröms who maintain that many a product line that has been abandoned due to unfavourable average costs could have been saved by appropriate analysis and pruning.

- Report by exception. Get accountants to think common cause and special cause. Only report special cause events.
- Reduce the frequency of reporting intervals. Ask what are the benefits and costs of various reporting intervals.
- Clarify the presentation of accounts so all can read them. This means that the word 'variance' should not appear on a Profit and Loss statement. Specifically report actual increases and decreases in inventory.
- Record inventory valuations in terms of raw material value only. Do not accrue value. Do not show 'deferred labour and overhead' as costs that have been accrued into inventory.
- Go through the implications of Lean implementation with senior managers beforehand. They need to know and expect the consequences of inventory reductions on Profit and Loss and Balance Sheet.
- Concentrate on Cash flows. It is money going into and out of the company that is of prime importance – not the transfer prices. Know the implications on cash of Lean implementations.
- If the company has constraint resources (and most do), focus costs around these constraints. Calculate contribution per constraint minute. Know what the opportunity cost of an hour lost or gained at a constraint will be, and get the accountants to cost it.
- Get accountants to participate on the assembly and evaluation of future State maps.

These are but a few of the possibilities. The potential is large.

Further reading:
Adrian Gordon, *The Lean Control Book*, MSc Lean Ops dissertation, Cardiff Business School, 1999
Richard Schonberger, *Let's Fix It!*, Free Press, 2001, Chapters 4 to 7
Orest Fiume, 'Lean Accounting and Finance', *Target*, Fourth quarter, 2002

Jean Cunningham and Orest Fiume, *Real Numbers*, Managing Times Press, 2003
H Thomas Johnson and Anders Bröms, *Profit Beyond Measure*, Nicholas Brealey, 2000.
John Darlington, *Notes on Costing*, MSc Lean Operations, Cardiff Business School.
Bruce Baggaley, (Brian Maskell Associates), *Learning to Count*, Proc. AME Conference, Chicago, 2002

Activity Based Costing

One reason why conventional or mass costing systems have run into trouble with modern manufacturing is that overhead costs are allocated in sometimes inappropriate ways, resulting in misleading product costs. Mass cost accounting allocates overhead to products by a two stage process: overhead costs are allocated to cost centres or departments, and are then reallocated from cost centres to products on the basis of (typically) labour hours or machine hours consumed by the product. When direct costs were a major proportion of total costs, this made sense. Today, however, overheads form the major proportion of costs, and direct labour and machine hours very little. Major distortions are possible, even likely. Mass costing usually uses a uniform cost centre rate to distribute costs. Kaplan and Cooper tell the story of two theoretical plants, Complex Factory and Simple Factory. They both make pencils in the same annual volume, but Simple makes only one variant whilst Complex makes a huge variety. As a result Complex has far higher overheads. Since the process is the same, cost accounting would allocate costs evenly between all variants. But clearly, those low volume unusual colours actually cost a whole lot more. So complex variants are undercosted whilst standard variants are overcosted. If this persists, and if pricing is based on cost, Complex can be driven out of business. Simple, however, has no real need for another accounting system - conventional costing works well; Activity Based Costing is not needed.

Under ABC the concept is that cost elements are allocated to activities that are in turn allocated to products via "cost drivers" (i.e. the quantity of that activity consumed, such as the number of inspection activities.) Direct costs elements such as raw materials and direct labour should be allocated directly to products.

An activity-traceable cost element is the most basic cost grouping in ABC. Examples are salaries, rent, office machines, and power. A primary activity is a defined, repetitive operation that is undertaken in the company - such as planning, storage, materials handling, inspecting, receiving, shipping, accounting - which is directly linked to the value adding stream. Secondary activities, such as personnel or training, support the primary activities and their costs should be recovered via the primary activities that they serve. Cost drivers are measures relating to the volume of an activity - for instance, the number of setups made, or the area of floor space used in storage. Minor cost categories are non-traceable costs such as library and postage that are difficult to trace to particular activities and can be allocated via a conventional rule such as direct machine hours.

The unit cost per activity is determined by dividing the total cost of the activity by the volume of the activity (for example the cost per inspection). These are the cost drivers that are "consumed" by the products. Since activities are not costed in conventional systems. ABC yields valuable insight into the underlying cost structure of the business even before product costs are calculated.

Notice the following:

- ABC is more likely to yield accurate costs than conventional costing, because there is greater traceability
- Even with ABC, there is still considerable judgement involved, so costs are never certain
- ABC is a fairly complex system
- ABC, like conventional costing, is based on assumptions about future activities which may change or whose volumes are likely not to materialise exactly. There will still be variances, so are variances worth tracking?
- There is a trade-off between accuracy and complexity; one could have a complex system with scores of drivers but is all this worth it? Better to get approximate answers faster and less expensively

If ABC is not properly used it can itself be very wasteful. It makes sense, therefore, to use it on a periodic or audit basis and not on a continual basis. You need to ask what benefit will be gained from running an ABC system continuously. Probably little.

Further reading:
Robert Kaplan and Robin Cooper, *Cost and Effect*, Harvard Business School Press, Boston, MA, 1998
Ernest Glad and Hugh Becker, *Activity Based Costing and Management*, Wiley, Chichester, 1996

Basic Measures for Lean

Begin any discussion on Lean measurement by recognizing that measurement is waste. It should be limited and minimised. 'You cannot fatten the calf by weighing it'.

Deming's Wise Words

Two quotations from W Edwards Deming's famous book, *Out of The Crisis*, serve as a salutary warning on measures:

"Rates for production are often set to accommodate the average worker. Naturally, half of them are above average and half below. What happens is that peer pressure holds the upper half to the rate, no more. The people below the average cannot make the rate. The result is loss, chaos, dissatisfaction, and turnover."

"If you have a stable system, then there is no use to specify a goal. You will get whatever the system will deliver. A goal beyond the capability of the system will not be reached…. If you have not a stable system, then there is again no point in setting a goal. There is no way to know what the system will produce: it has no capability."

Shewhart's Insight

First, we should note Shewhart's dictum, often forgotten, that measures should be seen as continuing and self-correcting, following the PDCA (Shewhart or Deming cycle). For Shewhart, measurement was part of a prediction cycle. Shewart saw measurement having three elements, the data, the human observer, and the conditions. Note that all three are subject to variation. The past is used to interpret the present in order to predict the future. Everyone develops a theory or model as to the relationship or system between data and effect. We all implicitly use models, good or bad – and they are uncertain. Since we are dealing with uncertainties in data, observation, and interpretation we should use control charts to assist in understanding the variation – whether special cause or common cause. And we should try to improve on the model and understand the system via Plan Do Check Act.

Virtually all measures should be tracked on an SPC-type chart, so as to distinguish common cause from special cause variation.

Beware of misleading measures. "Drowning in a river of average depth 3 feet", and "The next person to walk through the door will have more than the average number of legs."

Further reading:
W Edwards Deming, *Out of the Crisis*, Cambridge, 1986
Walter Shewhart, *Statistical Method from the viewpoint of Quality Control*, Dover, 1986 (reprint of 1939 book)
Mark Wilcox and Mike Bourne, Predictive Performance Measures, *EurOMA*, 2003

Relevant and Distant Measures

Richard Schonberger warns that bombarding employees with measures about which employees can do nothing and which the customer does not care about, can have adverse affects. Low productivity may not be their fault – a point made by Deming in his 85/15 rule of thumb – 85% of problems are due to the system which only management can fix; 15% is due to operators. Schonberger says we know a lot about getting gains – through blitz events, six sigma, value stream mapping etc. – but holding the gains and continuing to improve is

the real task, where measures have a real part to play. (See also Sustainability section). Schonberger's point is that measures must reflect an operator's 'zone of influence'. This idea is in line with the Hoshin (Policy Deployment) approach, but Hoshin can often fall down if control is emphasized – see below.

A chart of measures on the wall hardly motivates or inspires. But an active problem highlighting chart, requiring frequent record keeping, may well help. For instance, record stoppages and the reasons why, that build into a Pareto. Keep a tally chart of defects by source.

Schonberger argues that measures should not be primarily for 'control' purposes (negative connotations, often lagging the events, but sometimes required), but for encouragement and innovation. So 'controls' should be minimised. Like control charts, do not take action unless the process is out of control. On the other hand, measures that encourage improvement should be emphasized – like a receiving dock operator discussing delivery performance with drivers on a daily basis (rather than viewing delivery schedule achievement ratio), or plotting inventory time profiles at constraints (rather than viewing stock turns), or measuring minor stoppages and their reasons (rather than viewing last week's OEE data). This is in line with consultant Frank Devine's idea of 'Solution Space'. The "Whats" are defined by managers, but the "Hows" are worked out by operators.

Presumably this is also what Ohno was talking about when he said that 'excessive information must be suppressed'.

Likewise, Schonberger says that measures should be time appropriate. Category 1 measures can be influenced in the short term and a short-term expectation is appropriate. Examples are scrap, flow distance, WIP turns, changeover time, unsafe acts, capability index, skills mastered. Category 2 take longer to respond. Examples are throughput, raw material and finished goods turns, delivery performance, labour productivity, OEE, and employee satisfaction. Measuring and expecting short-term results could be counterproductive – improvement may be possible in the short term, but at the expense of medium term deterioration – like running inventories down, now but ignoring next quarter. Measurement trends should be interpreted over the medium term and are the responsibility of middle managers. Category 3 measures require longer-term interpretation, not short term reward or punishment. Examples are market share, customer retention, share price, new products launched. These are the responsibility of senior management. Once again, these ideas could have close agreement with the Hoshin process properly carried out.

Further reading:
Richard Schonberger, *Let's Fix It!*, Chapters 6 and 7, Free Press, 2001
Richard Schonberger, 'Performance Measures for a World Class Workforce', *Target*, v15, n4, 4th Q, 1999.

The Basic Measures

Arguably, there are four basic or prime measures for Lean. Each of them encourages 'all the right moves'. Each can be implemented on various levels from cell to plant, even supply chain. They are also a set, to be looked at together.

- *Lead time*. Measuring lead-time encourages reducing inventory, one-piece flow, reduction of flow length, and waste reduction. The measure is best done from receiving dock to dispatch. Next best is to track only work in process lead-time. Lead time can be measured on a sample basis, by tagging a small number of components each month at the receiving dock. Build up the distribution – do not just measure average lead-time. Alternately, but less good, you can use Little's Law – see the section on Factory Physics. A variation on this measure is to track 'Ohno's Time Line' – the time between receiving an order and receiving payment, expressed in $ per hour. This perhaps is even better since it includes transaction-processing time, and puts the emphasis on cash flow.
- *Customer Satisfaction*. Following the first Lean principle, monitoring customers is a basic requirement. If failure is indicated here, this has to be the first priority. Do get this measure from customers, not internally from shipments. An obvious question is – who are your customers, Final or intermediate. Answer: Both. Sample them across all relevant dimensions – cost, quality, delivery as basics, but note also soft measures such as the RATER framework: reliability, assurance, tangibles, empathy, responsiveness. (See Zeithaml and Bitner, *Service Management*, 2002)
- *Schedule Attainment*. An internal measure of consistency. Schedule attainment is the ability to hit the target for quantity and quality on a day-to-day basis line-by-line or cell-by-cell – not weekly for the plant. Again track the distribution. If you have a Heijunka system this is straightforward. Of course, if the schedule is out of line with customer demands, the measure is a waste of time.
- *Inventory Turns, and 'SWIP to WIP'*. Inventory turns is an established measure. An alternative is days of inventory. Arguably if you are measuring lead-time it is not necessary to track inventory turns but do track lead-time dock to dock and WIP inventory turns, rather than overall inventory turns. Why? Because WIP is fully under your own control, raw materials and finished goods are not fully under own control. SWIP is standard work in progess inventory, so measuring the variation between what should be and actual is useful.

QCDMMS

QCDMMS is an acronym for a set of measure categories widely used in Lean organizations and displayed at each line or area.

1. Quality. Internal scrap, rework, and first time through – expressed in parts per million. First time through percentage is parts entering minus parts scrapped or reworked at each stage. Because rework can happen several times this measure can be negative.
2. Cost. Typically a productivity measure – units per person per week. Usually not a monetary value. OEE performance may be shown here.
3. Delivery performance. Inbound from suppliers, outbound to customers. QOTIF. (Quality, OnTime in Full) A delivery that is not 100% perfect, on time, and in full scores zero.

4. Morale. Absenteeism, suggestions or improvements and possibly the result of an attitude audit.
5. Management. Communications, extent of cross training.
6. Safety. Accidents, Unsafe acts and audit of unsafe conditions

DTI 7 Measures

The British Department of Trade and Industry published a set of 7 measures that were developed out of Industry Forum's Improvement Events (Blitz events). These are now widely used in UK. As a set they are very useful; as individual measures they may have limitations. They are intended as a way of tracking trends within a company, rather than as benchmark measures.

1. Not Right First Time. NRFT = (Defective units x 1 million)/ Total units.
2. Productivity. P = No of units made / No of direct operator hours.
3. Stock turns = Sales turnover per product / (value of RM + WIP + FGI).
   It is useful to turn this measure into three measures – one for each of raw material, work in process, and finished goods since only WIP is fully under own control. The bad news is that value of inventory is subject to local accounting conventions and may be subject to manipulation. Best to define each category in terms of purchased material or parts value only, and not to assume any value is added until sold.
4. Delivery Schedule Attainment. This is the number of planned deliveries – (number late + number of part deliveries) as a percentage of total planned deliveries. A negative figure is possible. Note that quality does not figure, unless defectives are counted as part deliveries.
5. OEE – Overall Equipment Effectiveness. See discussion on OEE in Total Productive Maintenance (TPM) section.
6. Value Added per Person. (Output value – Input Value)/Direct Employees. Beware! May encourage inappropriate automation.
7. Floor Space Utilization = Sales turnover in area / Area in square metres.

Further reading:
DTI, *Quality Cost Delivery*, Dept of Trade and Industry, 1998 and DTI website.

Schonberger's Micro JIT Ratios

Richard Schonberger suggested three quick ratios in 1987 that are still very useful reminders of the real objectives of Lean. They are:

- Lead time to work content. Work content is actual work or value adding time. This encourages continuous flow, keep it moving, synchronised operations. Of course the ideal ratio is 1, but typical ratios run to 100 or even 1000.
- Process speed to sales rate. This ratio encourages uniform flow to takt. Ideal is 1 but typical is 5 to 1000. It addresses "Hurry up and wait", and batch and queue. The ratio discourages monuments and encourages a balanced line.
- Number of pieces to number of workstations. The ideal is one-piece flow with a ratio of one. A good ratio is 2. Typical is 50 or more. This encourages focused cells, and discourages stockrooms and excessive supermarkets.

Further reading:
Richard Schonberger, *World Class Manufacturing Casebook*, Introduction, Free Press, 1987.

Supply Chain Measures

Goldratt favours two complementary measures for supply chain effectiveness – Throughput Dollar Days and Inventory Dollar Days.

Throughput Dollar Days (TDD) is a measure that accumulates the cost of inventory only below an agreed 'emergency' level. The idea is that the potential of lost sales is tracked, so this measure focuses attention both on the item and the response time for replenishment. To set the emergency agreed stock level, consultation needs to take place between vendor and buyer. The emergency level is the level below which there is a high probability of losing sales. This is normally well below the safety stock level used in inventory control. If the inventory level falls below this emergency level the measure starts ticking, and accumulates the full throughput value day by day. Throughput is revenue minus direct variable costs. The measure accumulates every day the inventory is below target. So a shortage for 5 days is 5 times greater than the same shortage for one day. High throughput items, of course, attract higher penalties. There is therefore a motivation on the part of the vendor to focus on minimising delays for valuable items, and on installing the appropriate capacity. Where an item is a component of an assembly, throughput is defined as the revenue of the full end item minus the direct variable costs.

Inventory Dollar Days (IDD) is a measure that tracks flow through the supply chain. It measures both the value of the item and the length of time that it remains in the supply chain. This measure is taken periodically. Where the measure is used in a chain, the time is measured from manufacture to selling. Internally, the measure should be used for raw material, work in process, and finished goods, separately. The claim is that this measure is far more effective than the conventional inventory turn measure. Problems with the inventory turn measure that it is an overall average figure (some items may have very poor turns, other fairly good), and that it ignores the value of the inventory items.

The measures are complementary. TDD encourages the right minimum inventory to be held. IDD limits overproduction. Both have a time dimension. In a supply chain the measures would be communicated along the chain. The thought is that these measures send out the right messages for supply chain cooperation, that is flawed in conventional systems that tend to ignore the point that each player is in for essentially their own gain.

Checking out Measures

Andy Neely and Mike Bourne of Cranfield University suggest a framework for checking out each measure, based on Kipling's Six Honest Serving Men:

The Measure:	a self-explanatory title
Purpose:	why is it being measured?
Relates to:	to which business objective does this measure relate?
Target:	what is to be achieved, and by when?
Formula:	the formula or ratio used.
Frequency:	how often should the measure be taken, and reviewed
Who measures?	who is responsible for collection and reporting?
Source of data:	where does it come from
Who acts?	who is responsible for taking action?
What to do?	what action should be taken? and one could add
Limits:	what are the control limits within which no action is required?

The Hoshin Measurement Cascade

Hoshin or Policy Deployment, discussed in the Strategy section is a consistent way of evolving measures and gaining commitment. At each level, managers specify the whats, whens and whys, leaving the detail of the hows and whos to be worked out at the level below. Measures are then developed in an interactive way. Nevertheless, traditional Hoshin can be improved….

The Performance Prism

The Performance Prism is a framework measurement developed by the Centre for Performance at Cranfield University. It is gaining increased recognition and fits in well with Lean.

The Performance Prism has five faces, as shown. The argument is that each of these five categories should have a suitable set of measures.

The starting point is stakeholders, not strategy. An organisation exits for the satisfaction of its stakeholders, to achieve their goals, and strategy is the route map to get there. Stakeholders include shareholders, investors, customers, suppliers, employees, and communities. Also

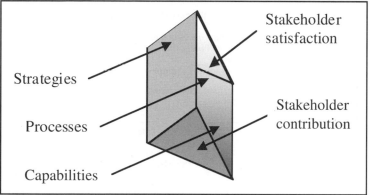

there may be regulators (such as a rail regulator) and pressure groups. Each stakeholder group has requirements from the organization. For instance, suppliers may require trust and a fair level of profit, and customers may require conforming products in a short lead-time. Measures are needed for each stakeholder group and requirement.

At the other end of the prism is stakeholder contribution. This covers the contribution that that the organization requires from each of the stakeholder groups. For example, suppliers should contribute competitively priced parts OTIF (on time in full), customers are required to pay on time and support improvement. Measures are needed.

Strategies, processes and capabilities are the means available to the organization to link stakeholder satisfaction and stakeholder contribution. Measures are needed in each category to track whether each is being implemented, to send out messages about the importance of initiatives in each category, to encourage behaviour, and to keep track of performance and if necessary to change the emphasis. Strategies are the

means to achieve the goals. Business processes are the cross functional 'value streams' and where improvements are necessary. Here it is useful to think of Jim Womack's primary processes (those that create value for the customer) and secondary processes (necessary but that don't add value directly for the customer – 'type1 muda'). Finally, there are capabilities. Again useful to think of Womack's requirements – each step is valuable (not waste, on time), capable (of meeting the requirements, quality capable, small variation), available (when needed – the OEE dimension), and sufficient (whether there is enough capacity and not too much capacity – Womack calls this 'adequate').

To develop appropriate measures
• Brainstorm out the stakeholders
• List their wants and needs from the organization, and what the organization wants and needs from them.
• List the strategies, processes and capabilities required to match these needs (these are a related set). Distinguish between primary and secondary processes.
• Check the existing measures against these strategies, processes, and capabilities.
• Develop the strategic measures – to cover implementation and behaviour
• Develop the process measures – to cover valuable, capable, available, sufficient

Further reading:
Check the Focus magazine website:www.focusmag.com
Andy Neely, et al, *The Performance Prism*, FT Pitman, 2003

Performance Measurement and Balanced Scorecard

Kaplan and Johnson, in their famous book *Relevance Lost*, attacked corporate reporting systems saying that they are oriented towards meeting the needs of the stockmarket, and that this was a major reason why

Western manufacturing was losing out to Japan For too long, performance measurement has been dominated by backward looking, and financial measures of performance.

It has been said that this is like a one-eyed person trying to drive a car by looking in the rear view mirror. Of course, what are needed are both financial and non-financial performance measures, looking forward as well as back.

The "Balanced Scorecard", developed by Kaplan and Norton, is now widely recognised as being a significant advance in performance measurement. Kaplan and Norton's work puts forward a methodology for a balanced set of measures, whereby financial measures are but one element. According to them, there are four aspects that any performance measurement system needs to cover. These are Financial, Customer (or externally) oriented, Business Process (or internally) oriented, and "Learning and Growth". All are necessary. Moreover, there is logic that sees financial performance emerging form customer understanding, from internal operations, and these last two being sustained and renewed by learning and growth. See the figure.

Kaplan and Norton suggest that there are generic measures in each area. Some examples are:

Financial	Return on investment, return on assets employed, economic value added, profitability, revenue
Supplier	Cost, quality, delivery performance, kaizen activity
Customer	Satisfaction, acquisition, retention, market share
Internal process	Cost, quality, response time, productivity, inventory days
People	Employee satisfaction, employee turnover
Learning & Innovation	New product introductions, improvements, suggestions.

Moreover, Kaplan and Norton maintain that measures should be capable of "telling the story"; that is that they should form a logical sequence showing how learning and growth lead to operational growth, which are both assisted by customer or market orientation, which

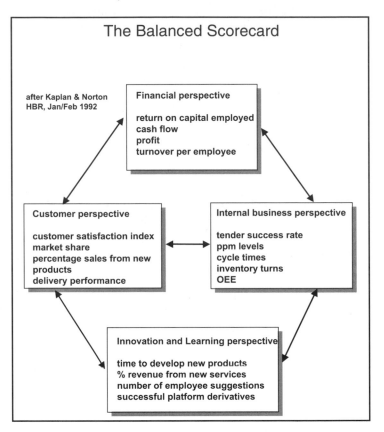

The Balanced Scorecard

after Kaplan & Norton HBR, Jan/Feb 1992

Financial perspective

return on capital employed
cash flow
profit
turnover per employee

Customer perspective

customer satisfaction index
market share
percentage sales from new products
delivery performance

Internal business perspective

tender success rate
ppm levels
cycle times
inventory turns
OEE

Innovation and Learning perspective

time to develop new products
% revenue from new services
number of employee suggestions
successful platform derivatives

finally result in financial return for shareholders. Such a framework can be both top-down and bottom-up, with participation at all levels in much the same way as the Hoshin framework (see separate section).

Further reading:
Robert Kaplan and David Norton, *The Balanced Scorecard,* Harvard Business School Press, 1996
Robert Kaplan and David Norton, *The Strategy Focused Organization*, Harvard Business School Press, 2001

Target Costing, Kaizen Costing and Cost Down

This final section is placed last in the book because it brings together many of the tools presented in earlier sections.

The concept of Target Costing is well established in Lean. The idea is simply that pricing begins with the market. Target cost = Market price - Target Profit. So, instead of the price being derived from cost plus profit, the cost is derived.

Notice Target costing is done in anticipation of future demand. In fact, the price may create the demand. Target costing begins with the customer's needs. A customer may in fact want to buy holes not drills, or 'power by the hour', not an aircraft engine.
It is proactive, not reactive.
It is a tough system, because there can be no compromise on the target cost.
There are variations - for example in the aircraft industry and in Formula 1 there is the target weight.

According to Cooper and Slagmulder, target costing has the cardinal rule "The target cost of a product can never be exceeded". Unless this rule is in place a target costing system will lose its effectiveness and will always be subject to the temptation of adding just a little bit more functionality at a little higher price.

There are three strands to target costing: allowable cost, product level target cost, and component target costs. Much of the following material on the three strands is derived from Cooper and Slagmulder.

Allowable cost is the maximum cost at which a product must be made so as to earn its target profit margin. The allowable cost is derived from target selling price - target profit margin. Target selling price is determined from three factors : customers, competitive offerings, and strategic objectives. The price customers can be expected to pay depends importantly upon their perception of value. So if a new product or variant is proposed, marketing must determine if and how much customers are prepared to pay for the new features. The position on the product life cycle is important. An innovative lead product may be able to command a higher price. Customer loyalty and brand name are influential. Then there are the competitive offerings : what functions are being, and are anticipated to be, offered at what prices. Finally there are strategic considerations as to, for example whether the product is to compete in a new market, and the importance of market share.

Target profit margin is the next factor in determining allowable cost. There are two approaches, according to Cooper and Slagmulder. The first uses the predecessor product and adjusts for market conditions. The second starts with the margin of the whole product line, and makes adjustments according to market conditions.

Product Level Target Costing begins with the Allowable Cost and challenges the designers to design a product with the required functionality at the allowable cost. Sometimes the design team will not know the real allowable cost, but will be set a target which is considered to be a difficult-to-achieve challenge, for motivational reasons. A useful concept is the Waste Free Cost. This concept, also found in value engineering, is the cost assuming that all avoidable waste has been taken out. Another guiding principle is the "cardinal rule" that cost must not be allowed to creep up: if an extra function is added, there must be a compensating cost reduction elsewhere. The process of moving in increments from the current cost to the target cost is referred to as "drifting" and is closely monitored. Once the target cost has been achieved, effort stops : there is no virtue in achieving more than is required.

Component target costing aims at setting the costs of each component. This is an important strategic consideration because it involves the question of supplier partnership and trust.

The figure shows a hierarchy of approaches and tools.

There are three routes to addressing component and product target costs. The first is through market-price tradeoffs, involving negotiations between designers and marketers and between OEM and suppliers, on the sensitivity of price, functionality and quality. Core tools here are the Kano model, QFD, increasingly design for six sigma, and centrally, value engineering. The design concept of the four objectives and six tradeoffs is also important. All of these are discussed in separate sections.

The second area is inter-organizational development. This involves working with supplier partners to achieve cost down. The various approaches used by Toyota and others were discussed in the Improvement section, and in the Supplier Partnership section - see particularly the

The third area is Concurrent Cost Management. This can take place both internally or with immediate suppliers. The idea is to address costs at each level, from concept to production. The stages used to be addressed sequentially, but are now increasingly being done concurrently. Concurrent engineering ideas are used. Of particular note is the Toyota 'set based' methodology that gradually homes in on the specifications whilst allowing flexibility and innovation until quite late into the process. Ramp up is an important

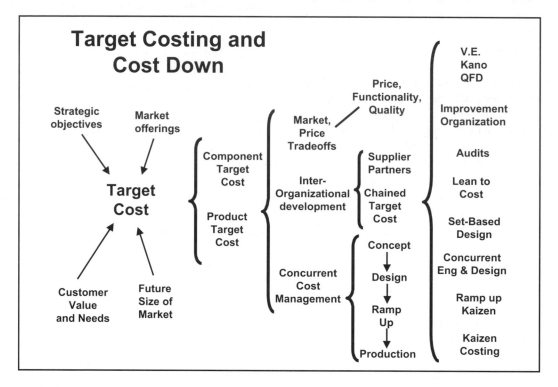

supplier association and purchasing association sections. Chained target costing extends this pressure, or co-operation, further upstream along the supply chain. Each company along the chain is expected (or forced to?) participate by a level-by-level process. Audits play a part here - for example Ford uses its FPS audit tool to assess suppliers and uses activity sampling to identify the extent of cost down opportunity. (See sections on these tools). Toyota uses their supplier support centre. When waste is identified it is either helped to be removed or expected to be removed. Ford uses a confidential costing system, called Lean to Cost, to translate the identified waste into money terms.

stage aimed at reducing problems before full scale production of the new product begins.

Once the product goes into production, three other actions may follow :

1. Further variants may be launched from the base product or platform at strategic intervals, to maintain competitiveness by either adding functionality or to pass on advances in technology, or to pass on price reductions.

2. Further value engineering (sometimes referred to

as value analysis after the initial launch) may take place at regular intervals. One Japanese company aims to do a value analysis on each of their continuing consumer electronics products once per year. The aim is to either reduce cost or improve functionality.

3. "Kaizen costing" is undertaken. Kaizen costing is the post-launch version of target costing, and aims to achieve target cost levels at specific points. Kaizen costing is not really costing in the conventional Western sense. The Westen way is to track variances. How feeble! The kaizen way is to target productivity improvements in people, materials, methods, and machines - as identified by audits, benchmarks, waste analysis, mapping, and activity sampling - in specific periods of time. What the paperwork says about the variances does not matter - what matters is the real tangible improvements in productivity.

Kaizen costing targets three areas: the method or facilities, the product, the overheads. Method is targeted by both the Policy Deployment process focusing on cost down initiatives, level by level, and by local initiatives carried out by the team with or without help from Lean Promotion Office or OEM staff. A typical improvement would be a cell re-balance as explained in the Layout and Cells section of this book. The product is targeted by value engineering. Overheads are targeted using Information value stream mapping and Brown paper mapping.

Further reading:
Robin Cooper and Regine Slagmulder, *Target Costing and Value Engineering*, Institute of Management Accountants / Productivity Press, 1997
Robin Cooper and Regine Slagmulder, *Supply Chain Development for the Lean Enterprise*, Institute of Management Accountants / Productivity Press, 1999
Robert Kaplan and Robin Cooper, *Cost and Effect*, Harvard Business School Press, 1998
Shahid Ansari et al, *Target Costing*, Irwin McGraw Hill, 1997

INDEX to Topics

INDEX to People

The Author

John Bicheno is Director of the MSc programme in Lean Operations at the Lean Enterprise Research Centre (LERC), Cardiff Business School, Wales. (Dan Jones was previously Director of LERC, now headed by Peter Hines.) At the time of writing, this is the only Masters programme in the world entirely devoted to Lean, and is taught on-site at factory locations. John has graduate degrees in Engineering, Systems, and Management, and is CFPIM certfied by APICS. Following 10 years in operations management and engineering, he started his Lean journey whilst at the University of the Witwatersrand in the early 1980s, and continues to learn. He has been a mentor, trainer and consultant to scores of companies, and is on the board of AME UK.

Books and Games from PICSIE

Books

Fishbone Flow   John Bicheno   2006   A5   122 pages

This book is an extensive revision of the bestselling booklet 'Cause and Effect Lean'. Lean is explained in over 50 fishbone diagrams and supporting text. The framework used is a development of the powerful 'Thinkflow' model of Creating Flow, Maintaining Flow, and Organising for Flow that has won many accolades. From this high level concept, several levels of detail are developed, resulting at the lowest levels in specific guidance. A feature of the new book is the integration of three other world-class concepts of Six Sigma, TPM, and TRIZ.

Six Sigma and The Quality Toolbox   Bicheno and Catherwood   A4   152 pages

This book is a companion volume to The New Lean Toolbox but focuses specifically on Six Sigma methodology and a large range of tools for quality improvement and problem solving. The book also includes a section on the theories of the major quality gurus and a section on tools and concepts relevant to service operations – whether in a specific service company or as part of the product-service bundle. The book has been reprinted by the Welsh Development Agency and is also used widely by consultants and prescribed by several universities. The no-padding, snappy style of former editions of the book has attracted wide non-solicited acclaim.

Games

The Buckingham Lean Game. An ideal game to lean Lean manufacturing. Unlike other games this game includes several products, changeover, quality and right size machines. Can be adapted to multiple environments.

The Buckingham Supply Chain Game and LEAP Game. These two bundled games are excellent simulations of both the distribution chain and the supply chain. The LEAP Game was developed at Cardiff University.

The Buckingham Heijunka Game. This more advanced game illustrates how to transform a current state into a future state using Heijunka principles. An extensive set of power point slides on lean scheduling and mapping concepts relating to the game (including batch sizing, mixed model, pitch, supermarkets, types of kanban, etc) is included.

The Buckingham Service Operations Game. Built around an actual situation, this game several lean service concepts including service mapping, failure demand, 5S in service, and customer interactions.